OXFORD PAPERBAC

THE
OXFORD-
PICTORIAL
DICTIONARY

Business and Technical

C000292190

9A9O

OXFORD PAPERBACK REFERENCE

THE
OXFORD-DUDEN
PICTORIAL ENGLISH
DICTIONARY

Business and Technical

THE
OXFORD–DUDEN
PICTORIAL ENGLISH
DICTIONARY

Business and Technical

Oxford   New York

OXFORD UNIVERSITY PRESS

1986

Oxford University Press, Walton Street, Oxford OX2 6DP

Oxford New York Toronto
Delhi Bombay Calcutta Madras Karachi
Petaling Jaya Singapore Hong Kong Tokyo
Nairobi Dar es Salaam Cape Town
Melbourne Auckland

and associated companies in
Beirut Berlin Ibadan Nicosia

Oxford is a trade mark of Oxford University Press

The word 'DUDEN' is a registered trademark of the
Bibliographisches Institut for books of any kind

Published in the United States
by Oxford University Press, New York

Illustrations © Bibliographisches Institut, Mannheim 1979
Text © Oxford University Press 1981

The Oxford–Duden Pictorial English Dictionary first published 1981
First issued as a paperback 1984
This edition, under the title The Oxford–Duden Pictorial
English Dictionary: Business and Technical,
first published 1986

All rights reserved. No part of this publication may be reproduced,
stored in a retrieval system, or transmitted, in any form or by any means,
electronic, mechanical, photocopying, recording, or otherwise, without
the prior permission of Oxford University Press

This book is sold subject to the condition that it shall not, by way
of trade or otherwise, be lent, re-sold, hired out, or otherwise circulated
without the publisher's prior consent in any form of binding or cover
other than that in which it is published and without a similar condition
including this condition being imposed on the subsequent purchaser

Edited by John Pheby, Oxford, with the assistance of
Roland Breitsprecher, Michael Clark, Judith Cunningham,
Derek Jordan, and Werner Scholze-Stubenrecht
Illustrations by Jochen Schmidt, Mannheim

British Library Cataloguing in Publication Data
The Oxford–Duden Pictorial English
dictionary.—(Oxford paperback reference)
Business and technical
1. Vocabulary—Pictorial works
428.1   PE1449
ISBN 0-19-281982-8

Printed in Hong Kong

Foreword

This pictorial dictionary is based on the Oxford–Duden Pictorial German-English Dictionary published in 1980. It was produced by the German Section of the Oxford University Press Dictionary Department in cooperation with the Dudenredaktion of the Bibliographisches Institut, Mannheim, and with the assistance of various British companies, institutions, and specialists. Numerous modifications of the text and illustrations of the original work have been carried out, especially regarding the depiction of everyday objects and situations, in order to allow greater scope for the treatment of these objects and situations in the context of English-speaking countries.

There are certain kinds of information which can be conveyed more readily and clearly by pictures than by definitions and explanations alone: an illustration will help the reader to visualize the object denoted by the word and to form an impression of the way in which objects function in their own technical field or in the everyday life of English-speaking countries. The layout of the illustrations and the text will be particularly useful to the learner. Each double page of the dictionary contains a list of the vocabulary of a subject together with a picture illustrating this vocabulary. This arrangement, and the presence of an alphabetical index, allows the book to be used in two ways: either as a key to the vocabulary of a subject or as an alphabetical dictionary in which the reader is referred to the section or sections in which the word is illustrated.

J.P.

Abbreviations

Am.	*American usage*
c.	*castrated (animal)*
coll.	*colloquial*
f.	*female (animal)*
form.	*formerly*
joc.	*jocular*
m.	*male (animal)*
poet.	*poetic*
sg.	*singular*
sim.	*similar*
y.	*young (animal)*

Contents

The arabic numerals are the numbers of the pictures

THE
OXFORD–DUDEN
PICTORIAL ENGLISH
DICTIONARY

Business and Technical

1 Sea Fishing

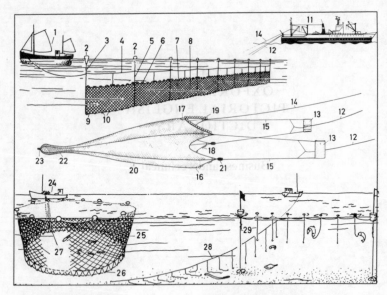

1–23 deep–sea fishing
1–10 drift net fishing
1 herring lugger (fishing lugger, lugger)
2–10 herring drift net
2 buoy
3 buoy rope
4 float line
5 seizing
6 wooden float
7 headline
8 net
9 footrope
10 sinkers (weights)
11–23 trawl fishing (trawling)
11 factory ship, a trawler
12 warp (trawl warp)
13 otter boards
14 net sonar cable
15 wire warp
16 wing
17 net sonar device
18 footrope
19 spherical floats
20 belly
21 1,800 kg iron weight
22 cod end (cod)
23 cod line for closing the cod end

24–29 inshore fishing
24 fishing boat
25 ring net cast in a circle
26 cable for closing the ring net
27 closing gear
28–29 long–line fishing (long–lining)
28 long line
29 suspended fishing tackle

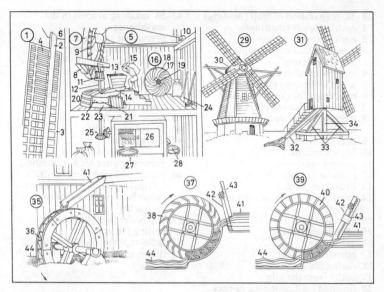

1-34 windmill
1 windmill vane (windmill sail, windmill arm)
2 stock (middling, back, radius)
3 frame
4 shutter
5 wind shaft (sail axle)
6 sail top
7 brake wheel
8 brake
9 wooden cog
10 pivot bearing (step bearing)
11 wallower
12 mill spindle
13 hopper
14 shoe (trough, spout)
15 miller
16 millstone
17 furrow (flute)
18 master furrow
19 eye
20 hurst (millstone casing)
21 set of stones (millstones)
22 runner (upper millstone)
23 bed stone (lower stone, bedder)
24 wooden shovel
25 bevel gear (bevel gearing)
26 bolter (sifter)

27 wooden tub (wooden tun)
28 flour
29 smock windmill (Dutch windmill)
30 rotating (revolving) windmill cap
31 post windmill (German windmill)
32 tailpole (pole)
33 base
34 post
35-44 watermill
35 overshot mill wheel (high-breast mill wheel), a mill wheel (waterwheel)
36 bucket (cavity)
37 middleshot mill wheel (breast mill wheel)
38 curved vane
39 undershot mill wheel
40 flat vane
41 headrace (discharge flume)
42 mill weir
43 overfall (water overfall)
44 millstream (millrace, *Am.* raceway)

3 Malting and Brewing I

1–41 preparation of malt (malting)
1 malting tower (maltings)
2 barley hopper
3 washing floor with compressed-air washing unit
4 outflow condenser
5 water–collecting tank
6 condenser for the steep liquor
7 coolant–collecting plant
8 steeping floor (steeping tank, dressing floor)
9 cold water tank
10 hot water tank
11 pump room
12 pneumatic plant
13 hydraulic plant
14 ventilation shaft (air inlet and outlet)
15 exhaust fan

16–18 kilning floors
16 drying floor
17 burner ventilator
18 curing floor
19 outlet from the kiln
20 finished malt collecting hopper
21 transformer station
22 cooling compressors
23 green malt (germinated barley)
24 turner (plough)
25 central control room with flow diagram
26 screw conveyor
27 washing floor
28 steeping floor
29 drying kiln
30 curing kiln
31 barley silo
32 weighing apparatus
33 barley elevator
34 three–way chute (three–way tippler)
35 malt elevator
36 cleaning machine
37 malt silo
38 corn removal by suction
39 sacker
40 dust extractor
41 barley reception

42–53 mashing process in the mashhouse
42 premasher (converter) for mixing grist and water
43 mash tub (mash tun) for mashing the malt
44 mash copper (mash tun, *Am.* mash kettle) for boiling the mash
45 dome of the tun
46 propeller (paddle)
47 sliding door
48 water (liquor) supply pipe
49 brewer (master brewer, masher)
50 lauter tun for settling the draff (grains) and filtering off the wort
51 lauter battery for testing the wort for quality
52 hop boiler (wort boiler) for boiling the wort
53 ladle–type thermometer (scoop thermometer)

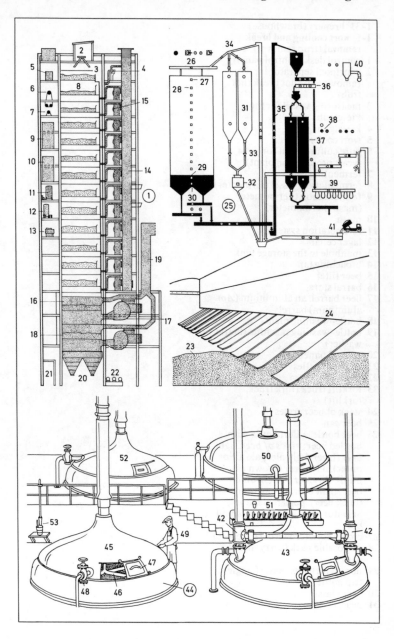

4 Brewing II

1-31 **brewery** (brewhouse)
1-5 **wort cooling and break removal** (trub removal)
1 control desk (control panel)
2 whirlpool separator for removing the hot break (hot trub)
3 measuring vessel for the kieselguhr
4 kieselguhr filter
5 wort cooler
6 pure culture plant for yeast (yeast propagation plant)
7 fermenting cellar
8 fermentation vessel (fermenter)
9 fermentation thermometer (mash thermometer)
10 mash
11 refrigeration system
12 lager cellar
13 manhole to the storage tank
14 broaching tap
15 beer filter
16 barrel store
17 beer barrel, an aluminium (*Am.* aluminum) barrel
18 bottle-washing plant
19 bottle-washing machine (bottle washer)
20 control panel
21 cleaned bottles
22 bottling
23 forklift truck (fork truck, forklift)
24 stack of beer crates
25 beer can
26 beer bottle, a Eurobottle with bottled beer; *kinds of beer:* light beer (lager, light ale, pale ale or bitter), dark beer (brown ale, mild), Pilsener beer, Munich beer, malt beer, strong beer (bock beer), porter, ale, stout, Salvator beer, wheat beer, small beer
27 crown cork (crown cork closure)
28 disposable pack (carry-home pack)
29 non-returnable bottle (single-trip bottle)
30 beer glass
31 head

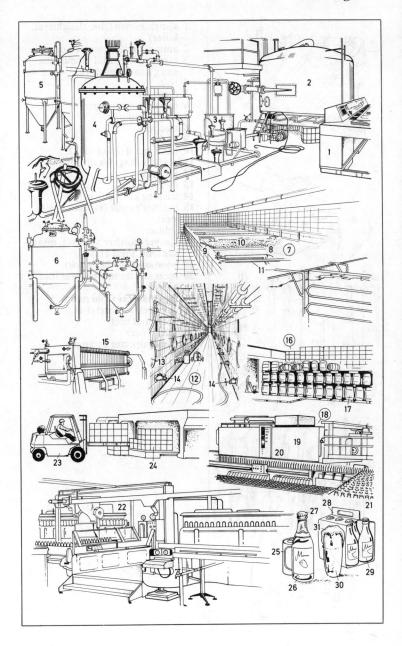

5 Slaughterhouse (Abattoir)

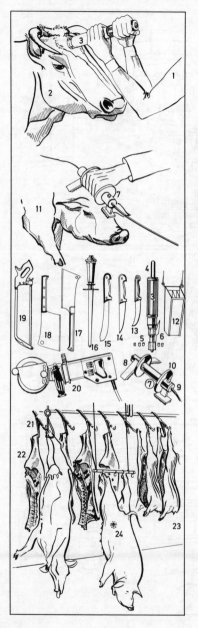

1 slaughterman (*Am.* slaughterer, killer)
2 animal for slaughter, an ox
3 captive-bolt pistol (pneumatic gun), a stunning device
4 bolt
5 cartridges
6 release lever (trigger)
7 electric stunner
8 electrode
9 lead
10 hand guard (insulation)
11 pig (*Am.* hog) for slaughter
12 knife case
13 flaying knife
14 sticking knife (sticker)
15 butcher's knife (butcher knife)
16 steel
17 splitter
18 cleaver (butcher's cleaver, meat axe (*Am.* meat ax))
19 bone saw (butcher's saw)
20 meat saw for sawing meat into cuts
21–24 **cold store** (cold room)
21 gambrel (gambrel stick)
22 quarter of beef
23 side of pork
24 meat inspector's stamp

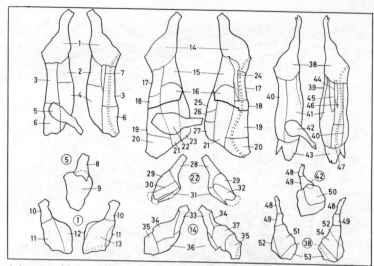

left: meat side;
right: bone side

1–13 *animal:* **calf**; *meat:* **veal**
1 leg with hind knuckle
2 flank
3 loin and rib
4 breast (breast of veal)
5 shoulder with fore knuckle
6 neck with scrag (scrag end)
7 best end of loin (of loin of veal)
8 fore knuckle
9 shoulder
10 hind knuckle
11 roasting round (oyster round)
12 cutlet for frying or braising
13 undercut (fillet)
14–37 *animal:* **ox**; *meat:* **beef**
14 round with rump and shank
15–16 flank
15 thick flank
16 thin flank
17 sirloin
18 prime rib (fore ribs, prime fore rib)
19 middle rib and chuck
20 neck
21 flat rib
22 leg of mutton piece (bladebone) with shin
23 brisket (brisket of beef)
24 fillet (fillet of beef)

25 hind brisket
26 middle brisket
27 breastbone
28 shin
29 leg of mutton piece
30 bladebone [meat side]
31 part of top rib
32 bladebone [bone side]
33 shank
34 silverside
35 rump
36 thick flank
37 top side
38–54 *animal:* **pig**; *meat:* **pork**
38 leg with knuckle and trotter
39 ventral part of the belly
40 back fat
41 belly
42 bladebone with knuckle and trotter
43 head (pig's head)
44 fillet (fillet of pork)
45 leaf fat (pork flare)
46 loin (pork loin)
47 spare rib
48 trotter
49 knuckle
50 butt
51 fore end (ham)
52 round end for boiling
53 fat end
54 gammon steak

7 Butcher's Shop

1–30 butcher's shop
1–4 meat
1 ham on the bone
2 flitch of bacon
3 smoked meat
4 piece of loin (piece of sirloin)
5 lard
6–11 sausages
6 price label
7 mortadella
8 scalded sausage; *kinds:* Vienna sausage (Wiener), Frankfurter sausage (Frankfurter)
9 collared pork (*Am.* headcheese)
10 ring of Lyoner sausage
11 pork sausages; *also:* beef sausages
12 cold shelves
13 meat salad (diced meat salad)
14 cold meats (*Am.* cold cuts)
15 pâté
16 mince (mincemeat, minced meat)
17 knuckle of pork

18 basket for special offers
19 price list for special offers
20 special offer
21 freezer
22 pre-packed joints
23 deep-frozen ready-to-eat meal
24 chicken
25 canned food
26 can
27 canned vegetables
28 canned fish
29 salad cream
30 soft drinks

31–59 manufacture of sausages
31–37 butcher's knives
31 slicer
32 knife blade
33 saw teeth
34 knife handle
35 carver (carving knife)
36 boning knife
37 butcher's knife (butcher knife)
38 butcher (master butcher)
39 butcher's apron
40 meat–mixing trough
41 sausage meat
42 scraper
43 skimmer
44 sausage fork
45 scalding colander
46 waste bin (*Am.* trash bin)
47 cooker, for cooking with steam or hot air
48 smoke house
49 sausage filler (sausage stuffer)
50 feed pipe (supply pipe)
51 containers for vegetables

52 mincing machine for sausage meat
53 mincing machine (meat mincer, mincer, *Am.* meat grinder)
54 plates (steel plates)
55 meathook (butcher's hook)
56 bone saw
57 chopping board
58 butcher, cutting meat
59 piece of meat

8 Bakery

1–54 baker's shop
1 shop assistant (*Am.* salesgirl, saleslady)
2 bread (loaf of bread, loaf)
3 crumb
4 crust (bread crust)
5 crust (*Am.* heel)
6–12 kinds of bread (breads)
6 round loaf, a wheat and rye bread
7 small round loaf
8 long loaf (bloomer), a wheat and rye bread
9 white loaf
10 pan loaf, a wholemeal rye bread
11 yeast bread (*Am.* stollen)
12 French loaf (baguette, French stick)
13–16 rolls
13 brown roll
14 white roll
15 finger roll
16 rye-bread roll
17–47 cakes (confectionery)
17 cream roll
18 vol-au-vent, a puff pastry (*Am.* puff paste)
19 Swiss roll (*Am.* jelly roll)
20 tartlet
21 slice of cream cake
22–24 flans (*Am.* pies) and gateaux (torten)
22 fruit flan (*kinds:* strawberry flan, cherry flan, gooseberry flan, peach flan, rhubarb flan)
23 cheesecake
24 cream cake (*Am.* cream pie) (*kinds:* butter-cream cake, Black Forest gateau)
25 cake plate
26 meringue
27 cream puff
28 whipped cream
29 doughnut (*Am.* bismarck)
30 Danish pastry
31 saltstick (saltzstange) (*also:* caraway roll, caraway stick)
32 croissant (crescent roll, *Am.* crescent)
33 ring cake (gugelhupf)
34 slab cake with chocolate icing
35 streusel cakes
36 marshmallow

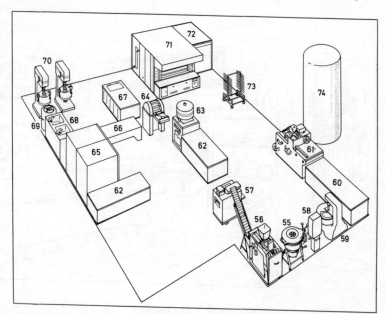

37 coconut macaroon
38 pastry whirl
39 iced bun
40 sweet bread
41 plaited bun (plait)
42 Frankfurter garland cake
43 slices (*kinds:* streusel slices, sugared slices, plum slices)
44 pretzel
45 wafer (*Am.* waffle)
46 tree cake (baumkuchen)
47 flan case
48–50 wrapped bread
48 wholemeal bread (*also:* wheatgerm bread)
49 pumpernickel (wholemeal rye bread)
50 crispbread
51 gingerbread (*Am.* lebkuchen)
52 flour (*kinds:* wheat flour, rye flour)
53 yeast (baker's yeast)
54 rusks (French toast)
55–74 bakery (bakehouse)
55 kneading machine (dough mixer)

56–57 bread unit
56 divider
57 moulder (*Am.* molder)
58 premixer
59 dough mixer
60 workbench
61 roll unit
62 workbench
63 divider and rounder (rounding machine)
64 crescent–forming machine
65 freezers
66 oven [for baking with fat]
67–70 confectionery unit
67 cooling table
68 sink
69 boiler
70 whipping unit [with beater]
71 reel oven (oven)
72 fermentation room
73 fermentation trolley
74 flour silo

9 Grocer's Shop (*Am.* Grocery Store)

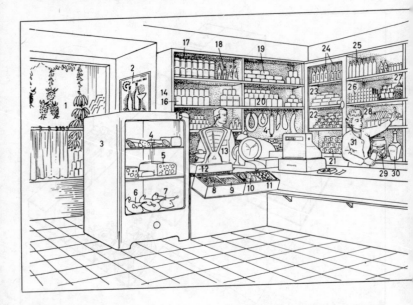

1–87 grocer's shop (grocer's, delicatessen shop, *Am.* grocery store, delicatessen store), a retail shop (*Am.* retail store)
1 window display
2 poster (advertisement)
3 cold shelves
4 sausages
5 cheese
6 roasting chicken (broiler)
7 poulard, a fattened hen
8–11 baking ingredients
8 raisins; *sim.:* sultanas
9 currants
10 candied lemon peel
11 candied orange peel
12 computing scale, a rapid scale
13 shop assistant (*Am.* salesclerk)
14 goods shelves (shelves)
15–20 canned food
15 canned milk
16 canned fruit (cans of fruit)
17 canned vegetables
18 fruit juice
19 sardines in oil, a can of fish
20 canned meat (cans of meat)
21 margarine

22 butter
23 coconut oil, a vegetable oil
24 oil; *kinds:* salad oil, olive oil, sunflower oil, wheatgerm oil, ground–nut oil
25 vinegar
26 stock cube
27 bouillon cube
28 mustard
29 gherkin (pickled gherkin)
30 soup seasoning
31 shop assistant (*Am.* salesgirl, saleslady)
32–34 pastas
32 spaghetti
33 macaroni
34 noodles
35–39 cereal products
35 pearl barley
36 semolina
37 rolled oats (porridge oats, oats)
38 rice
39 sago
40 salt
41 grocer (*Am.* groceryman), a shopkeeper (tradesman, retailer, *Am.* storekeeper)

42 capers	64 red wine
43 customer	**65–68 tea, coffee, etc.**
44 receipt (sales check)	65 coffee (pure coffee)
45 shopping bag	66 cocoa
46–49 wrapping material	67 coffee
46 wrapping paper	68 tea bag
47 adhesive tape	69 electric coffee grinder
48 paper bag	70 coffee roaster
49 cone-shaped paper bag	71 roasting drum
50 blancmange powder	72 sample scoop
51 whole-fruit jam (preserve)	73 price list
52 jam	74 freezer
53–55 sugar	**75–86 confectionery** (*Am.* candies)
53 cube sugar	75 sweet (*Am.* candy)
54 icing sugar (*Am.* confectioner's sugar)	76 drops
	77 toffees
55 refined sugar in crystals	78 bar of chocolate
56–59 spirits	79 chocolate box
56 whisky (whiskey)	80 chocolate, a sweet
57 rum	81 nougat
58 liqueur	82 marzipan
59 brandy (cognac)	83 chocolate liqueur
60–64 wine in bottles (bottled wine)	84 Turkish delight
60 white wine	85 croquant
61 Chianti	86 truffle
62 vermouth	87 soda water
63 sparkling wine	

10 Supermarket

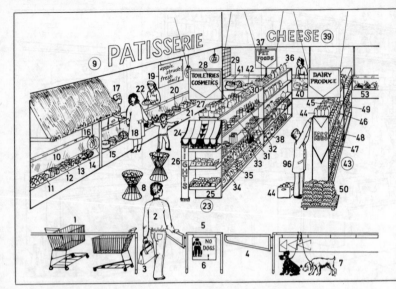

1-96 **supermarket**, a self-service food store
1 shopping trolley
2 customer
3 shopping bag
4 entrance to the sales area
5 barrier
6 sign (notice) banning dogs
7 dogs tied by their leads
8 basket
9 **bread and cake counter** (bread counter, cake counter)
10 display counter for bread and cakes
11 kinds of bread (breads)
12 rolls
13 croissants (crescent rolls, *Am.* crescents)
14 round loaf
15 gateau
16 pretzel [made with yeast dough]
17 shop assistant (*Am.* salesgirl, saleslady)
18 customer
19 sign listing goods
20 fruit flan
21 slab cake
22 ring cake
23 **cosmetics gondola,** a gondola (sales shelves)

24 canopy
25 hosiery shelf
26 stockings (nylons)
27-35 **toiletries** (cosmetics)
27 jar of cream (*kinds:* moisturising cream, day cream, night-care cream, hand cream)
28 packet of cotton wool
29 talcum powder
30 packet of cotton wool balls
31 toothpaste
32 nail varnish (nail polish)
33 shaving cream
34 bath salts
35 sanitary articles
36-37 **pet foods**
36 complete dog food
37 packet of dog biscuits
38 bag of cat litter
39 **cheese counter**
40 whole cheese
41 Swiss cheese (Emmental cheese) with holes
42 Edam cheese, a round cheese
43 gondola for dairy products
44 long-life milk; *also:* pasteurized milk, homogenized milk
45 plastic milk bag
46 cream

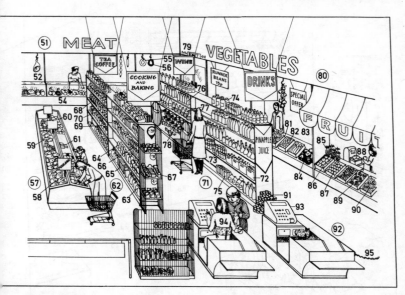

47 butter
48 margarine
49 box of cheeses
50 box of eggs
51 **fresh meat counter** (meat counter)
52 ham on the bone
53 meat (meat products)
54 sausages
55 ring of pork sausage
56 ring of blood sausage
57 freezer
58–61 **frozen food**
58 poulard
59 turkey leg (drumstick)
60 boiling fowl
61 frozen vegetables
62 **gondola for baking ingredients and cereal products**
63 wheat flour
64 sugar loaf
65 packet of noodles
66 salad oil
67 packet of spice
68–70 **tea, coffee, etc.**
68 coffee
69 packet of tea
70 instant coffee

71 **drinks gondola**
72 soft drinks
73 can of beer (canned beer)
74 bottle of fruit juice (bottled fruit juice)
75 can of fruit juice (canned fruit juice)
76 bottle of wine
77 bottle of Chianti
78 bottle of champagne
79 emergency exit
80 **fruit and vegetable counter**
81 vegetable basket
82 tomatoes
83 cucumbers
84 cauliflower
85 pineapple
86 apples
87 pears
88 scales for weighing fruit
89 grapes (bunches of grapes)
90 bananas
91 can
92 **checkout**
93 cash register
94 cashier
95 chain

17

11 Shoemaker (Bootmaker)

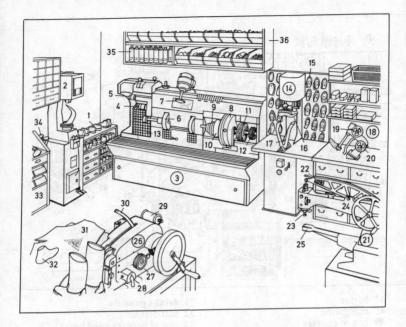

1-68 shoemaker's workshop
   (bootmaker's workshop)
1 finished (repaired) shoes
2 auto-soling machine
3 finishing machine
4 heel trimmer
5 sole trimmer
6 scouring wheel
7 naum keag
8 drive unit (drive wheel)
9 iron
10 buffing wheel
11 polishing brush
12 horsehair brush
13 extractor grid
14 automatic sole press
15 press attachment
16 pad
17 press bar
18 stretching machine
19 width adjustment
20 length adjustment
21 stitching machine
22 power regulator (power control)
23 foot

24 handwheel
25 arm
26 sole stitcher (sole-stitching
   machine)
27 foot bar lever
28 feed adjustment (feed setting)
29 bobbin (cotton bobbin)
30 thread guide (yarn guide)
31 sole leather
32 [wooden] last
33 workbench
34 last
35 dye spray
36 shelves for materials

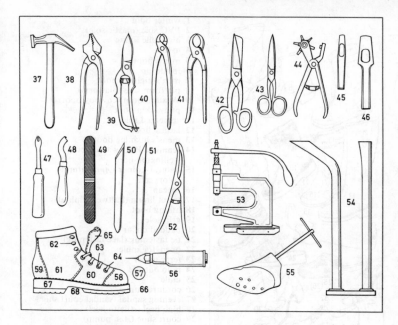

37 shoemaker's hammer
38 shoemaker's pliers (welt pincers)
39 sole-leather shears
40 small pincers (nippers)
41 large pincers (nippers)
42 upper-leather shears
43 scissors
44 revolving punch (rotary punch)
45 punch
46 punch with handle
47 nail puller
48 welt cutter
49 shoemaker's rasp
50 cobbler's knife (shoemaker's knife)
51 skiving knife (skife knife, paring knife)
52 toecap remover
53 eyelet, hook, and press-stud setter
54 stand with iron lasts
55 width-setting tree
56 nail grip
57 boot
58 toecap

59 counter
60 vamp
61 quarter
62 hook
63 eyelet
64 lace (shoelace, bootlace)
65 tongue
66 sole
67 heel
68 shank (waist)

12 Shoes (Footwear)

1 winter boot
2 PVC sole (plastic sole)
3 high-pile lining
4 nylon
5 men's boot
6 inside zip
7 men's high leg boot
8 platform sole (platform)
9 Western boot (cowboy boot)
10 pony-skin boot
11 cemented sole
12 ladies' boot
13 mens's high leg boot
14 seamless PVC waterproof wellington boot
15 natural-colour (*Am.* natural-color) sole
16 toecap
17 tricot lining (knitwear lining)
18 hiking boot
19 grip sole
20 padded collar
21 tie fastening (lace fastening)
22 open-toe mule
23 terry upper
24 polo outsole
25 mule
26 corduroy upper
27 evening sandal (sandal court shoe)
28 high heel (stiletto heel)
29 court shoe (*Am.* pump)
30 moccasin
31 shoe, a tie shoe (laced shoe, Oxford shoe, *Am.* Oxford)
32 tongue
33 high-heeled shoe (shoe with raised heel)
34 casual
35 trainer (training shoe)
36 tennis shoe
37 counter (stiffening)
38 natural-colour (*Am.* natural-color) rubber sole
39 heavy-duty boot (*Am.* stogy, stogie)
40 toecap
41 slipper
42 woollen (*Am.* woolen) slip sock
43 knit stitch (knit)
44 clog
45 wooden sole
46 soft-leather upper
47 sabot
48 toe post sandal
49 ladies' sandal
50 surgical footbed (sock)
51 sandal
52 shoe buckle (buckle)
53 sling-back court shoe (*Am.* sling pump)
54 fabric court shoe
55 wedge heel
56 baby's first walking boot

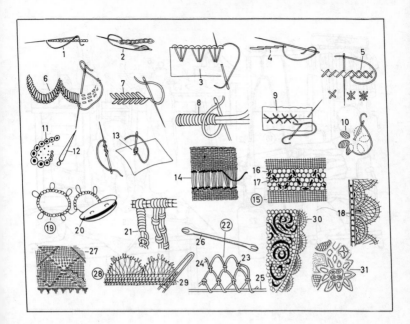

1 backstitch seam
2 chain stitch
3 ornamental stitch
4 stem stitch
5 cross stitch
6 buttonhole stitch (button stitch)
7 fishbone stitch
8 overcast stitch
9 herringbone stitch (Russian stitch, Russian cross stitch)
10 satin stitch (flat stitch)
11 eyelet embroidery (broderie anglaise)
12 stiletto
13 French knot (French dot, knotted stitch, twisted knot stitch)
14 hem stitch work
15 tulle work (tulle lace)
16 tulle background (net background)
17 darning stitch
18 pillow lace (bobbin lace, bone lace); kinds: Valenciennes, Brussels lace
19 tatting
20 tatting shuttle (shuttle)
21 knotted work (macramé)
22 filet (netting)
23 netting loop
24 netting thread
25 mesh pin (mesh gauge)
26 netting needle
27 open work
28 gimping (hairpin work)
29 gimping needle (hairpin)
30 needlepoint lace (point lace, needlepoint); kinds: reticella lace, Venetian lace, Alençon lace; sim. with metal thread: filigree work
31 braid embroidery (braid work)

14 Dressmaker

1–27 dressmaker's workroom
1 dressmaker
2 tape measure (measuring tape), a metre (*Am*. meter) tape measure
3 cutting shears
4 cutting table
5 model dress
6 dressmaker's model (dressmaker's dummy, dress form)
7 model coat
8 sewing machine
9 drive motor
10 drive belt
11 treadle
12 sewing machine cotton (sewing machine thread) [on bobbin]
13 cutting template
14 seam binding
15 button box
16 remnant
17 movable clothes rack
18 hand-iron press
19 presser (ironer)
20 steam iron
21 water feed pipe
22 water container
23 adjustable–tilt ironing surface
24 lift device for the iron
25 steam extractor
26 foot switch controlling steam extraction
27 pressed non–woven woollen (*Am*. woolen) fabric

1–32 tailor's workroom

1 triple mirror
2 lengths of material
3 suiting
4 fashion journal (fashion magazine)
5 ashtray
6 fashion catalogue
7 workbench
8 wall shelves (wall shelf unit)
9 cotton reel
10 small reels of sewing silk
11 hand shears
12 combined electric and treadle sewing machine
13 treadle
14 dress guard
15 band wheel
16 bobbin thread
17 sewing machine table
18 sewing machine drawer
19 seam binding
20 pincushion
21 marking out
22 tailor
23 shaping pad
24 tailor's chalk (French chalk)
25 workpiece
26 steam press (steam pressing unit)
27 swivel arm
28 pressing cushion (pressing pad)
29 iron
30 hand-ironing pad
31 clothes brush
32 pressing cloth

16 Ladies' Hairdresser

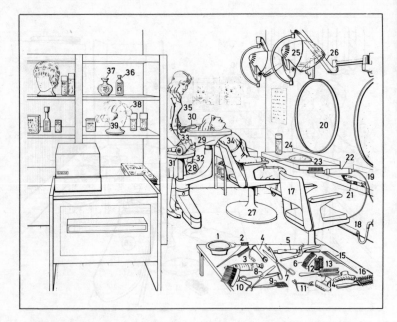

1–39 ladies' hairdressing salon and beauty salon (*Am.* beauty parlor, beauty shop)

1–16 hairdresser's tools
1 bowl containing bleach
2 detangling brush
3 bleach tube
4 curler [used in dyeing]
5 curling tongs (curling iron)
6 comb (back comb, side comb)
7 haircutting scissors
8 thinning scissors (*Am.* thinning shears)
9 thinning razor
10 hairbrush
11 hair clip
12 roller
13 curl brush
14 curl clip
15 dressing comb
16 stiff-bristle brush
17 adjustable hairdresser's chair
18 footrest
19 dressing table
20 salon mirror (mirror)
21 electric clippers
22 warm-air comb
23 hand mirror (hand glass)
24 hair spray (hair-fixing spray)
25 drier, a swivel-mounted drier
26 swivel arm of the drier
27 round base
28 shampoo unit
29 shampoo basin
30 hand spray (shampoo spray)
31 service tray
32 shampoo bottle
33 hair drier (hand hair drier, hand-held hair drier)
34 cape (gown)
35 hairdresser
36 perfume bottle
37 bottle of toilet water
38 wig
39 wig block

1–42 men's salon (men's hairdressing salon, barber's shop, *Am.* barbershop)

1 hairdresser (barber)
2 overalls (hairdresser's overalls)
3 hairstyle (haircut)
4 cape (gown)
5 paper towel
6 salon mirror (mirror)
7 hand mirror (hand glass)
8 light
9 toilet water
10 hair tonic
11 shampoo unit
12 shampoo basin
13 hand spray (shampoo spray)
14 mixer tap (*Am.* mixing faucet)
15 sockets, e.g. for hair drier
16 adjustable hairdresser's chair (barber's chair)
17 height-adjuster bar (height adjuster)
18 armrest
19 footrest
20 shampoo
21 perfume spray

22 hair drier (hand hair drier, hand-held hair drier)
23 setting lotion in a spray can
24 hand towels for drying hair
25 towels for face compresses
26 crimping iron
27 neck brush
28 dressing comb
29 warm-air comb
30 warm-air brush
31 curling tongs (hair curler, curling iron)
32 electric clippers
33 thinning scissors (*Am.* thinning shears)
34 haircutting scissors; *sim.:* styling scissors
35 scissor-blade
36 pivot
37 handle
38 open razor (straight razor)
39 razor handle
40 edge (cutting edge, razor's edge, razor's cutting edge)
41 thinning razor
42 diploma

18 Tobacco and Smoking Requisites

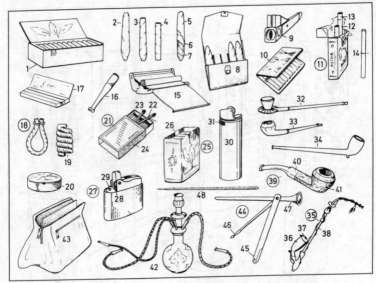

1 cigar box
2 cigar; *kinds:* Havana cigar (Havana), Brazilian cigar, Sumatra cigar
3 cigarillo
4 cheroot
5 wrapper
6 binder
7 filler
8 cigar case
9 cigar cutter
10 cigarette case
11 cigarette packet (*Am.* pack)
12 cigarette, a filter-tipped cigarette
13 cigarette tip; *kinds:* cork tip, gold tip
14 Russian cigarette
15 cigarette roller
16 cigarette holder
17 packet of cigarette papers
18 pigtail (twist of tobacco)
19 chewing tobacco; *a piece:* plug (quid, chew)
20 snuff box, containing snuff
21 matchbox
22 match
23 head (match head)
24 striking surface
25 packet of tobacco; *kinds:* fine cut, shag, navy plug
26 revenue stamp
27 petrol cigarette lighter (petrol lighter)
28 flint
29 wick
30 gas cigarette lighter (gas lighter), a disposable lighter
31 flame regulator
32 chibonk (chibonque)
33 short pipe
34 clay pipe (Dutch pipe)
35 long pipe
36 pipe bowl (bowl)
37 bowl lid
38 pipe stem (stem)
39 briar pipe
40 mouthpiece
41 sand-blast finished or polished briar grain
42 hookah (narghile, narghileh), a water pipe
43 tobacco pouch
44 smoker's companion
45 pipe scraper
46 pipe cleaner
47 tobacco presser
48 pipe cleaner

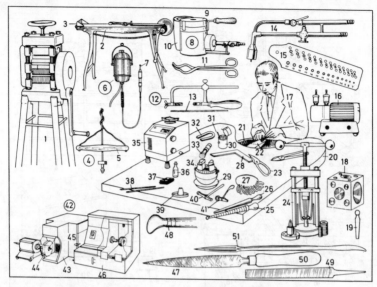

1 wire and sheet roller
2 drawbench (drawing bench)
3 wire (gold or silver wire)
4 archimedes drill (drill)
5 crossbar
6 suspended (pendant) electric
   drilling machine
7 spherical cutter (cherry)
8 melting pot
9 fireclay top
10 graphite crucible
11 crucible tongs
12 piercing saw (jig saw)
13 piercing saw blade
14 soldering gun
15 thread tapper
16 blast burner (blast lamp) for
   soldering
17 goldsmith
18 swage block
19 punch
20 workbench (bench)
21 bench apron
22 needle file
23 metal shears
24 wedding ring sizing machine
25 ring gauge (*Am.* gage)
26 ring–rounding tool

27 ring gauge (*Am.* gage)
28 steel set–square
29 leather pad
30 box of punches
31 punch
32 magnet
33 bench brush
34 engraving ball (joint vice, clamp)
35 gold and silver balance (assay
   balance), a precision balance
36 soldering flux (flux)
37 charcoal block
38 stick of solder
39 soldering borax
40 shaping hammer
41 chasing (enchasing) hammer
42 polishing and burnishing
   machine
43 dust exhauster (vacuum cleaner)
44 polishing wheel
45 dust collector (dust catcher)
46 buffing machine
47 round file
48 bloodstone (haematite, hematite)
49 flat file
50 file handle
51 polishing iron (burnisher)

20 Watchmaker, Clockmaker

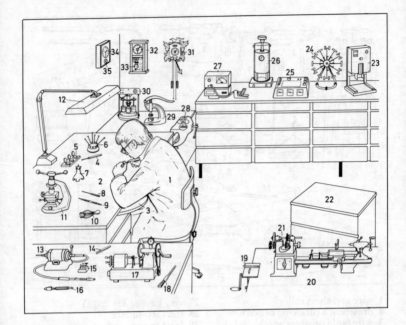

1 watchmaker; *also*: clockmaker
2 workbench
3 armrest
4 oiler
5 oil stand
6 set of screwdrivers
7 clockmaker's anvil
8 broach, a reamer
9 spring pin tool
10 hand–removing tool
11 watchglass–fitting tool
12 workbench lamp, a multi–purpose lamp
13 multi–purpose motor
14 tweezers
15 polishing machine attachments
16 pin vice (pin holder)
17 burnisher, for burnishing, polishing, and shortening of spindles
18 dust brush
19 cutter for metal watch straps
20 precision bench lathe (watchmaker's lathe)
21 drive–belt gear

22 workshop trolley for spare parts
23 ultrasonic cleaner
24 rotating watch–testing machine for automatic watches
25 watch–timing machine for electronic components
26 testing device for waterproof watches
27 electronic timing machine
28 vice (*Am.* vise)
29 watchglass–fitting tool for armoured (*Am.* armored) glasses
30 [automatic] cleaning machine for conventional cleaning
31 cuckoo clock (Black Forest clock)
32 wall clock (regulator)
33 compensation pendulum
34 kitchen clock
35 timer

1 electronic wristwatch
2 digital readout, a light–emitting diode (LED) readout; *also:* liquid crystal readout
3 hour and minute button
4 date and second button
5 strap (watch strap)
6 tuning fork principle (principle of the tuning fork watch)
7 power source (battery cell)
8 transformer
9 tuning fork element (oscillating element)
10 wheel ratchet
11 wheels
12 minute hand
13 hour hand
14 principle of the electronic quartz watch
15 quartz
16 integrated circuit
17 oscillation counter
18 decoder
19 calendar clock (alarm clock)
20 digital display with flip–over numerals
21 second indicator
22 stop button
23 forward and backward wind knob
24 grandfather clock
25 face
26 clock case
27 pendulum
28 striking weight
29 time weight
30 sundial
31 hourglass (egg timer)
32–43 components of an automatic watch (automatic wristwatch)
32 weight (rotor)
33 stone (jewel, jewelled bearing), a synthetic ruby
34 click
35 click wheel
36 clockwork (clockwork mechanism)
37 bottom train plate
38 spring barrel
39 balance wheel
40 escape wheel
41 crown wheel
42 winding crown
43 drive mechanism

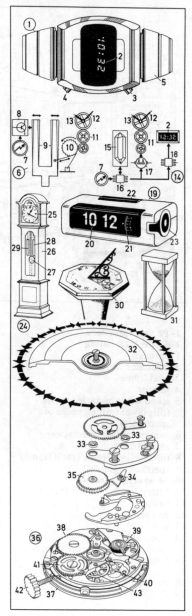

22 Optician

1–19 sales premises
1–4 spectacle fitting
1 optician
2 customer
3 trial frame
4 mirror
5 stand with spectacle frames
  (display of frames, range of
  spectacles)
6 sunglasses (sun spectacles)
7 metal frame
8 tortoiseshell frame (shell frame)
9 spectacles (glasses)
10–14 spectacle frame
10 fitting (mount) of the frame
11 bridge
12 pad bridge
13 side
14 side joint
15 spectacle lens, a bifocal lens
16 hand mirror (hand glass)
17 binoculars
18 monocular telescope (tube)
19 microscope

20–47 optician's workshop
20 workbench
21 universal centring (centering)
   apparatus
22 centring (centering) suction
   holder
23 sucker
24 edging machine
25 formers for the lens edging
   machine
26 inserted former
27 rotating printer
28 abrasive wheel combination
29 control unit
30 machine part
31 cooling water pipe
32 cleaning fluid
33 focimeter (vertex
   refractionometer)
34 metal–blocking device
35 abrasive wheel combination and
   forms of edging
36 roughing wheel for preliminary
   surfacing

37 fining lap for positive and
   negative lens surfaces
38 fining lap for special and flat
   lenses
39 plano–concave lens with a flat
   surface
40 plano–concave lens with a
   special surface
41 concave and convex lens with a
   special surface
42 convex and concave lens with a
   special surface
43 ophthalmic test stand
44 phoropter with ophthalmometer
   and optometer (refractometer)
45 trial lens case
46 collimator
47 acuity projector

23 Optical Instruments I

1 laboratory and research microscope, *Leitz system*
2 stand
3 base
4 coarse adjustment
5 fine adjustment
6 illumination beam path (illumination path)
7 illumination optics
8 condenser
9 microscope (microscopic, object) stage
10 mechanical stage
11 objective turret (revolving nosepiece)
12 binocular head
13 beam-splitting prisms
14 transmitted-light microscope with camera and polarizer, *Zeiss system*
15 stage base
16 aperture-stop slide
17 universal stage
18 lens panel
19 polarizing filter
20 camera
21 focusing screen
22 discussion tube arrangement
23 wide-field metallurgical microscope, a reflected-light microscope (microscope for reflected light)
24 matt screen (ground glass screen, projection screen)
25 large-format camera
26 miniature camera
27 base plate
28 lamphouse
29 mechanical stage
30 objective turret (revolving nosepiece)
31 surgical microscope
32 pillar stand
33 field illumination
34 photomicroscope
35 miniature film cassette
36 photomicrographic camera attachment for large-format or television camera
37 surface-finish microscope
38 light section tube
39 rack and pinion
40 zoom stereomicroscope

41 zoom lens
42 dust counter
43 measurement chamber
44 data output
45 analogue (*Am.* analog) output
46 measurement range selector
47 digital display (digital readout)
48 dipping refractometer for examining food
49 microscopic photometer
50 photometric light source
51 measuring device (photomultiplier, multiplier phototube)
52 light source for survey illumination
53 remote electronics
54 universal wide-field microscope
55 adapter for camera or projector attachment
56 eyepiece focusing knob
57 filter pick-up
58 handrest
59 lamphouse for incident (vertical) illumination
60 lamphouse connector for transillumination
61 wide-field stereomicroscope
62 interchangeable lenses (objectives)
63 incident (vertical) illumination (incident top lighting)
64 fully automatic microscope camera, a camera with photomicro mount adapter
65 film cassette
66 universal condenser for research microscope 1
67 universal-type measuring machine for photogrammetry (phototheodolite)
68 photogrammetric camera
69 motor-driven level, a compensator level
70 electro-optical distance-measuring instrument
71 stereometric camera
72 horizontal base
73 one-second theodolite

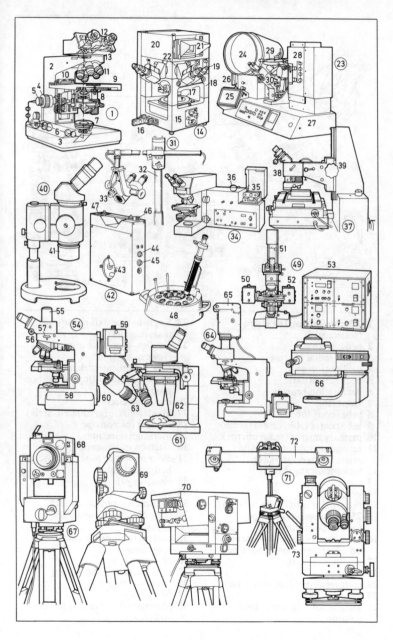

24 Optical Instruments II

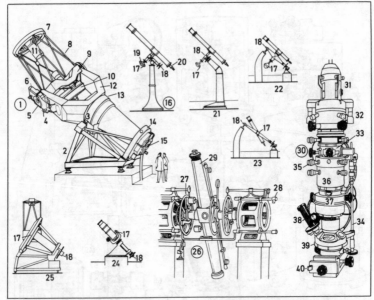

1 **2.2 m reflecting telescope**
  (reflector)
2 pedestal (base)
3 axial–radial bearing
4 declination gear
5 declination axis
6 declination bearing
7 front ring
8 tube (body tube)
9 tube centre (*Am.* center) section
10 primary mirror (main mirror)
11 secondary mirror (deviation
   mirror, corrector plate)
12 fork mounting (fork)
13 cover
14 guide bearing
15 main drive unit of the polar axis
16–25 **telescope mountings**
   (telescope mounts)
16 refractor (refracting telescope)
   on a German–type mounting
17 declination axis
18 polar axis
19 counterweight (counterpoise)
20 eyepiece
21 knee mounting with a bent
   column

22 English–type axis mounting
   (axis mount)
23 English–type yoke mounting
   (yoke mount)
24 fork mounting (fork mount)
25 horseshoe mounting (horseshoe
   mount)
26 meridian circle
27 divided circle (graduated circle)
28 reading microscope
29 meridian telescope
30 electron microscope
31–39 microscope tube (microscope
   body, body tube)
31 electron gun
32 condensers
33 specimen insertion air lock
34 control for specimen stage
   adjustment
35 control for the objective
   apertures
36 objective lens
37 intermediate image screen
38 telescope magnifier
39 final image tube
40 photographic chamber for film
   and plate magazines

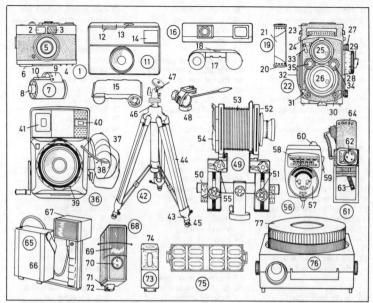

1 miniature camera (35 mm camera)
2 viewfinder eyepiece
3 meter cell
4 accessory shoe
5 flush lens
6 rewind handle (rewind, rewind crank)
7 miniature film cassette (135 film cassette, 35 mm cassette)
8 film spool
9 film with leader
10 cassette slit (cassette exit slot)
11 cartridge-loading camera
12 shutter release (shutter release button)
13 flash cube contact
14 rectangular viewfinder
15 126 cartridge (instamatic cartridge)
16 pocket camera (subminiature camera)
17 110 cartridge (subminiature cartridge)
18 film window
19 120 rollfilm
20 rollfilm spool
21 backing paper
22 twin-lens reflex camera
23 folding viewfinder hood (focusing hood)
24 meter cell
25 viewing lens

26 object lens
27 spool knob
28 distance setting (focus setting)
29 exposure meter using needle-matching system
30 flash contact
31 shutter release
32 film transport (film advance, film wind)
33 flash switch
34 aperture-setting control
35 shutter speed control
36 large-format hand camera (press camera)
37 grip (handgrip)
38 cable release
39 distance-setting ring (focusing ring)
40 multiple-frame viewfinder (universal viewfinder)
41 multiple-frame viewfinder (universal viewfinder)
42 tripod
43 tripod leg
44 tubular leg
45 rubber foot
46 central column
47 ball and socket head
48 cine camera pan and tilt head
49 large-format folding camera
50 optical bench
51 standard adjustment

52 lens standard
53 bellows
54 camera back
55 back standard adjustment
56 hand-held exposure meter (exposure meter)
57 calculator dial
58 scales (indicator scales) with indicator needle (pointer)
59 range switch (high/low range selector)
60 diffuser for incident light measurement
61 probe exposure meter for large format cameras
62 meter
63 probe
64 dark slide
65 battery-portable electronic flash (battery-portable electronic flash unit)
66 powerpack unit (battery)
67 flash head
68 single-unit electronic flash (flashgun)
69 swivel-mounted reflector
70 photodiode
71 foot
72 hot-shoe contact
73 flash cube unit
74 flash cube
75 flash bar
76 slide projector
77 rotary magazine

26 Photography II

1-105 system camera
1 miniature single–lens reflex camera
2 camera body
3-8 lens, a normal lens (standard lens)
3 lens barrel
4 distance scale in metres and feet
5 aperture ring (aperture-setting ring, aperture control ring)
6 front element mount with filter mount
7 front element
8 focusing ring (distance-setting ring)
9 ring for the carrying strap
10 battery chamber
11 screw-in cover
12 rewind handle (rewind, rewind crank)
13 battery switch
14 flash socket for F and X contact
15 self-time lever (setting lever for the self-timer, setting lever for the delayed-action release)
16 single-stroke film advance lever
17 exposure counter (frame counter)
18 shutter release (shutter release button)
19 shutter speed setting knob (shutter speed control)
20 accessory shoe
21 hot-shoe flash contact
22 viewfinder eyepiece with correcting lens
23 camera back
24 pressure plate
25 take-up spool of the rapid-loading system
26 transport sprocket
27 rewind release button (reversing clutch)
28 film window
29 rewind cam
30 tripod socket (tripod bush)
31 reflex system (mirror reflex system)
32 lens
33 reflex mirror
34 film window
35 path of the image beam
36 path of the sample beam
37 meter cell

38 auxiliary mirror
39 focusing screen
40 field lens
41 pentaprism
42 eyepiece
43–105 system of accessories
43 interchangeable lenses
44 fisheye lens (fisheye)
45 wide-angle lens (short focal length lens)
46 normal lens (standard lens)
47 medium focal length lens
48 telephoto lens (long focal length lens)
49 long-focus lens
50 mirror lens
51 viewfinder image
52 signal to switch to manual control
53 matt collar (ground glass collar)
54 microprism collar
55 split-image rangefinder (focusing wedges)
56 aperture scale
57 exposure meter needle
58-66 interchangeable focusing screens
58 all-matt screen (ground glass screen) with microprism spot
59 all-matt screen (ground glass screen) with microprism spot and split-image rangefinder
60 all-matt screen (ground glass screen) without focusing aids
61 matt screen (ground glass screen) with reticule
62 microprism spot for lenses with a large aperture
63 microprism spot for lenses with an aperture of f = 1 : 3.5 or larger
64 Fresnel lens with matt collar (ground glass collar) and split-image rangefinder
65 all-matt screen (ground glass screen) with finely matted central spot and graduated markings
66 matt screen (ground glass screen) with clear spot and double cross hairs

67 data recording back for exposing data about shots
68 viewfinder hood (focusing hood)
69 interchangeable penta-prism viewfinder
70 pentaprism
71 right-angle viewfinder
72 correction lens
73 eyecup
74 focusing telescope
75 battery unit
76 combined battery holder and control grip for the motor drive
77 rapid-sequence camera
78 attachable motor drive
79 external (outside) power supply
80 ten meter film back (magazine back)
81-98 close-up and macro equipment
81 extension tube
82 adapter ring
83 reversing ring
84 lens in retrofocus position
85 bellows unit (extension bellows, close-up bellows attachment)
86 focusing stage
87 slide-copying attachment
88 slide-copying adapter
89 micro attachment (photomicroscope adapter)
90 copying stand (copy stand, copypod)
91 spider legs
92 copying stand (copy stand)
93 arm of the copying stand (copy stand)
94 macrophoto stand
95 stage plates for the macrophoto stand
96 insertable disc (disk)
97 Lieberkühn reflector
98 mechanical stage
99 table tripod (table-top tripod)
100 rifle grip
101 cable release
102 double cable release
103 camera case (ever-ready case)
104 lens case
105 soft–leather lens pouch

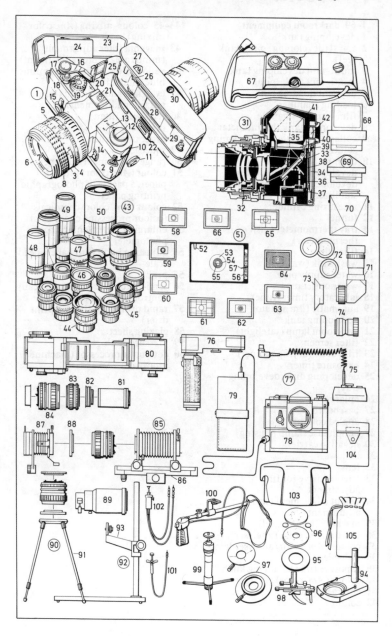

27 Photography III

1–60 darkroom equipment
1 developing tank
2 spiral (developing spiral, tank reel)
3 multi–unit developing tank
4 multi–unit tank spiral
5 daylight–loading tank
6 loading chamber
7 film transport handle
8 developing tank thermometer
9 collapsible bottle for developing solution
10 chemical bottles for first developer, stop bath, colour developer, bleach–hardener, stabilizer
11 measuring cylinders
12 funnel
13 tray thermometer (dish thermometer)
14 film clip
15 wash tank (washer)
16 water supply pipe
17 water outlet pipe
18 laboratory timer (timer)
19 automatic film agitator
20 developing tank
21 darkroom lamp (safelight)
22 filter screen
23 film drier (drying cabinet)
24 exposure timer
25 developing dish (developing tray)
26 enlarger
27 baseboard
28 angled column
29 lamphouse (lamp housing)
30 negative carrier
31 bellows
32 lens
33 friction drive for fine adjustment
34 height adjustment (scale adjustment)
35 masking frame (easel)
36 colour (*Am.* color) analyser
37 colour (*Am.* color) analyser lamp
38 probe lead
39 exposure time balancing knob
40 colour (*Am.* color) enlarger
41 enlarger head
42 column

43–45 colour–mixing (*Am.* color–mixing) knob
43 magenta filter adjustment (minus green filter adjustment)
44 yellow filter adjustment (minus blue filter adjustment)
45 cyan filter adjustment (minus red filter adjustment)
46 red swing filter
47 print tongs
48 processing drum
49 squeegee
50 range (assortment) of papers
51 colour (*Am.* color) printing paper, a packet of photographic printing paper
52 colour (*Am.* color) chemicals (colour processing chemicals)
53 enlarging meter (enlarging photometer)
54 adjusting knob with paper speed scale
55 probe
56 semi–automatic thermostatically controlled developing dish
57 rapid print drier (heated print drier)
58 glazing sheet
59 pressure cloth
60 automatic processor (machine processor)

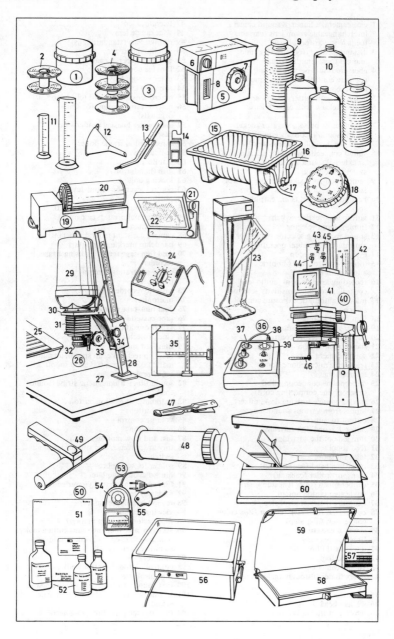

28 Cine Film

1 **cine camera,** a Super-8 sound camera
2 interchangeable zoom lens (variable focus lens, varifocal lens)
3 distance setting (focus setting) and manual focal length setting
4 aperture ring (aperture-setting ring, aperture control ring) for manual aperture setting
5 handgrip with battery chamber
6 shutter release with cable release socket
7 pilot tone or pulse generator socket for the sound recording equipment (with the dual film-tape system)
8 sound connecting cord for microphone or external sound source (in single-system recording)
9 remote control socket (remote control jack)
10 headphone socket (*sim.:* earphone socket)
11 autofocus override switch
12 filming speed selector
13 sound recording selector switch for automatic or manual operation
14 eyepiece with eyecup
15 diopter control ring (dioptric adjustment ring)
16 recording level control (audio level control, recording sensitivity selector)
17 manual/automatic exposure control switch
18 film speed setting
19 power zooming arrangement
20 automatic aperture control
21 **sound track system**
22 sound camera
23 telescopic microphone boom
24 microphone
25 microphone connecting lead (microphone connecting cord)
26 **mixing console** (mixing desk, mixer)
27 inputs from various sound sources
28 output to camera
29 **Super-8 sound film cartridge**
30 film gate of the cartridge
31 feed spool
32 take-up spool
33 recording head (sound head)
34 transport roller (capstan)
35 rubber pinch roller (capstan idler)
36 guide step (guide notch)
37 exposure meter control step
38 conversion filter step (colour, *Am.* color, conversion filter step)
39 **single-8 cassette**
40 film gate opening
41 unexposed film
42 exposed film
43 **16 mm camera**
44 reflex finder (through-the-lens reflex finder)
45 magazine
46–49 **lens head**
46 lens turret (turret head)

47 telephoto lens
48 wide-angle lens
49 normal lens (standard lens)
50 winding handle
51 **compact Super-8 camera**
52 footage counter
53 macro zoom lens
54 zooming lever
55 macro lens attachment (close-up lens)
56 macro frame (mount for small originals)
57 **underwater housing** (underwater case)
58 direct-vision frame finder
59 measuring rod
60 stabilizing wing
61 grip (handgrip)
62 locking bolt
63 control lever (operating lever)
64 porthole
65 **synchronization start** (sync start)
66 professional press-type camera
67 cameraman
68 camera assistant (sound assistant)
69 handclap marking sync start
70 **dual film-tape recording using a tape recorder**
71 pulse-generating camera
72 pulse cable
73 cassette recorder
74 microphone
75 **dual film-tape reproduction**
76 tape cassette
77 synchronization unit
78 cine projector
79 film feed spool
80 take-up reel (take-up spool), an automatic take-up reel (take-up spool)
81 **sound projector**
82 sound film with magnetic stripe (sound track, track)
83 automatic-threading button
84 trick button
85 volume control
86 reset button
87 fast and slow motion switch
88 forward, reverse, and still projection switch
89 splicer for wet splices
90 hinged clamping plate
91 **film viewer** (animated viewer editor)
92 foldaway reel arm
93 rewind handle (rewinder)
94 viewing screen
95 film perforator (film marker)
96 **six-turn able film and sound cutting table** (editing table, cutting bench, animated sound editor)
97 monitor
98 control buttons (control well)
99 film turntable
100 first sound turntable, e.g. for live sound
101 second sound turntable for post-sync sound
102 film and tape synchronizing head

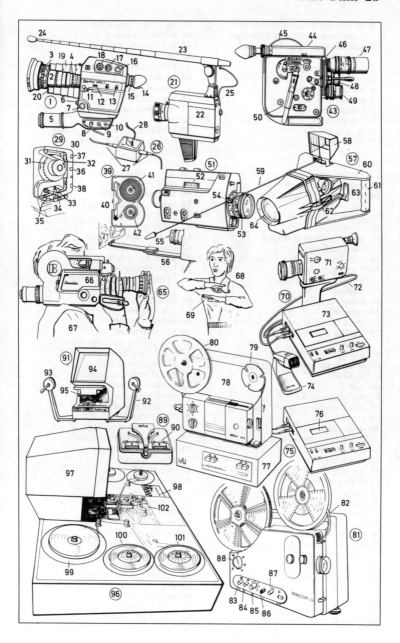

29 Building Site (Construction Site) I

1-49 carcase (carcass, fabric)
[house construction, carcassing]
1 basement of tamped (rammed)
concrete
2 concrete base course
3 cellar window (basement window)
4 outside cellar steps
5 utility room window
6 utility room door
7 ground floor (*Am.* first floor)
8 brick wall
9 lintel (window head)
10 reveal
11 jamb
12 window ledge (window sill)
13 reinforced concrete lintel
14 upper floor (first floor, *Am.*
second floor)
15 hollow-block wall
16 concrete floor
17 work platform (working
platform)
18 bricklayer (*Am.* brickmason)
19 bricklayer's labourer (*Am.*
laborer); *also:* builder's
labourer
20 mortar trough
21 chimney
22 cover (boards) for the staircase
23 scaffold pole (scaffold
standard)
24 platform railing
25 angle brace (angle tie) in the
scaffold
26 ledger
27 putlog (putlock)
28 plank platform (board platform)
29 guard board
30 scaffolding joint with chain or
lashing or whip or bond
31 builder's hoist
32 mixer operator
33 concrete mixer, a gravity mixer
34 mixing drum
35 feeder skip
36 concrete aggregate [sand and
gravel]
37 wheelbarrow
38 hose (hosepipe)
39 mortar pan (mortar trough,
mortar tub)
40 stack of bricks
41 stacked shutter boards (lining
boards)
42 ladder
43 bag of cement
44 site fence, a timber fence

45 signboard (billboard)
46 removable gate
47 contractors' name plates
48 site hut (site office)
49 building site latrine
50-57 bricklayer's (*Am.*
brickmason's) **tools**
50 plumb bob (plummet)
51 thick lead pencil
52 trowel
53 bricklayer's (*Am.* brickmason's)
hammer (brick hammer)
54 mallet
55 spirit level
56 laying-on trowel
57 float
58-68 masonry bonds
58 brick (standard brick)
59 stretching bond
60 heading bond
61 racking (raking) back
62 English bond
63 stretching course
64 heading course
65 English cross bond (Saint
Andrew's cross bond)
66 chimney bond
67 first course
68 second course
69-82 excavation
69 profile (*Am.* batterboard)
[fixed on edge at the corner]
70 intersection of strings
71 plumb bob (plummet)
72 excavation side
73 upper edge board
74 lower edge board
75 foundation trench
76 navvy (*Am.* excavator)
77 conveyor belt (conveyor)
78 excavated earth
79 plank roadway
80 tree guard
81 mechanical shovel
(excavator)
82 shovel bucket (bucket)
83-91 plastering
83 plasterer
84 mortar trough
85 screen
86-89 ladder scaffold
86 standard ladder
87 boards (planks, platform)
88 diagonal strut (diagonal brace)
89 railing
90 guard netting
91 rope-pulley hoist

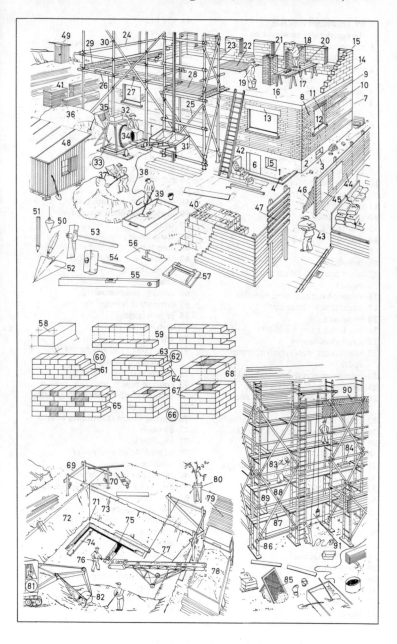

30 Building Site (Construction Site) II

1-89 reinforced concrete (ferroconcrete) construction
1 reinforced concrete (ferro-concrete) skeleton construction
2 reinforced concrete (ferroconcrete) frame
3 inferior purlin
4 concrete purlin
5 ceiling joist
6 arch (flank)
7 rubble concrete wall
8 reinforced concrete (ferroconcrete) floor
9 concreter (concretor), flattening out
10 projecting reinforcement (*Am.* connection rebars)
11 column box
12 joist shuttering
13 shuttering strut
14 diagonal bracing
15 wedge
16 board
17 sheet pile wall (sheet pile, sheet piling)
18 shutter boards (lining boards)
19 circular saw (buzz saw)
20 bending table
21 bar bender (steel bender)
22 hand steel shears
23 reinforcing steel (reinforcement rods)
24 pumice concrete hollow block
25 partition wall, a timber wall
26 concrete aggregate [gravel and sand of various grades]
27 crane track
28 tipping wagon (tipping truck)
29 concrete mixer
30 cement silo
31 tower crane (tower slewing crane)
32 bogie (*Am.* truck)
33 counterweight
34 tower
35 crane driver's cabin (crane driver's cage)
36 jib (boom)
37 bearer cable
38 concrete bucket
39 sleepers (*Am.* ties)
40 chock
41 ramp
42 wheelbarrow
43 safety rail
44 site hut
45 canteen
46 tubular steel scaffold (scaffolding)
47 standard
48 ledger tube
49 tie tube
50 shoe
51 diagonal brace
52 planking (platform)
53 coupling (coupler)
54-76 formwork (shuttering) and reinforcement
54 bottom shuttering (lining)
55 side shutter of a purlin
56 cut-in bottom
57 cross beam
58 cramp iron (cramp, dog)
59 upright member, a standard
60 strap
61 cross piece
62 stop fillet
63 strut (brace, angle brace)
64 frame timber (yoke)
65 strap
66 reinforcement binding
67 cross strut (strut)
68 reinforcement
69 distribution steel
70 stirrup
71 projecting reinforcement (*Am.* connection rebars)
72 concrete (heavy concrete)
73 column box
74 bolted frame timber (bolted yoke)
75 nut (thumb nut)
76 shutter board (shuttering board)
77-89 tools
77 bending iron
78 adjustable service girder
79 adjusting screw
80 round bar reinforcement
81 distance piece (separator, spacer)
82 Torsteel
83 concrete tamper
84 mould (*Am.* mold) for concrete test cubes
85 concreter's tongs
86 sheeting support
87 hand shears
88 immersion vibrator (concrete vibrator)
89 vibrating cylinder (vibrating head, vibrating poker)

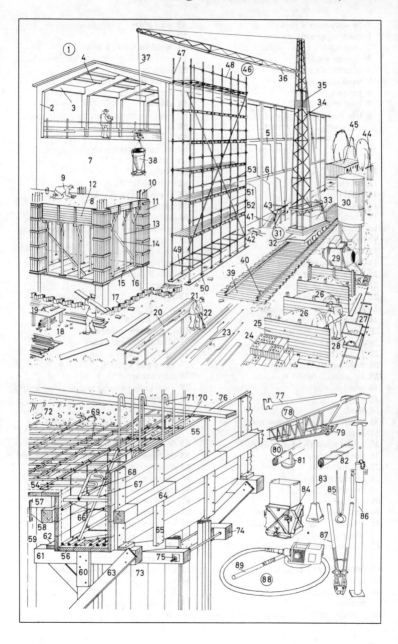

31 Carpenter

1-59 carpenter's yard
1 stack of boards (planks)
2 long timber (*Am.* lumber)
3 sawing shed
4 carpenter's workshop
5 workshop door
6 handcart
7 roof truss
8 tree [used for topping out ceremony], with wreath
9 timber wall
10 squared timber (building timber, scantlings)
11 drawing floor
12 carpenter
13 safety helmet
14 cross-cut saw, a chain saw
15 chain guide
16 saw chain
17 mortiser (chain cutter)
18 trestle (horse)
19 beam mounted on a trestle
20 set of carpenter's tools
21 electric drill
22 dowel hole
23 mark for the dowel hole
24 beams
25 post (stile, stud, quarter)
26 corner brace
27 brace (strut)
28 base course (plinth)
29 house wall (wall)
30 window opening
31 reveal
32 jamb
33 window ledge (window sill)
34 cornice
35 roundwood (round timber)
36 floorboards
37 hoisting rope
38 ceiling joist (ceiling beam, main beam)
39 wall joist
40 wall plate
41 trimmer (trimmer joist, *Am.* header, header joist)
42 dragon beam (dragon piece)
43 false floor (inserted floor)
44 floor filling of breeze, loam, etc.
45 fillet (cleat)
46 stair well (well)
47 chimney
48 framed partition (framed wall)
49 wall plate
50 girt
51 window jamb, a jamb
52 corner stile (corner strut, corner stud)
53 principal post
54 brace (strut) with skew notch
55 nogging piece
56 sill rail
57 window lintel (window head)
58 head (head rail)
59 filled-in panel (bay, pan)

60-82 carpenter's tools
60 hand saw
61 bucksaw
62 saw blade
63 compass saw (keyhole saw)
64 plane
65 auger (gimlet)
66 screw clamp (cramp, holdfast)
67 mallet
68 two-handed saw
69 try square
70 broad axe (*Am.* broadax)
71 chisel
72 mortise axe (mortice axe, *Am.* mortise ax)
73 axe (*Am.* ax)
74 carpenter's hammer
75 claw head (nail claw)
76 folding rule
77 carpenter's pencil
78 iron square
79 drawknife (drawshave, drawing knife)
80 shaving
81 bevel
82 mitre square (*Am.* miter square, miter angle)

83-96 building timber
83 undressed timber (*Am.* rough lumber)
84 heartwood (duramen)
85 sapwood (sap, alburnum)
86 bark (rind)
87 baulk (balk)
88 halved timber
89 wane (waney edge)
90 quarter baulk (balk)
91 plank (board)
92 end-grained timber
93 heartwood plank (heart plank)
94 unsquared (untrimmed) plank (board)
95 squared (trimmed) board
96 slab (offcut)

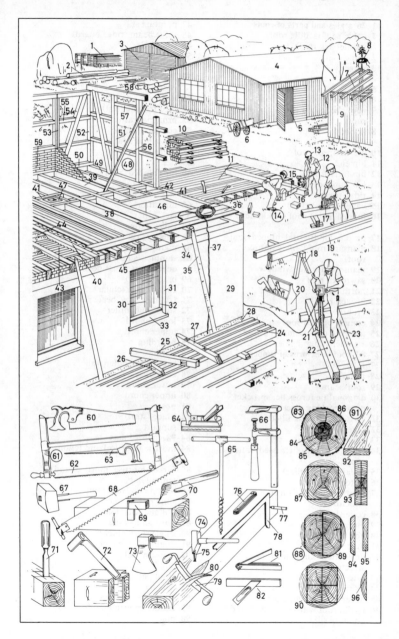

32 Roof, Timber Joints

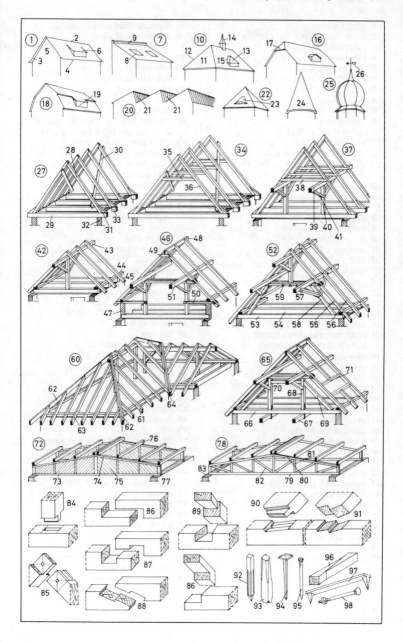

33 Roof and Roofer

1 tiled roof
2 plain-tile double-lap roofing
3 ridge tile
4 ridge course tile
5 under-ridge tile
6 plain (plane) tile
7 ventilating tile
8 ridge tile
9 hip tile
10 hipped end
11 valley (roof valley)
12 skylight
13 chimney
14 chimney flashing, made of sheet zinc
15 ladder hook
16 snow guard bracket
17 battens (slating and tiling battens)
18 batten gauge (*Am.* gage)
19 rafter
20 tile hammer
21 lath axe (*Am.* ax)
22 hod
23 hod hook
24 opening (hatch)
25 gable (gable end)
26 toothed lath
27 soffit
28 gutter
29 rainwater pipe (downpipe)
30 swan's neck (swan-neck)
31 pipe clip
32 gutter bracket
33 tile cutter
34 scaffold
35 safety wall
36 eaves
37 outer wall
38 exterior rendering
39 frost-resistant brickwork
40 inferior purlin
41 rafter head (rafter end)
42 eaves fascia
43 double lath (tilting lath)
44 insulating boards
45-60 tiles and tile roofings
45 split-tiled roof
46 plain (plane) tile
47 ridge course
48 slip
49 eaves course
50 plain-tiled roof
51 nib
52 ridge tile
53 pantiled roof
54 pantile
55 pointing

56 Spanish-tiled roof (*Am.* mission-tiled roof)
57 under tile
58 over tile
59 interlocking tile
60 flat interlocking tile
61-89 slate roof
61 roof boards (roof boarding, roof sheathing)
62 roofing paper (sheathing paper); *also:* roofing felt (*Am.* rag felt)
63 cat ladder (roof ladder)
64 coupling hook
65 ridge hook
66 roof trestle
67 trestle rope
68 knot
69 ladder hook
70 scaffold board
71 slater
72 nail bag
73 slate hammer
74 slate nail, a galvanized wire nail
75 slater's shoe, a bast or hemp shoe
76 eaves course (eaves joint)
77 corner bottom slate
78 roof course
79 ridge course (ridge joint)
80 gable slate
81 tail line
82 valley (roof valley)
83 box gutter (trough gutter, parallel gutter)
84 slater's iron
85 slate
86 back
87 head
88 front edge
89 tail
90-103 asphalt-impregnated paper roofing and corrugated asbestos cement roofing
90 asphalt-impregnated paper roof
91 width [parallel to the gutter]
92 gutter
93 ridge
94 join
95 width [at right angles to the gutter]
96 felt nail (clout nail)
97 corrugated asbestos cement roof
98 corrugated sheet
99 ridge capping piece
100 lap
101 wood screw
102 rust-proof zinc cup
103 lead washer

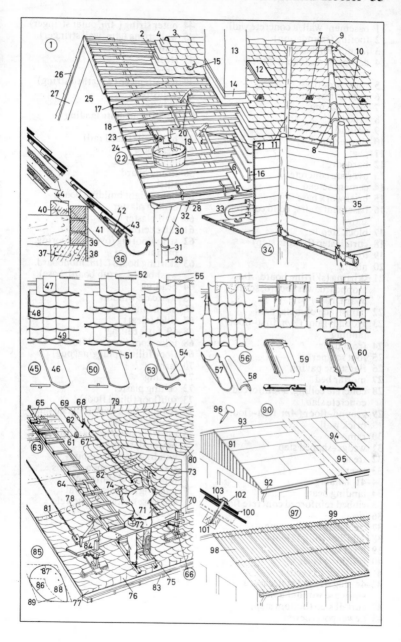

34 Floor, Ceiling, Staircase Construction

1 basement wall, a concrete wall
2 footing (foundation)
3 foundation base
4 damp course (damp-proof course)
5 waterproofing
6 rendering coat
7 brick paving
8 sand bed
9 ground
10 shuttering
11 peg
12 hardcore
13 oversite concrete
14 cement screed
15 brickwork base
16 basement stairs, solid concrete stairs
17 block step
18 curtail step (bottom step)
19 top step
20 nosing
21 skirting (skirting board, *Am.* mopboard, washboard, scrub board, base)
22 balustrade of metal bars
23 ground-floor (*Am.* first-floor) landing
24 front door
25 foot scraper
26 flagstone paving
27 mortar bed
28 concrete ceiling, a reinforced concrete slab
29 ground-floor (*Am.* first-floor) brick wall
30 ramp
31 wedge-shaped step
32 tread
33 riser
34-41 landing
34 landing beam
35 ribbed reinforced concrete floor
36 rib
37 steel-bar reinforcement
38 subfloor (blind floor)
39 level layer
40 finishing layer
41 top layer (screed)
42-44 dog-legged staircase, a staircase without a well
42 curtail step (bottom step)
43 newel post (newel)

44 outer string (*Am.* outer stringer)
45 wall string (*Am.* wall stringer)
46 staircase bolt
47 tread
48 riser
49 wreath piece (wreathed string)
50 balustrade
51 baluster
52-62 intermediate landing
52 wreath
53 handrail (guard rail)
54 head post
55 landing beam
56 lining board
57 fillet
58 lightweight building board
59 ceiling plaster
60 wall plaster
61 false ceiling
62 strip flooring (overlay flooring, parquet strip)
63 skirting board (*Am.* mopboard, washboard, scrub board, base)
64 beading
65 staircase window
66 main landing beam
67 fillet (cleat)
68-69 false ceiling
68 false floor (inserted floor)
69 floor filling (plugging, pug)
70 laths
71 lathing
72 ceiling plaster
73 subfloor (blind floor)
74 parquet floor with tongued-and-grooved blocks
75 quarter-newelled (*Am.* quarter-neweled) staircase
76 winding staircase (spiral staircase) with open newels (open-newel staircase)
77 winding staircase (spiral staircase) with solid newels (solid-newel staircase)
78 newel (solid newel)
79 handrail

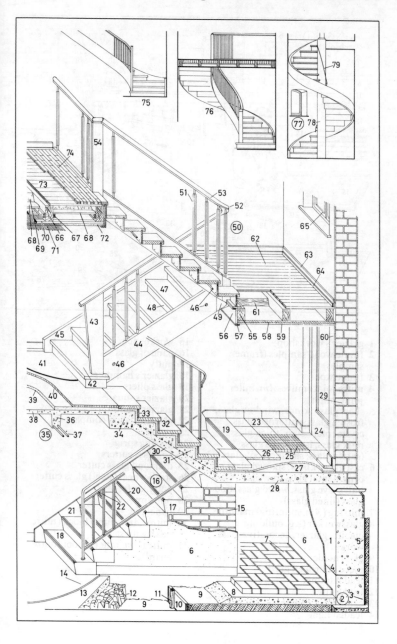

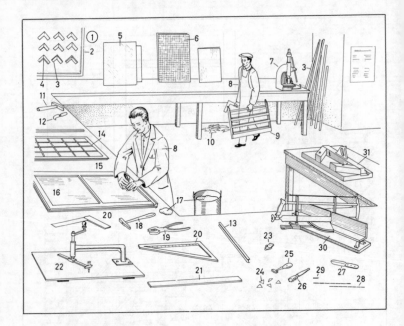

1 glazier's workshop
2 frame wood samples (frame samples)
3 frame wood
4 mitre joint (mitre, *Am.* miter joint, miter)
5 sheet glass; *kinds:* window glass, frosted glass, patterned glass, crystal plate glass, thick glass, milk glass, laminated glass (safety glass, shatterproof glass)
6 cast glass; *kinds:* stained glass, ornamental glass, raw glass, bull's-eye glass, wired glass, line glass (lined glass)
7 mitring (*Am.* mitering) machine
8 glassworker (*e.g.* building glazier, glazier, decorative glass worker)
9 glass holder
10 piece of broken glass
11 lead hammer
12 lead knife
13 came (lead came)
14 leaded light

15 workbench
16 pane of glass
17 putty
18 glazier's hammer
19 glass pliers
20 glazier's square
21 glazier's rule
22 glazier's beam compass
23 eyelet
24 glazing sprig
25-26 glass cutters
25 diamond glass cutter
26 steel-wheel (steel) glass cutter
27 putty knife
28 pin wire
29 panel pin
30 mitre (*Am.* miter) block (mitre box) [with saw]
31 mitre (*Am.* miter) shoot (mitre board)

1 metal shears (tinner's snips, *Am.* tinner's shears)
2 elbow snips (angle shears)
3 gib
4 lapping plate
5–7 propane soldering apparatus
5 propane soldering iron, a hatchet iron
6 soldering stone, a sal-ammoniac block
7 soldering fluid (flux)
8 beading iron for forming reinforcement beading
9 angled reamer
10 workbench (bench)
11 beam compass (trammel, *Am.* beam trammel)
12 electric hand die
13 hollow punch
14 chamfering hammer
15 beading swage (beading hammer)
16 abrasive-wheel cutting-off machine
17 plumber
18 mallet
19 mandrel
20 socket (tinner's socket)
21 block
22 anvil
23 stake
24 circular saw (buzz saw)
25 flanging, swaging, and wiring machine
26 sheet shears (guillotine)
27 screw-cutting machine (thread-cutting machine, die stocks)
28 pipe-bending machine (bending machine, pipe bender)
29 welding transformer
30 bending machine (rounding machine) for shaping funnels

37 Plumber, Gas Fitter, Heating Engineer

1 gas fitter and plumber
2 stepladder
3 safety chain
4 stop valve
5 gas meter
6 bracket
7 service riser
8 distributing pipe
9 supply pipe
10 pipe-cutting machine
11 pipe repair stand
12-25 gas and water appliances
12-13 geyser, an instantaneous water heater
12 gas water heater
13 electric water heater
14 toilet cistern
15 float
16 bell
17 flush pipe
18 water inlet
19 flushing lever (lever)
20 radiator
21 radiator rib
22 two-pipe system
23 flow pipe
24 return pipe
25 gas heater
26-37 plumbing fixtures
26 trap (anti-syphon trap)
27 mixer tap (*Am.* mixing faucet) for washbasins
28 hot tap
29 cold tap
30 extendible shower attachment
31 water tap (pillar tap) for washbasins
32 spindle top
33 shield
34 draw-off tap (*Am.* faucet)
35 supatap
36 swivel tap
37 flushing valve
38-52 fittings
38 joint with male thread
39 reducing socket (reducing coupler)
40 elbow screw joint (elbow coupling)
41 reducing socket (reducing coupler) with female thread
42 screw joint
43 coupler (socket)

44 T-joint (T-junction joint, tee)
45 elbow screw joint with female thread
46 bend
47 T-joint (T-junction joint, tee) with female taper thread
48 ceiling joint
49 reducing elbow
50 cross
51 elbow joint with male thread
52 elbow joint
53-57 pipe supports
53 saddle clip
54 spacing bracket
55 plug
56 pipe clips
57 two-piece spacing clip
58-86 plumber's tools, gas fitter's tools
58 gas pliers
59 footprints
60 combination cutting pliers
61 pipe wrench
62 flat-nose pliers
63 nipple key
64 round-nose pliers
65 pincers
66 adjustable S-wrench
67 screw wrench
68 shifting spanner
69 screwdriver
70 compass saw (keyhole saw)
71 hacksaw frame
72 hand saw
73 soldering iron
74 blowlamp (blowtorch) [for soldering]
75 sealing tape
76 tin-lead solder
77 club hammer
78 hammer
79 spirit level
80 steel-leg vice (*Am.* vise)
81 pipe vice (*Am.* vise)
82 pipe-bending machine
83 former (template)
84 pipe cutter
85 hand die
86 screw-cutting machine (thread-cutting machine)

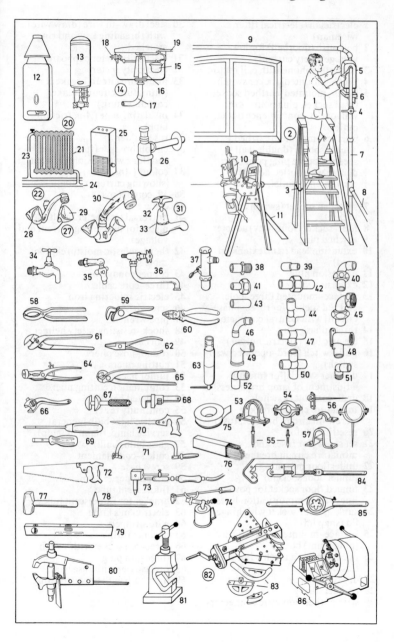

38 Electrician

1 electrician (electrical fitter, wireman)
2 bell push (doorbell) for low-voltage safety current
3 house telephone with call button
4 [flush-mounted] rocker switch
5 [flush-mounted] earthed socket (wall socket, plug point, *Am.* wall outlet, convenience outlet, outlet)
6 [surface-mounted] earthed double socket (double wall socket, double plug point, *Am.* double wall outlet, double convenience outlet, double outlet)
7 switched socket (switch and socket)
8 four-socket (four-way) adapter
9 earthed plug
10 extension lead (*Am.* extension cord)
11 extension plug
12 extension socket
13 surface-mounted three-pole earthed socket [for three-phase circuit] with neutral conductor
14 three-phase plug
15 electric bell (electric buzzer)
16 pull-switch (cord-operated wall switch)
17 dimmer switch [for smooth adjustment of lamp brightness]
18 drill-cast rotary switch
19 miniature circuit breaker (screw-in circuit breaker, fuse)
20 resetting button
21 set screw [for fuses and miniature circuit breakers]
22 underfloor mounting (underfloor sockets)
23 hinged floor socket for power lines and communication lines
24 sunken floor socket with hinged lid (snap lid)
25 surface-mounted socket outlet (plug point) box
26 pocket torch, a torch (*Am.* flashlight)
27 dry cell battery
28 contact spring
29 strip of thermoplastic connectors
30 steel draw-in wire (draw wire) with threading key, and ring attached
31 electricity meter cupboard
32 electricity meter
33 miniature circuit breakers (miniature circuit breaker consumer unit)
34 insulating tape (*Am.* friction tape)
35 fuse holder
36 circuit breaker (fuse), a fuse cartridge with fusible element
37 colour (*Am.* color) indicator [showing current rating]
38-39 contact maker
40 cable clip
41 universal test meter (multiple meter for measuring current and voltage)
42 thermoplastic moisture-proof cable
43 copper conductor
44 three-core cable
45 electric soldering iron
46 screwdriver
47 pipe wrench
48 shock-resisting safety helmet
49 tool case
50 round-nose pliers
51 cutting pliers
52 junior hacksaw
53 combination cutting pliers
54 insulated handle
55 continuity tester
56 electric light bulb (general service lamp, filament lamp)
57 glass bulb (bulb)
58 coiled-coil filament
59 screw base
60 lampholder
61 fluorescent tube
62 bracket for fluorescent tubes
63 electrician's knife
64 wire strippers
65 bayonet fitting
66 three-pin socket with switch
67 three-pin plug
68 fuse carrier with fuse wire
69 light bulb with bayonet fitting

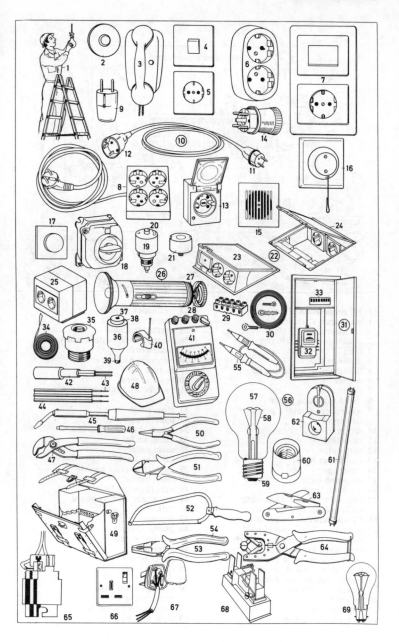

39 Paperhanger

1 **painting**
2 painter
3 paintbrush
4 emulsion paint (emulsion)
5 stepladder
6 can (tin) of paint
7-**8** cans (tins) of paint
7 can (tin) with fixed handle
8 paint kettle
9 drum of paint
10 paint bucket
11 paint roller
12 grill [for removing excess paint from the roller]
13 stippling roller
14 **varnishing**
15 oil-painted dado
16 canister for thinner
17 flat brush for larger surfaces (flat wall brush)
18 stippler
19 fitch
20 cutting-in brush
21 radiator brush (flay brush)
22 paint scraper
23 scraper
24 putty knife
25 sandpaper
26 sandpaper block
27 floor brush
28 **sanding and spraying**
29 grinder

30 sander
31 pressure pot
32 spray gun
33 compressor (air compressor)
34 flow coating machine for flow coating radiators, etc.
35 hand spray
36 airless spray unit
37 airless spray gun
38 efflux viscometer
39 seconds timer
40 **lettering and gilding**
41 lettering brush (signwriting brush, pencil)
42 tracing wheel
43 stencil knife
44 oil gold size
45 gold leaf
46 outline drawing
47 mahlstick
48 pouncing
49 pounce bag
50 gilder's cushion
51 gilder's knife
52 sizing gold leaf
53 filling in the letters with stipple paint
54 gilder's mop

41 Cooper and Tank Construction Engineer

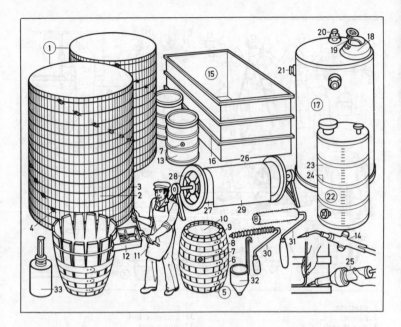

1–33 cooper's and tank construction engineer's workshops

1 tank
2 circumference made of staves (staved circumference)
3 iron rod
4 turnbuckle
5 barrel (cask)
6 body of barrel (of cask)
7 bunghole
8 band (hoop) of barrel
9 barrel stave
10 barrelhead (heading)
11 cooper
12 trusser
13 drum
14 gas welding torch
15 staining vat, made of thermoplastics
16 iron reinforcing bands
17 storage container, made of glass fibre (*Am.* glass fiber) reinforced polyester resin
18 manhole

19 manhole cover with handwheel
20 flange mount
21 flange–type stopcock
22 measuring tank
23 shell (circumference)
24 shrink ring
25 hot–air gun
26 roller made of glass fibre (*Am.* glass fiber) reinforced synthetic resin
27 cylinder
28 flange
29 glass cloth
30 grooved roller
31 lambskin roller
32 ladle for testing viscosity
33 measuring vessel for hardener

1-25 furrier's workroom
1 furrier
2 steam spray gun
3 steam iron
4 beating machine
5 cutting machine for letting out furskins
6 uncut furskin
7 let-out strips (let-out sections)
8 fur worker
9 fur-sewing machine
10 blower for letting out
11-21 furskins
11 mink skin
12 fur side
13 leather side
14 cut furskin
15 lynx skin before letting out
16 let-out lynx skin
17 fur side
18 leather side
19 let-out mink skin
20 lynx fur, sewn together (sewn)
21 broadtail

22 fur marker
23 fur worker
24 mink coat
25 ocelot coat

43 Joiner I

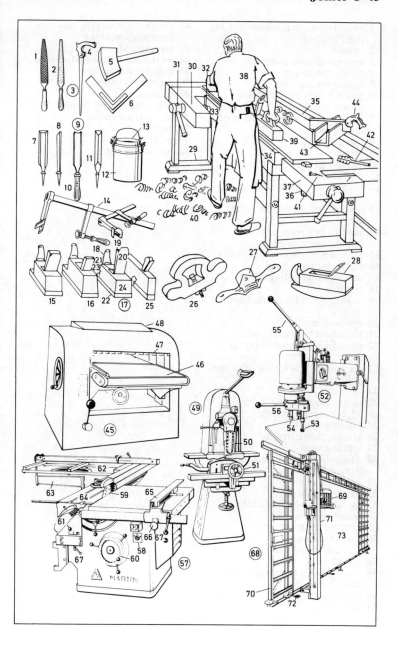

44 Joiner II

1 veneer-peeling machine (peeling machine, peeler)
2 veneer
3 veneer-splicing machine
4 nylon-thread cop
5 sewing mechanism
6 dowel hole boring machine (dowel hole borer)
7 boring motor with hollow-shaft boring bit
8 clamp handle
9 clamp
10 clamping shoe
11 stop bar
12 edge sander (edge-sanding machine)
13 tension roller with extension arm
14 sanding belt regulator (regulating handle)
15 endless sanding belt (sand belt)
16 belt-tensioning lever
17 canting table (tilting table)
18 belt roller
19 angling fence for mitres (*Am.* miters)
20 opening dust hood
21 rise adjustment of the table
22 rise adjustment wheel for the table
23 clamping screw for the table rise adjustment
24 console
25 foot of the machine
26 edge-veneering machine
27 sanding wheel
28 sanding dust extractor
29 splicing head
30 single-belt sanding machine (single-belt sander)
31 belt guard
32 bandwheel cover
33 extractor fan (exhaust fan)
34 frame-sanding pad
35 sanding table
36 fine adjustment
37 fine cutter and jointer
38 saw carriage
39 trailing cable hanger (trailing cable support)
40 air extractor pipe
41 rail

42 frame-cramping (frame-clamping) machine
43 frame stand
44 workpiece, a window frame
45 compressed-air line
46 pressure cylinder
47 pressure foot
48 frame-mounting device
49 rapid-veneer press
50 bed
51 press
52 pressure piston

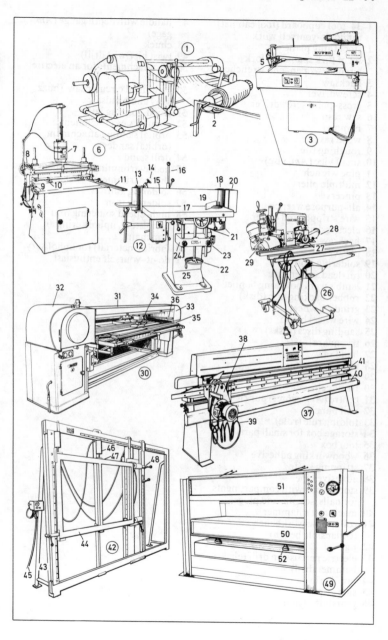

45 Do-it-yourself

1-34 tool cupboard (tool cabinet) for do-it-yourself work
1 smoothing plane
2 set of fork spanners (fork wrenches, open-end wrenches)
3 hacksaw
4 screwdriver
5 cross-point screwdriver
6 saw rasp
7 hammer
8 wood rasp
9 roughing file
10 small vice (*Am.* vise)
11 pipe wrench
12 multiple pliers
13 pincers
14 all-purpose wrench
15 wire stripper and cutter
16 electric drill
17 hacksaw
18 plaster cup
19 soldering iron
20 tin-lead solder wire
21 lamb's wool polishing bonnet
22 rubber backing disc (disk)
23 grinding wheel
24 wire wheel brush
25 sanding discs (disks)
26 try square
27 hand saw
28 universal cutter
29 spirit level
30 firmer chisel
31 centre (*Am.* center) punch
32 nail punch
33 folding rule (rule)
34 storage box for small parts
35 tool box
36 woodworking adhesive
37 stripping knife
38 adhesive tape
39 storage box with compartments for nails, screws, and plugs
40 machinist's hammer
41 collapsible workbench (collapsible bench)
42 jig
43 electric percussion drill (electric hammer drill)
44 pistol grip
45 side grip
46 gearshift switch
47 handle with depth gauge (*Am.* gage)
48 chuck
49 twist bit (twist drill)
50-55 attachments for an electric drill
50 combined circular saw (buzz saw) and bandsaw
51 wood-turning lathe
52 circular saw attachment
53 orbital sanding attachment (orbital sander)
54 drill stand
55 hedge-trimming attachment (hedge trimmer)
56 soldering gun
57 soldering iron
58 high-speed soldering iron
59 upholstery, upholstering an armchair
60 fabric (material) for upholstery
61 do-it-yourself enthusiast

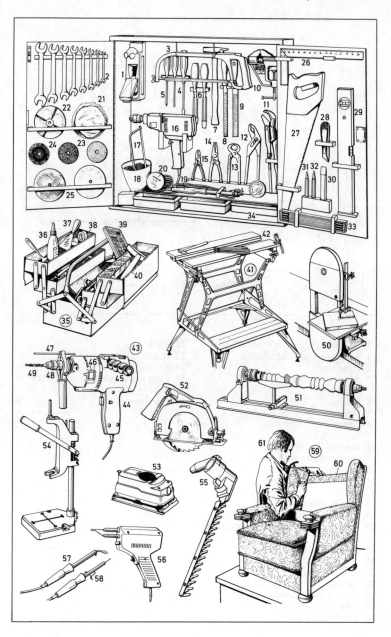

46 Turner (Ivory Carver)

1-26 **turnery** (turner's workshop)
1 wood-turning lathe (lathe)
2 lathe bed
3 starting resistance (starting resistor)
4 gearbox
5 tool rest
6 chuck
7 tailstock
8 centre (*Am.* center)
9 driving plate with pin
10 two-jaw chuck
11 live centre (*Am.* center)
12 fretsaw
13 fretsaw blade
14, 15, 24 turning tools
14 thread chaser, for cutting threads in wood
15 gouge, for rough turning
16 spoon bit (shell bit)
17 hollowing tool
18 outside calliper (caliper)
19 turned work (turned wood)
20 master turner (turner)
21 [piece of] rough wood

22 drill
23 inside calliper (caliper)
24 parting tool
25 glass paper (sandpaper, emery paper)
26 shavings

1–40 basket making (basketry, basketwork)
1–4 weaves (strokes)
1 randing
2 rib randing
3 oblique randing
4 randing, a piece of wickerwork (screen work)
5 weaver
6 stake
7 workboard; *also:* lapboard
8 screw block
9 hole for holding the block
10 stand
11 chip basket (spale basket)
12 chip (spale)
13 soaking tub
14 willow stakes (osier stakes)
15 willow rods (osier rods)
16 basket, a piece of wickerwork (basketwork)
17 border
18 woven side
19 round base
20 woven base
21 slath
22–24 covering a frame
22 frame
23 end
24 rib
25 upsett
26 grass; *kinds:* esparto grass, alfalfa grass
27 rush (bulrush, reed mace)
28 reed
29 raffia (bast)
30 straw
31 bamboo cane
32 rattan (ratan) chair cane
33 basket maker
34 bending tool
35 cutting point (bodkin)
36 rapping iron
37 pincers
38 picking knife
39 shave
40 hacksaw

48 Blacksmith (Smith) I

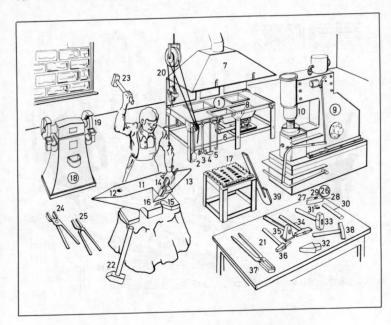

1–8 hearth (forge) with blacksmith's fire
1 hearth (forge)
2 shovel (slice)
3 swab
4 rake
5 poker
6 blast pipe (tue iron)
7 chimney (cowl, hood)
8 water trough (quenching trough, bosh)
9 power hammer
10 ram (tup)
11–16 anvil
11 anvil
12 flat beak (beck, bick)
13 round beak (beck, bick)
14 auxiliary table
15 foot
16 upsetting block
17 swage block
18 tool-grinding machine (tool grinder)
19 grinding wheel
20 block and tackle

21 workbench (bench)
22–39 blacksmith's tools
22 sledge hammer
23 blacksmith's hand hammer
24 flat tongs
25 round tongs
26 parts of the hammer
27 peen (pane, pein)
28 face
29 eye
30 haft
31 cotter punch
32 hardy (hardie)
33 set hammer
34 sett (set, sate)
35 flat-face hammer (flatter)
36 round punch
37 angle tongs
38 blacksmith's chisel (scaling hammer, chipping hammer)
39 moving iron (bending iron)

1 compressed-air system
2 electric motor
3 compressor
4 compressed-air tank
5 compressed-air line
6 percussion screwdriver
7 pedestal grinding machine (floor grinding machine)
8 grinding wheel
9 guard
10 trailer
11 brake drum
12 brake shoe
13 brake lining
14 testing kit
15 pressure gauge (*Am.* gage)
16 brake-testing equipment, a rolling road
17 pit
18 braking roller
19 meter (recording meter)
20 precision lathe for brake drums
21 lorry wheel
22 boring mill

23 power saw, a hacksaw (power hacksaw)
24 vice (*Am.* vise)
25 saw frame
26 coolant supply pipe
27 riveting machine
28 trailer frame (chassis) under construction
29 inert-gas welding equipment
30 rectifier
31 control unit
32 CO_2 cylinder
33 anvil
34 hearth (forge) with blacksmith's fire
35 trolley for gas cylinders
36 vehicle under repair, a tractor

50 Hammer Forging (Smith Forging) and Drop Forging

1 continuous furnace with grid hearth for annealing of round stock
2 discharge opening (discharge door)
3 gas burners
4 charging door
5 counterblow hammer
6 upper ram
7 lower ram
8 ram guide
9 hydraulic drive
10 column
11 short–stroke drop hammer
12 ram (tup)
13 upper die block
14 lower die block
15 hydraulic drive
16 frame
17 anvil
18 forging and sizing press
19 standard
20 table
21 disc (disk) clutch
22 compressed–air pipe
23 solenoid valve
24 air–lift gravity hammer (air–lift drop hammer)
25 drive motor
26 hammer (tup)
27 foot control (foot pedal)
28 preshaped (blocked) workpiece
29 hammer guide
30 hammer cylinder
31 anvil
32 mechanical manipulator to move the workpiece in hammer forging
33 dogs
34 counterweight
35 hydraulic forging press
36 crown
37 cross head
38 upper die block
39 lower die block
40 anvil
41 hydraulic piston
42 pillar guide
43 rollover device
44 burden chain (chain sling)
45 crane hook
46 workpiece
47 gas furnace (gas–fired furnace)

48 gas burner
49 charging opening
50 chain curtain
51 vertical–lift door
52 hot–air duct
53 air preheater
54 gas pipe
55 electric door–lifting mechanism
56 air blast

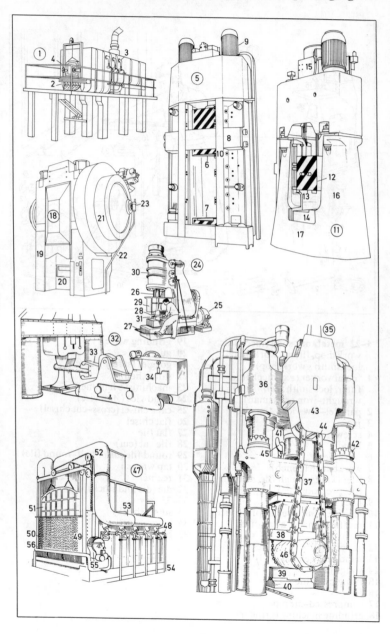

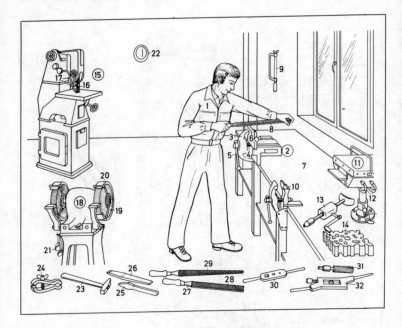

1–22 metalwork shop (mechanic's
workshop, fitter's workshop,
locksmith's workshop)
1 metalworker (*e.g.* mechanic,
fitter, locksmith; *form. also:*
wrought–iron craftsman)
2 parallel–jaw vice (*Am.* vise)
3 jaw
4 screw
5 handle
6 workpiece
7 workbench (bench)
8 files (*kinds:* rough file, smooth
file, precision file)
9 hacksaw
10 leg vice (*Am.* vise), a spring vice
11 muffle furnace, a gas–fired
furnace
12 gas pipe
13 hand brace (hand drill)
14 swage block
15 filing machine
16 file
17 compressed–air pipe
18 grinding machine (grinder)

19 grinding wheel
20 guard
21 goggles (safety glasses)
22 safety helmet
23 machinist's hammer
24 hand vice (*Am.* vise)
25 cape chisel (cross–cut chisel)
26 flat chisel
27 flat file
28 file cut (cut)
29 round file (*also:* half–round file)
30 tap wrench
31 reamer
32 die (die and stock)
33–35 key
33 stem (shank)
34 bow
35 bit

36–43 door lock, a mortise (mortice) lock

36 back plate
37 spring bolt (latch bolt)
38 tumbler
39 bolt
40 keyhole
41 bolt guide pin
42 tumbler spring
43 follower, with square hole
44 cylinder lock (safety lock)
45 cylinder (plug)
46 spring
47 pin
48 safety key, a flat key
49 lift–off hinge
50 hook–and–ride band
51 strap hinge
52 vernier calliper (caliper) gauge (*Am.* gage)
53 feeler gauge (*Am.* gage)
54 vernier depth gauge (*Am.* gage)
55 vernier
56 straightedge
57 square
58 breast drill
59 twist bit (twist drill)
60 screw tap (tap)
61 halves of a screw die
62 screwdriver
63 scraper (*also:* pointed triangle scraper)
64 centre (*Am.* center) punch
65 round punch
66 flat–nose pliers
67 detachable–jaw cut nippers
68 gas pliers
69 pincers

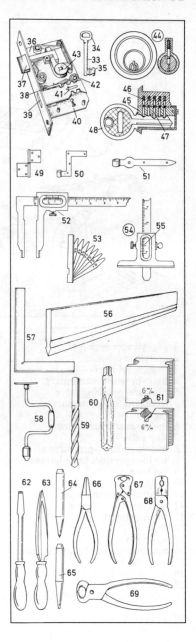

52 Gas Welder

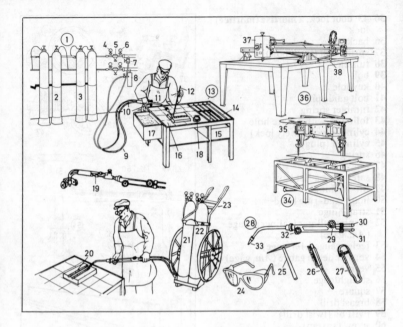

1 gas cylinder manifold
2 acetylene cylinder
3 oxygen cylinder
4 high–pressure manometer
5 pressure–reducing valve
  (reducing valve, pressure
  regulator)
6 low–pressure manometer
7 stop valve
8 hydraulic back–pressure valve
  for low–pressure installations
9 gas hose
10 oxygen hose
11 welding torch (blowpipe)
12 welding rod (filler rod)
13 welding bench
14 grating
15 scrap box
16 bench covering of chamotte slabs
17 water tank
18 welding paste (flux)
19 welding torch (blowpipe) with
  cutting attachment and guide
  tractor
20 workpiece

21 oxygen cylinder
22 acetylene cylinder
23 cylinder trolley
24 welding goggles
25 chipping hammer
26 wire brush
27 torch lighter (blowpipe lighter)
28 welding torch (blowpipe)
29 oxygen control
30 oxygen connection
31 gas connection (acetylene
  connection)
32 gas control (acetylene control)
33 welding nozzle
34 cutting machine
35 circular template
36 universal cutting machine
37 tracing head
38 cutting nozzle

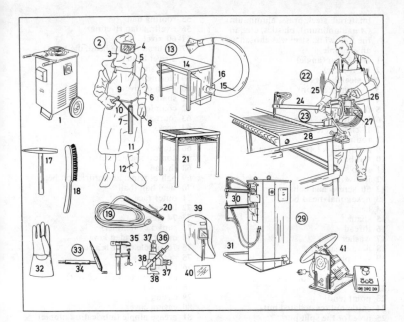

1 welding transformer
2 arc welder
3 arc welding helmet
4 flip-up window
5 shoulder guard
6 protective sleeve
7 electrode case
8 three-fingered welding glove
9 electrode holder
10 electrode
11 leather apron
12 shin guard
13 welding table with fume extraction equipment
14 table top
15 movable extractor duct
16 extractor support
17 chipping hammer
18 wire brush
19 welding lead
20 electrode holder
21 welding bench
22 spot welding
23 spot welding electrode holder
24 electrode arm

25 power supply (lead)
26 electrode-pressure cylinder
27 welding transformer
28 workpiece
29 foot-operated spot welder
30 welder electrode arms
31 foot pedal for welding pressure adjustment
32 five-fingered welding glove
33 inert-gas torch for inert-gas welding (gas-shielded arc welding)
34 inert-gas (shielding-gas) supply
35 work clamp (earthing clamp)
36 fillet gauge (*Am.* gage) (weld gauge) [for measuring throat thickness]
37 micrometer
38 measuring arm
39 arc welding helmet
40 filter lens
41 small turntable

54 Sections, Bolts, and Machine Parts

[material: steel, brass, aluminium
(*Am.* aluminum), plastics, etc.; in
the following, steel was chosen as
an example]

1 angle iron (angle)
2 leg (flange)
3-7 steel girders
3 T-iron (tee-iron)
4 vertical leg
5 flange
6 H-girder (H-beam)
7 E-channel (channel iron)
8 round bar
9 square iron (*Am.* square stock)
10 flat bar
11 strip steel
12 iron wire
13-50 screws and bolts
13 hexagonal-head bolt
14 head
15 shank
16 thread
17 washer
18 hexagonal nut
19 split pin
20 rounded end
21 width of head (of flats)
22 stud
23 point (end)
24 castle nut (castellated nut)
25 hole for the split pin
26 cross-head screw, a sheet-metal
   screw (self-tapping screw)
27 hexagonal socket head screw
28 countersunk-head bolt
29 catch
30 locknut (locking nut)
31 bolt (pin)
32 collar-head bolt
33 set collar (integral collar)
34 spring washer (washer)
35 round nut, an adjusting nut
36 cheese-head screw, a slotted screw
37 tapered pin
38 screw slot (screw slit, screw groove)
39 square-head bolt
40 grooved pin, a cylindrical pin
41 T-head bolt
42 wing nut (fly nut, butterfly nut)
43 rag bolt
44 barb
45 wood screw
46 countersunk head
47 wood screw thread
48 grub screw
49 pin slot (pin slit, pin groove)
50 round end
51 nail (wire nail)
52 head
53 shank
54 point

55 roofing nail
56 riveting (lap riveting)
57-60 rivet
57 set head (swage head, die head),
   a rivet head
58 rivet shank
59 closing head
60 pitch of rivets
61 shaft
62 chamfer (bevel)
63 journal
64 neck
65 seat
66 keyway
67 conical seat (cone)
68 thread
69 ball bearing, an antifriction bearing
70 steel ball (ball)
71 outer race
72 inner race
73-74 keys
73 sunk key (feather)
74 gib (gib-headed key)
75-76 needle roller bearing
75 needle cage
76 needle
77 castle nut (castellated nut)
78 split pin
79 casing
80 casing cover
81 grease nipple (lubricating nipple)
82-96 gear wheels, cog wheels
82 stepped gear wheel
83 cog (tooth)
84 space between teeth
85 keyway (key seat, key slot)
86 bore
87 herringbone gear wheel
88 spokes (arms)
89 helical gearing (helical spur wheel)
90 sprocket
91 bevel gear wheel (bevel wheel)
92-93 spiral toothing
92 pinion
93 crown wheel
94 epicyclic gear (planetary gear)
95 internal toothing
96 external toothing
97-107 absorption dynamometer
97 shoe brake (check brake, block brake)
98 brake pulley
99 brake shaft (brake axle)
100 brake block (brake shoe)
101 pull rod
102 brake magnet
103 brake weight
104 band brake
105 brake band
106 brake lining
107 adjusting screw, for even
    application of the brake

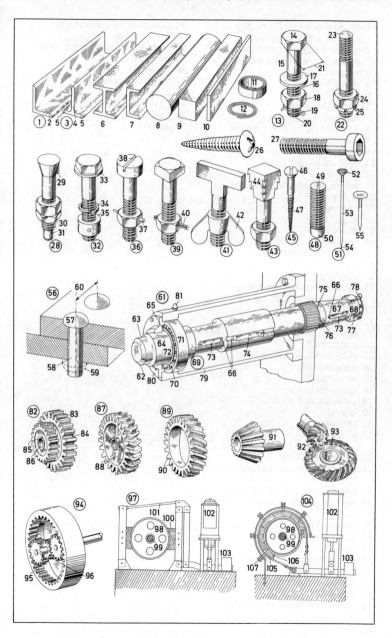

55 Coal Mine

1-51 coal mine (colliery, pit)
1 pithead gear (headgear)
2 winding engine house
3 pithead frame (head frame)
4 pithead building
5 processing plant
6 sawmill
7-11 coking plant
7 battery of coke ovens
8 larry car (larry, charging car)
9 coking coal tower
10 coke-quenching tower
11 coke-quenching car
12 gasometer
13 power plant (power station)
14 water tower
15 cooling tower
16 mine fan
17 depot
18 administration building (office building, offices)
19 tip heap (spoil heap)
20 cleaning plant
21-51 underground workings (underground mining)
21 ventilation shaft
22 fan drift
23 cage-winding system with cages
24 main shaft
25 skip-winding system
26 winding inset
27 staple shaft
28 spiral chute
29 gallery along seam
30 lateral
31 cross-cut
32 tunnelling (*Am.* tunneling) machine
33-37 longwall faces
33 horizontal ploughed longwall face
34 horizontal cut longwall face
35 vertical pneumatic pick longwall face
36 diagonal ram longwall face
37 goaf (gob, waste)
38 air lock
39 transportation of men by cars
40 belt conveying
41 raw coal bunker
42 charging conveyor
43 transportation of supplies by monorail car

44 transportation of men by monorail car
45 transportation of supplies by mine car
46 drainage
47 sump (sink)
48 capping
49 [layer of] coal-bearing rock
50 coal seam
51 fault

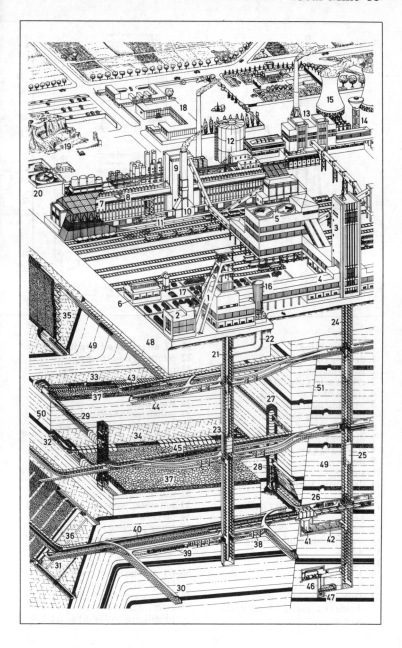

56 Mineral Oil (Oil, Petroleum)

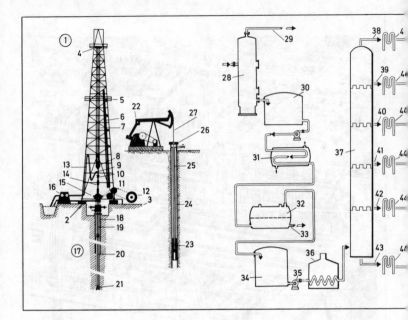

1–21 oil drilling
1 drilling rig
2 substructure
3 crown safety platform
4 crown blocks
5 working platform, an intermediate platform
6 drill pipes
7 drilling cable (drilling line)
8 travelling (*Am.* traveling) block
9 hook
10 swivel
11 draw works, a hoist
12 engine
13 standpipe and rotary hose
14 kelly
15 rotary table
16 slush pump (mud pump)
17 well
18 casing
19 drilling pipe
20 tubing
21 drilling bit; *kinds:* fishtail (blade) bit, rock (*Am.* roller) bit, core bit

22–27 oil (crude oil) production
22 pumping unit (pump)
23 plunger
24 tubing
25 sucker rods (pumping rods)
26 stuffing box
27 polish (polished) rod
28–35 treatment of crude oil [diagram]
28 gas separator
29 gas pipe (gas outlet)
30 wet oil tank (wash tank)
31 water heater
32 water and brine separator
33 salt water pipe (salt water outlet)
34 oil tank
35 trunk pipeline for oil [to the refinery or transport by tanker lorry (*Am.* tank truck), oil tanker, or pipeline]
36–64 processing of crude oil [diagram]
36 oil furnace (pipe still)
37 fractionating column (distillation column) with trays

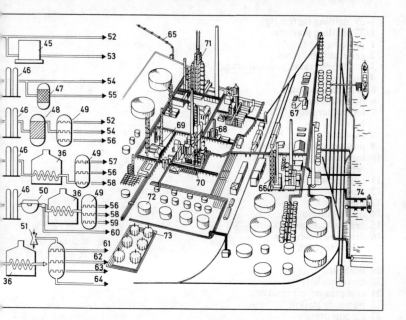

38 top gases (tops)
39 light distillation products
40 heavy distillation products
41 petroleum
42 gas oil component
43 residue
44 condenser (cooler)
45 compressor
46 desulphurizing
  (desulphurization, *Am.*
  desulfurizing, desulfurization)
  plant
47 reformer (hydroformer,
  platformer)
48 catalytic cracker (cat cracker)
49 distillation column
50 de-waxing (wax separation)
51 vacuum equipment
52–64 oil products
52 fuel gas
53 liquefied petroleum gas (liquid
  gas)
54 regular grade petrol (*Am.*
  gasoline)
55 super grade petrol (*Am.* gasoline)

56 diesel oil
57 aviation fuel
58 light fuel oil
59 heavy fuel oil
60 paraffin (paraffin oil, kerosene)
61 spindle oil
62 lubricating oil
63 cylinder oil
64 bitumen
65–74 oil refinery
65 pipeline (oil pipeline)
66 distillation plants
67 lubricating oil refinery
68 desulphurizing
  (desulphurization, *Am.*
  desulfurizing, desulfurization)
  plant
69 gas-separating plant
70 catalytic cracking plant
71 catalytic reformer
72 storage tank
73 spherical tank
74 tanker terminal

57 Offshore Drilling

1–39 drilling rig (oil rig)
1–37 drilling platform
1 power station
2 generator exhausts
3 revolving crane (pedestal crane)
4 piperack
5 turbine exhausts
6 materials store
7 helicopter deck (heliport deck, heliport)
8 elevator
9 production oil and gas separator
10 test oil and gas separators (test separators)
11 emergency flare stack
12 derrick
13 diesel tank
14 office building
15 cement storage tanks
16 drinking water tank
17 salt water tank
18 jet fuel tanks
19 lifeboats
20 elevator shaft
21 compressed–air reservoir
22 pumping station
23 air compressor
24 air lock
25 seawater desalination plant
26 inlet filters for diesel fuel
27 gas cooler
28 control panel for the separators
29 toilets (lavatories)
30 workshop
31 pig trap [the 'pig' is used to clean the oil pipeline]
32 control room
33 accommodation modules (accommodation)
34 high–pressure cementing pumps
35 lower deck
36 middle deck
37 top deck (main deck)
38 substructure
39 mean sea level

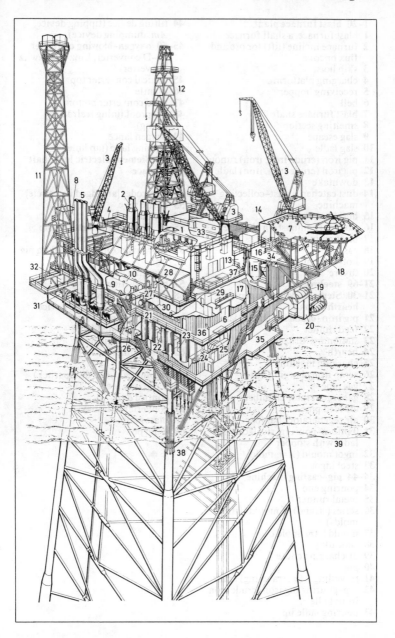

58 Iron and Steel Works

1-20 blast furnace plant
1 blast furnace, a shaft furnace
2 furnace incline (lift) for ore and flux or coke
3 skip hoist
4 charging platform
5 receiving hopper
6 bell
7 blast furnace shaft
8 smelting section
9 slag escape
10 slag ladle
11 pig iron (crude iron, iron) runout
12 pig iron (crude iron, iron) ladle
13 downtake
14 dust catcher, a dust-collecting machine
15 hot-blast stove
16 external combustion chamber
17 blast main
18 gas pipe
19 hot-blast pipe
20 tuyère
21-69 steelworks
21-30 Siemens-Martin open-hearth furnace
21 pig iron (crude iron, iron) ladle
22 feed runner
23 stationary furnace
24 hearth
25 charging machine
26 scrap iron charging box
27 gas pipe
28 gas regenerator chamber
29 air feed pipe
30 air regenerator chamber
31 [bottom-pouring] steel-casting ladle with stopper
32 ingot mould (*Am.* mold)
33 steel ingot
34-44 pig-casting machine
34 pouring end
35 metal runner
36 series (strand) of moulds (*Am.* molds)
37 mould (*Am.* mold)
38 catwalk
39 discharging chute
40 pig
41 travelling (*Am.* traveling) crane
42 top-pouring pig iron (crude iron, iron) ladle
43 pouring ladle lip

44 tilting device (tipping device, *Am.* dumping device)
45-50 oxygen-blowing converter (L-D converter, Linz-Donawitz converter)
45 conical converter top
46 mantle
47 solid converter bottom
48 fireproof lining (refractory lining)
49 oxygen lance
50 tapping hole (tap hole)
51-54 Siemens electric low-shaft furnace
51 feed
52 electrodes [arranged in a circle]
53 bustle pipe
54 runout
55-69 Thomas converter (basic Bessemer converter)
55 charging position for molten pig iron
56 charging position for lime
57 blow position
58 discharging position
59 tilting device (tipping device, *Am.* dumping device)
60 crane-operated ladle
61 auxiliary crane hoist
62 lime bunker
63 downpipe
64 tipping car (*Am.* dump truck)
65 scrap iron feed
66 control desk
67 converter chimney
68 blast main
69 wind box

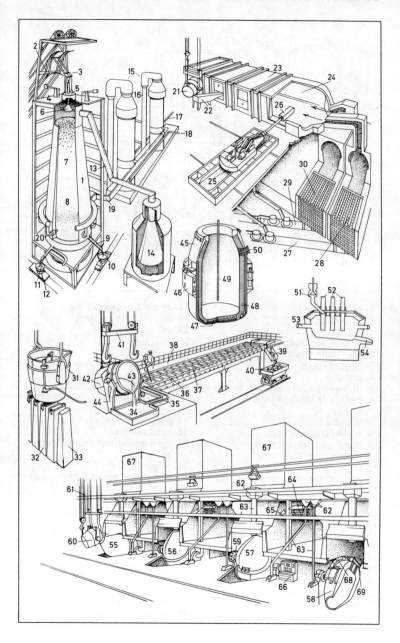

59 Iron Foundry and Rolling Mill

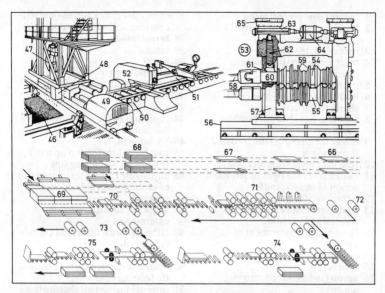

46–75 rolling mill
46 soaking pit
47 soaking pit crane
48 ingot
49 ingot tipper
50 blooming train (roller path)
51 workpiece
52 bloom shears
53 two-high mill
54–55 set of rolls (set of rollers)
54 upper roll (upper roller)
55 lower roll (lower roller)
56–60 roll stand
56 base plate
57 housing (frame)
58 coupling spindle
59 groove
60 roll bearing
61–65 adjusting equipment
61 chock
62 main screw
63 gear
64 motor
65 indicator for rough and fine adjustment

66–75 continuous rolling mill train for the manufacture of strip [diagram]
66–68 processing of semi-finished product
66 semi-finished product
67 gas cutting installation
68 stack of finished steel sheets
69 continuous reheating furnaces
70 blooming train
71 finishing train
72 coiler
73 collar bearing for marketing
74 5 mm shearing train
75 10 mm shearing train

60 Machine Tools I

1 **centre** (*Am*. center) **lathe**
2 headstock with gear control (geared headstock)
3 reduction drive lever
4 lever for normal and coarse threads
5 speed change lever
6 leadscrew reverse-gear lever
7 change-gear box
8 feed gearbox (Norton tumbler gear)
9 levers for changing the feed and thread pitch
10 feed gear lever (tumbler lever)
11 switch lever for right or left hand action of main spindle
12 lathe foot (footpiece)
13 leadscrew handwheel for traversing of saddle (longitudinal movement of saddle)
14 tumbler reverse lever
15 feed screw
16 apron (saddle apron, carriage apron)
17 lever for longitudinal and transverse motion
18 drop (dropping) worm (feed trip, feed tripping device) for engaging feed mechanisms
19 lever for engaging half nut of leadscrew (lever for clasp nut engagement)
20 lathe spindle
21 tool post
22 top slide (tool slide, tool rest)
23 cross slide
24 bed slide
25 coolant supply pipe
26 tailstock centre (*Am*. center)
27 barrel (tailstock barrel)
28 tailstock barrel clamp lever
29 tailstock
30 tailstock barrel adjusting handwheel
31 lathe bed
32 leadscrew
33 feed shaft
34 reverse shaft for right and left hand motion and engaging and disengaging
35 four-jaw chuck (four-jaw independent chuck)
36 gripping jaw

37 three-jaw chuck (three-jaw self-centring, self-centering, chuck)
38 **turret lathe**
39 cross slide
40 turret
41 combination toolholder (multiple turning head)
42 top slide
43 star wheel
44 coolant tray for collecting coolant and swarf
45-53 **lathe tools**
45 tool bit holder (clamp tip tool) for adjustable cutting tips
46 adjustable cutting tip (clamp tip) of cemented carbide or oxide ceramic
47 shapes of adjustable oxide ceramic tips
48 lathe tool with cemented carbide cutting edge
49 tool shank
50 brazed cemented carbide cutting tip (cutting edge)
51 internal facing tool (boring tool) for corner work
52 general-purpose lathe tool
53 parting (parting-off) tool
54 lathe carrier
55 driving (driver) plate
56-72 **measuring instruments**
56 plug gauge (*Am*. gage)
57 'GO' gauging (*Am*. gaging) member (end)
58 'NOT GO' gauging (*Am*. gaging) member (end)
59 calliper (caliper, snap) gauge (*Am*. gage)
60 'GO' side
61 'NOT GO' side
62 micrometer
63 measuring scale
64 graduated thimble
65 frame
66 spindle (screwed spindle)
67 vernier calliper (caliper) gauge (*Am*. gage)
68 depth gauge (*Am*. gage) attachment rule
69 vernier scale
70 outside jaws
71 inside jaws
72 vernier depth gauge (*Am*. gage)

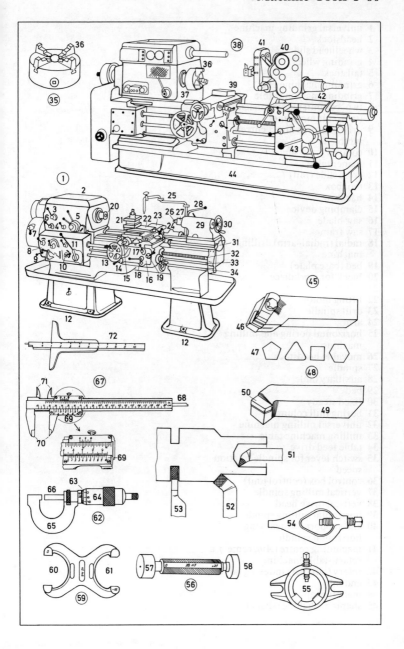

61 Machine Tools II

1 universal grinding machine
2 headstock
3 wheelhead slide
4 grinding wheel
5 tailstock
6 grinding machine bed
7 grinding machine table
8 two–column planing machine
  (two–column planer)
9 drive motor, a direct current
  motor
10 column
11 planer table
12 cross slide (rail)
13 tool box
14 hacksaw
15 clamping device
16 saw blade
17 saw frame
18 radial (radial–arm) drilling
  machine
19 bed (base plate)
20 block for workpiece
21 pillar
22 lifting motor
23 drill spindle
24 arm
25 horizontal boring and milling
  machine
26 movable headstock
27 spindle
28 auxiliary table
29 bed
30 fixed steady
31 boring mill column
32 universal milling machine
33 milling machine table
34 table feed drive
35 switch lever for spindle rotation
  speed
36 control box (control unit)
37 vertical milling spindle
38 vertical drive head
39 horizontal milling spindle
40 end support for steadying
  horizontal spindle
41 machining centre (*Am.* center), a
  rotary–table machine
42 rotary (circular) indexing table
43 end mill
44 machine tap
45 shaping machine (shaper)

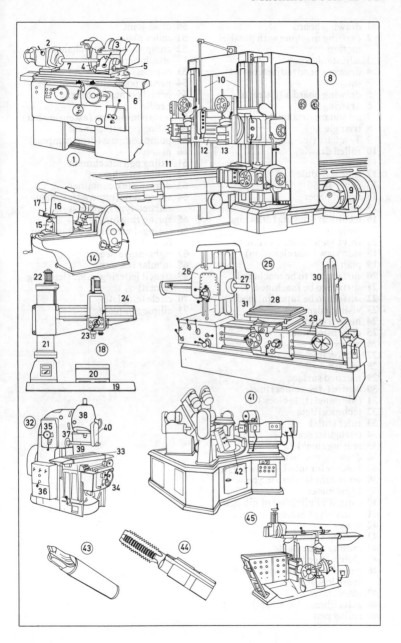

62 Drawing Office

1 drawing board
2 drafting machine with parallel motion
3 adjustable knob
4 drawing head (adjustable set square)
5 drawing board adjustment
6 drawing table
7 set square (triangle)
8 triangle
9 T-square (tee-square)
10 rolled drawing
11 diagram
12 time schedule
13 paper stand
14 roll of paper
15 cutter
16 technical drawing (drawing, design)
17 front view (front elevation)
18 side view (side elevation)
19 plan
20 surface not to be machined
21 surface to be machined
22 surface to be superfinished
23 visible edge
24 hidden edge
25 dimension line
26 arrow head
27 section line
28 section A-B
29 hatched surface
30 centre (Am. center) line
31 title panel (title block)
32 technical data
33 ruler (rule)
34 triangular scale
35 erasing shield
36 drawing ink cartridge
37 holders for tubular drawing pens
38 set of tubular drawing pens
39 hygrometer
40 cap with indication of nib size
41 pencil-type eraser
42 eraser
43 erasing knife
44 erasing knife blade
45 clutch-type pencil
46 pencil lead (refill lead, refill, spare lead)
47 glass eraser
48 glass fibres (Am. fibers)
49 ruling pen

50 cross joint
51 index plate
52 compass with interchangeable attachments
53 compass head
54 needle point attachment
55 pencil point attachment
56 needle
57 lengthening arm (extension bar)
58 ruling pen attachment
59 pump compass (drop compass)
60 piston
61 ruling pen attachment
62 pencil attachment
63 drawing ink container
64 spring bow (rapid adjustment, ratchet-type) compass
65 spring ring hinge
66 spring-loaded fine adjustment for arcs
67 right-angle needle
68 tubular ink unit
69 stencil lettering guide (lettering stencil)
70 circle template
71 ellipse template

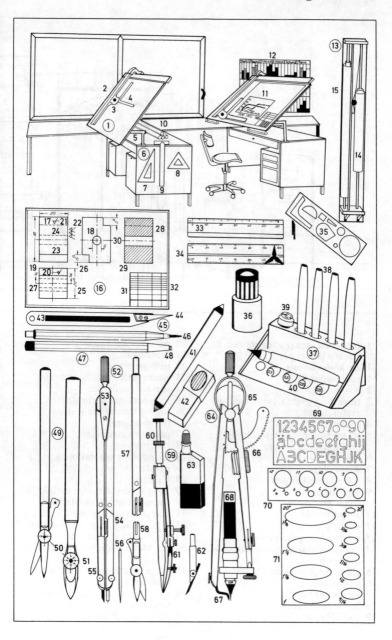

63 Power Plant (Power Station) I

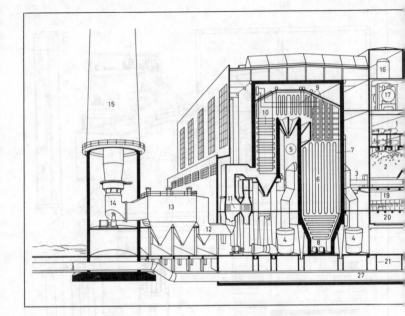

1-28 steam-generating station, an electric power plant
1-21 boiler house
1 coal conveyor
2 coal bunker
3 travelling-grate (*Am.* traveling-grate) stoker
4 coal mill
5 steam boiler, a water-tube boiler (radiant-type boiler)
6 burners
7 water pipes
8 ash pit (clinker pit)
9 superheater
10 water preheater
11 air preheater
12 gas flue
13 electrostatic precipitator
14 induced-draught (*Am.* induced-draft) fan
15 chimney (smokestack)
16 de-aerator
17 feedwater tank
18 boiler feed pump
19 control room

20 cable tunnel
21 cable vault
22 turbine house
23 steam turbine with alternator
24 surface condenser
25 low-pressure preheater
26 high-pressure preheater (economizer)
27 cooling water pipe
28 control room
29-35 outdoor substation, a substation
29 busbars
30 power transformer, a mobile (transportable) transformer
31 stay poles (guy poles)
32 high-voltage transmission line
33 high-voltage conductor
34 air-blast circuit breaker (circuit breaker)
35 surge diverter (*Am.* lightning arrester, arrester)
36 overhead line support, a lattice steel tower
37 cross arm (traverse)

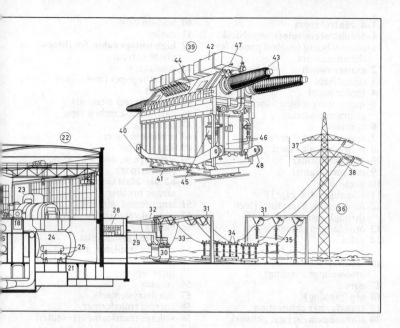

38 strain insulator
39 **mobile (transportable)**
transformer (power transformer,
transformer)
40 transformer tank
41 bogie (*Am.* truck)
42 oil conservator
43 primary voltage terminal
(primary voltage bushing)
44 low–voltage terminals (low–
voltage bushings)
45 oil–circulating pump
46 oil cooler
47 arcing horn
48 transport lug

64 Power Plant (Power Station) II

1-8 control room
1-6 control console (control desk)
1 control board (control panel) for the alternators
2 master switch
3 signal light
4 feeder panel
5 monitoring controls for the switching systems
6 controls
7 revertive signal panel
8 matrix mimic board
9-18 transformer
9 oil conservator
10 breather
11 oil gauge (*Am.* gage)
12 feed-through terminal (feed-through insulator)
13 on-load tap changer
14 yoke
15 primary winding (primary)
16 secondary winding (secondary, low-voltage winding)
17 core
18 tap (tapping)
19 transformer connection
20 star connection (star network, Y-connection)
21 delta connection (mesh connection)
22 neutral point
23-30 steam turbine, a turbogenerator unit
23 high-pressure cylinder
24 medium-pressure cylinder
25 low-pressure cylinder
26 three-phase generator (generator)
27 hydrogen cooler
28 leakage steam path
29 jet nozzle
30 turbine monitoring panel with measuring instruments
31 automatic voltage regulator
32 synchro
33 cable box
34 conductor
35 feed-through terminal (feed-through insulator)
36 core
37 casing
38 filling compound (filler)
39 lead sheath

40 lead-in tube
41 cable
42 high voltage cable, for three-phase current
43 conductor
44 metallic paper (metallized paper)
45 tracer (tracer element)
46 varnished-cambric tape
47 lead sheath
48 asphalted paper
49 jute serving
50 steel tape or steel wire armour (*Am.* armor)
51-62 air-blast circuit breaker, a circuit breaker
51 compressed-air tank
52 control valve (main operating valve)
53 compressed-air inlet
54 support insulator, a hollow porcelain supporting insulator
55 interrupter
56 resistor
57 auxiliary contacts
58 current transformer
59 voltage transformer (potential transformer)
60 operating mechanism housing
61 arcing horn
62 spark gap

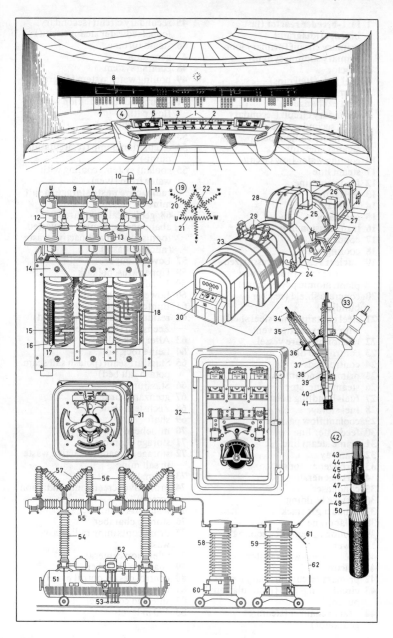

65 Nuclear Energy

1 **fast–breeder reactor** (fast breeder) [diagram]
2 primary circuit (primary loop, primary sodium system)
3 reactor
4 fuel rods (fuel pins)
5 primary sodium pump
6 heat exchanger
7 secondary circuit (secondary loop, secondary sodium system)
8 secondary sodium pump
9 steam generator
10 cooling water flow circuit
11 steam line
12 feedwater line
13 feed pump
14 steam turbine
15 generator
16 transmission line
17 condenser
18 cooling water
19 **nuclear reactor,** a pressurized–water reactor (nuclear power plant, atomic power plant)
20 concrete shield (reactor building)
21 steel containment (steel shell) with air extraction vent
22 reactor pressure vessel
23 control rod drive
24 control rods
25 primary coolant pump
26 steam generator
27 fuel–handling hoists
28 fuel storage
29 coolant flow passage
30 feedwater line
31 prime steam line
32 manway
33 turbogenerator set
34 turbogenerator
35 condenser
36 service building
37 exhaust gas stack
38 polar crane
39 cooling tower, a dry cooling tower
40 pressurized–water system
41 reactor
42 primary circuit (primary loop)
43 circulation pump (recirculation pump)
44 heat exchanger (steam generator)
45 secondary circuit (secondary loop, feedwater steam circuit)
46 steam turbine
47 generator
48 cooling system
49 boiling water system [diagram]
50 reactor
51 steam and recirculation water flow paths
52 steam turbine
53 generator
54 circulation pump (recirculation pump)
55 coolant system (cooling with water from river)
56 **radioactive waste storage in salt mine**
57–68 geological structure of abandoned salt mine converted for disposal of radioactive waste (nuclear waste)
57 Lower Keuper
58 Upper Muschelkalk
59 Middle Muschelkalk
60 Lower Muschelkalk
61 Bunter downthrow
62 residue of leached (lixiviated) Zechstein (Upper Permian)
63 Aller rock salt
64 Leine rock salt
65 Stassfurt seam (potash salt seam, potash salt bed)
66 Stassfurt salt
67 grenzanhydrite
68 Zechstein shale
69 shaft
70 minehead buildings
71 storage chamber
72 storage of medium–active waste in salt mine
73 511 m level
74 protective screen (anti–radiation screen)
75 lead glass window
76 storage chamber
77 drum containing radioactive waste
78 television camera
79 charging chamber
80 control desk (control panel)
81 upward ventilator
82 shielded container
83 490 m level

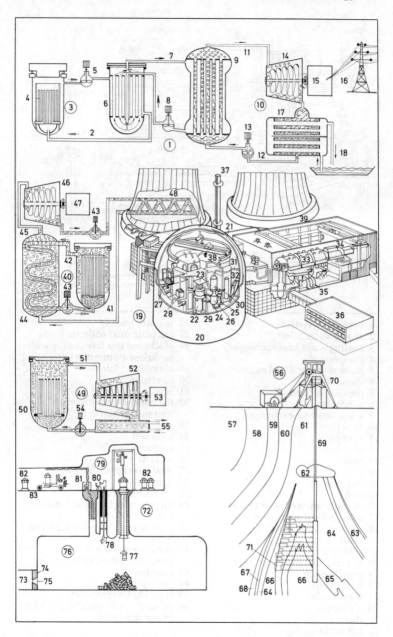

66 Modern Sources of Energy

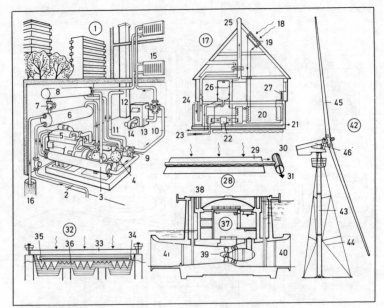

1 **heat pump system**
2 source water inlet
3 cooling water heat exchanger
4 compressor
5 natural-gas or diesel engine
6 evaporator
7 pressure release valve
8 condenser
9 waste-gas heat exchanger
10 flow pipe
11 vent pipe
12 chimney
13 boiler
14 fan
15 radiator
16 sink
17–36 **utilization of solar energy**
17 solar (solar-heated) house
18 solar radiation (sunlight, insolation)
19 collector
20 hot reservoir (heat reservoir)
21 power supply
22 heat pump
23 water outlet
24 air supply
25 flue
26 hot water supply

27 radiator heating
28 flat plate solar collector
29 blackened receiver surface with asphalted aluminium (*Am.* aluminum) foil
30 steel tube
31 heat transfer fluid
32 flat plate solar collector, containing solar cell
33 glass cover
34 solar cell
35 air ducts
36 insulation
37 **tidal power plant** [section]
38 dam
39 reversible turbine
40 turbine inlet for water from the sea
41 turbine inlet for water from the basin
42 **wind power plant** (wind generator, aerogenerator)
43 truss tower
44 guy wire
45 rotor blades (propeller)
46 generator with variable pitch for power regulation

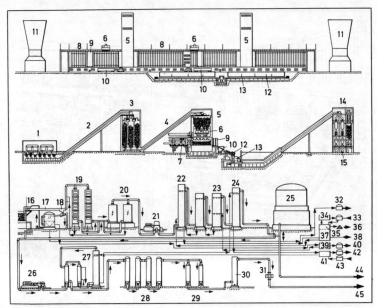

1-15 coking plant
1 dumping of coking coal
2 belt conveyor
3 service bunker
4 coal tower conveyor
5 coal tower
6 larry car (larry, charging car)
7 pusher ram
8 battery of coke ovens
9 coke guide
10 quenching car, with engine
11 quenching tower
12 coke loading bay (coke wharf)
13 coke side bench
14 screening of lump coal and culm
15 coke loading

16-45 coke-oven gas processing
16 discharge (release) of gas from the coke ovens
17 gas-collecting main
18 coal tar extraction
19 gas cooler
20 electrostatic precipitator
21 gas extractor
22 hydrogen sulphide (*Am.* hydrogen sulfide) scrubber (hydrogen sulphide wet collector)
23 ammonia scrubber (ammonia wet collector)
24 benzene (benzol) scrubber

25 gas holder
26 gas compressor
27 debenzoling by cooler and heat exchanger
28 desulphurization (*Am.* desulfurization) of pressure gas
29 gas cooling
30 gas drying
31 gas meter
32 crude tar tank
33 sulphuric acid (*Am.* sulfuric acid) supply
34 production of sulphuric acid (*Am.* sulfuric acid)
35 production of ammonium sulphate (*Am.* ammonium sulfate)
36 ammonium sulphate (*Am.* ammonium sulfate)
37 recovery plant for recovering the scrubbing agents
38 waste water discharge
39 phenol extraction from the gas water
40 crude phenol tank
41 production of crude benzol (crude benzene)
42 crude benzol (crude benzene) tank
43 scrubbing oil tank
44 low-pressure gas main
45 high-pressure gas main

1 sawmill
2 vertical frame saw (*Am.* gang mill)
3 saw blades
4 feed roller
5 guide roller
6 fluting (grooving, grooves)
7 oil pressure gauge (*Am.* gage)
8 saw frame
9 feed indicator
10 log capacity scale
11 auxiliary carriage
12 carriage
13 log grips
14 remote control panel
15 carriage motor
16 truck for splinters (splints)
17 endless log chain (*Am.* jack chain)
18 stop plate
19 log-kicker arms
20 cross conveyor
21 washer (washing machine)
22 cross chain conveyor for sawn timber

23 roller table
24 undercut swing saw
25 piling
26 roller trestles
27 gantry crane
28 crane motor
29 pivoted log grips
30 roundwood (round timber)
31 log dump
32 squared timber store
33 sawn logs
34 planks
35 boards (planks)
36 squared timber
37 stack bearer
38 automatic cross-cut chain saw
39 log grips
40 feed roller
41 chain-tensioning device
42 saw-sharpening machine
43 grinding wheel (teeth grinder)
44 feed pawl
45 depth adjustment for the teeth grinder

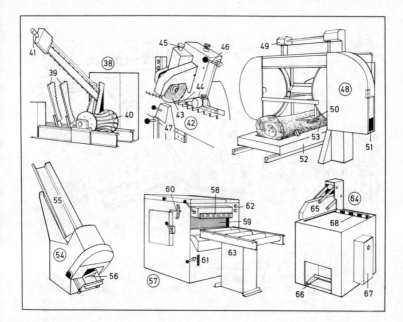

46 lifter (lever) for the grinder chuck
47 holding device for the saw blade
48 horizontal bandsaw for sawing logs
49 height adjustment
50 chip remover
51 chip extractor
52 carriage
53 bandsaw blade
54 automatic blocking saw
55 feed channel
56 discharge opening
57 twin edger (double edger)
58 breadth scale (width scale)
59 kick–back guard
60 height scale
61 in–feed scale
62 indicator lamps
63 feed table
64 undercut swing saw
65 automatic hold–down with protective hood
66 foot switch
67 distribution board (panelboard)
68 length stop

69 Quarry

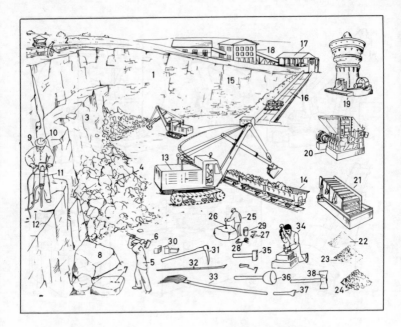

1 **quarry**, an open-cast working
2 overburden
3 working face
4 loose rock pile (blasted rock)
5 quarryman (quarrier), a quarry worker
6 sledge hammer
7 wedge
8 block of stone
9 driller
10 safety helmet
11 hammer drill (hard-rock drill)
12 borehole
13 universal excavator
14 large-capacity truck
15 rock face
16 inclined hoist
17 primary crusher
18 stone-crushing plant
19 coarse rotary (gyratory) crusher; *sim.:* fine rotary (gyratory) crusher
20 hammer crusher (impact crusher)

21 vibrating screen
22 screenings (fine dust)
23 stone chippings
24 crushed stone
25 shot firer
26 measuring rod
27 blasting cartridge
28 fuse (blasting fuse)
29 plugging sand (stemming sand) bucket
30 dressed stone
31 pick
32 crowbar (pinch bar)
33 fork
34 stonemason
35-38 **stonemason's tools**
35 stonemason's hammer
36 mallet
37 drove chisel (drove, boaster, broad chisel)
38 dressing axe (*Am.* ax)

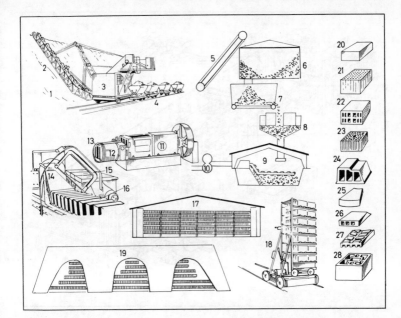

1 clay pit
2 loam, an impure clay (raw clay)
3 overburden excavator, a large-scale excavator
4 narrow-gauge (*Am.* narrow-gage) track system
5 inclined hoist
6 souring chambers
7 box feeder (feeder)
8 edge runner mill (edge mill, pan grinding mill)
9 rolling plant
10 double-shaft trough mixer (mixer)
11 extrusion press (brick-pressing machine)
12 vacuum chamber
13 die
14 clay column
15 cutter (brick cutter)
16 unfired brick (green brick)
17 drying shed
18 mechanical finger car (stacker truck)
19 circular kiln (brick kiln)

20 solid brick (building brick)
21-22 perforated bricks and hollow blocks
21 perforated brick with vertical perforations
22 hollow clay block with horizontal perforations
23 hollow clay block with vertical perforations
24 floor brick
25 compass brick (radial brick, radiating brick)
26 hollow flooring block
27 paving brick
28 cellular brick [for fireplaces] (chimney brick)

71 Cement Works (Cement Factory)

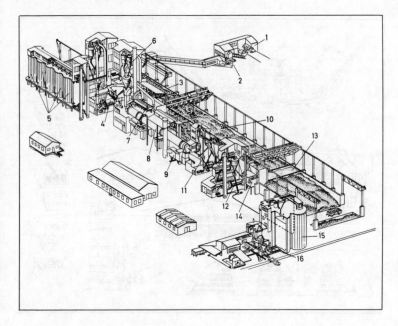

1 raw materials (limestone, clay, and marl)
2 hammer crusher (hammer mill)
3 raw material store
4 raw mill for simultaneously grinding and drying the raw materials with exhaust gas from the heat exchanger
5 raw meal silos
6 heat exchanger (cyclone heat exchanger)
7 dust collector (an electrostatic precipitator) for the heat exchanger exhaust from the raw mill
8 rotary kiln
9 clinker cooler
10 clinker store
11 primary air blower
12 cement-grinding mill
13 gypsum store
14 gypsum crusher
15 cement silo
16 cement-packing plant

1 grinding cylinder (ball mill) for the preparation of the raw material in water
2 sample sagger (saggar, seggar), with aperture for observing the firing process
3 bottle kiln (beehive kiln) [diagram]
4 firing mould (*Am*. mold)
5 tunnel kiln
6 Seger cone (pyrometric cone, *Am*. Orton cone) for measuring high temperatures
7 de-airing pug mill (de-airing pug press), an extrusion press
8 clay column
9 thrower throwing a ball (bat) of clay
10 slug of clay
11 turntable; *sim.:* potter's wheel
12 filter press
13 filter cake
14 jiggering, with a profiling tool; *sim.:* jollying

15 plaster mould (*Am*. mold) for slip casting
16 turntable glazing machine
17 porcelain painter (china painter)
18 hand–painted vase
19 repairer
20 pallet (modelling, *Am*. modeling, tool)
21 shards (sherds, potsherds)

73 Glass Production

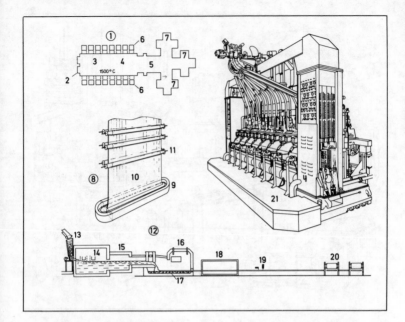

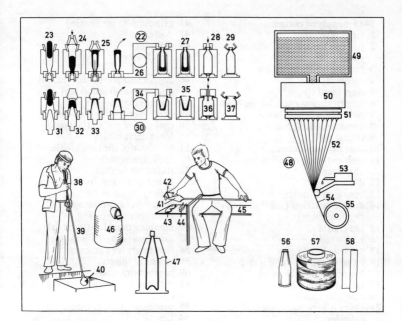

35 reheating
36 blowing (suction, final shaping)
37 delivery of the completed vessel
38–47 glassmaking (glassblowing,
  glassblowing by hand, glass
  forming)
38 glassmaker (glassblower)
39 blowing iron
40 gob
41 hand–blown goblet
42 clappers for shaping the base
  (foot) of the goblet
43 trimming tool
44 tongs
45 glassmaker's chair (gaffer's
  chair)
46 covered glasshouse pot
47 mould (*Am.* mold), into which
  the parison is blown
48–55 production of glass fibre
  (*Am.* glass fiber)
48 continuous filament process
49 glass furnace
50 bushing containing molten glass
51 bushing tips

52 glass filaments
53 sizing
54 strand (thread)
55 spool
56–58 glass fibre (*Am.* **glass fiber**)
  products
56 glass yarn (glass thread)
57 sleeved glass yarn (glass thread)
58 glass wool

74 Cotton Spinning I

1-13 supply of cotton
1 ripe cotton boll
2 full cop (cop wound with weft yarn)
3 compressed cotton bale
4 jute wrapping
5 steel band
6 identification mark of the bale
7 bale opener (bale breaker)
8 cotton-feeding brattice
9 cotton feed
10 dust extraction fan
11 duct to the dust-collecting chamber
12 drive motor
13 conveyor brattice
14 double scutcher (machine with two scutchers)
15 lap cradle
16 rack head
17 starting handle
18 handwheel, for raising and lowering the rack head
19 movable lap-turner
20 calender rollers
21 cover for the perforated cylinders
22 dust escape flue (dust discharge flue)
23 drive motors (beater drive motors)
24 beater driving shaft
25 three-blade beater (Kirschner beater)
26 grid [for impurities to drop]
27 pedal roller (pedal cylinder)
28 control lever for the pedal roller, a pedal lever
29 variable change-speed gear
30 cone drum box
31 stop and start levers for the hopper
32 wooden hopper delivery roller
33 hopper feeder
34 carding machine (card, carding engine)
35 card can (carding can), for receiving the coiled sliver
36 can holder
37 calender rollers
38 carded sliver (card sliver)
39 vibrating doffer comb
40 start-stop lever

41 grinding-roller bearing
42 doffer
43 cylinder
44 flat clearer
45 flats
46 supporting pulleys for the flats
47 scutcher lap (carded lap)
48 scutcher lap holder
49 drive motor with flat belt
50 main drive pulley (fast-and-loose drive pulley)
51 principle of the card (of the carding engine)
52 fluted feed roller
53 licker-in (taker-in, licker-in roller)
54 licker-in undercasing
55 cylinder undercasing
56 combing machine (comber)
57 drive gearbox (driving gear)
58 laps ready for combing
59 calender rollers
60 comber draw box
61 counter
62 coiler top
63 principle of the comber
64 lap
65 bottom nipper
66 top nipper
67 top comb
68 combing cylinder
69 plain part of the cylinder
70 needled part of the cylinder
71 detaching rollers
72 carded and combed sliver

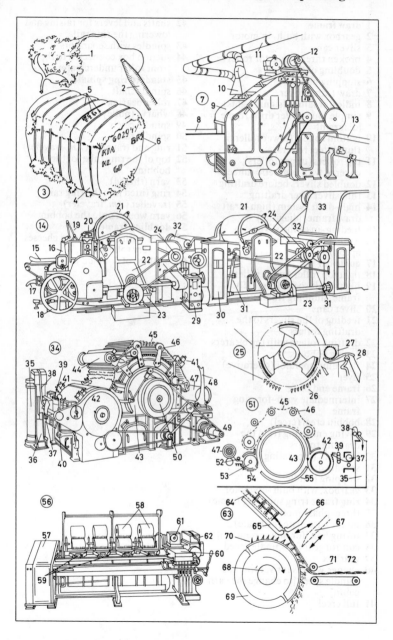

75 Cotton Spinning II

1 **draw frame**
2 gearbox with built-in motor
3 sliver cans
4 broken thread detector roller
5 doubling of the slivers
6 stopping handle
7 draw frame cover
8 indicator lamps (signal lights)
9 simple four-roller draw frame [diagram]
10 bottom rollers (lower rollers), fluted steel rollers
11 top rollers (upper rollers) covered with synthetic rubber
12 doubled slivers before drafting
13 thin sliver after drafting
14 high-draft system (high-draft draw frame) [diagram]
15 feeding-in of the sliver
16 leather apron (composition apron)
17 guide bar
18 light top roller (guide roller)
19 high-draft speed frame (fly frame, slubbing frame)
20 sliver cans
21 feeding of the slivers to the drafting rollers
22 drafting rollers with top clearers
23 roving bobbins
24 fly frame operator (operative)
25 flyer
26 frame end plate
27 intermediate yarn-forming frame
28 bobbin creel (creel)
29 roving emerging from the drafting rollers
30 lifter rail (separating rail)
31 spindle drive
32 stopping handle
33 gearbox, with built-on motor
34 **ring frame** (ring spinning frame)
35 three-phase motor
36 motor base plate (bedplate)
37 lifting bolt [for motor removal]
38 control gear for spindle speed
39 gearbox
40 change wheels for varying the spindle speed [to change the yarn count]
41 full creel

42 shafts and levers for raising and lowering the ring rail
43 spindles with separators
44 suction box connected to the front roller underclearers
45 **standard ring spindle**
46 spindle shaft
47 roller bearing
48 wharve (pulley)
49 spindle catch
50 spindle rail
51 ring and traveller (*Am.* traveler)
52 top of the ring tube (of the bobbin)
53 yarn (thread)
54 ring fitted into the ring rail
55 traveller (*Am.* traveler)
56 yarn wound onto the bobbin
57 **doubling frame**
58 creel, with cross-wound cheeses
59 delivery rollers
60 bobbins of doubled yarn

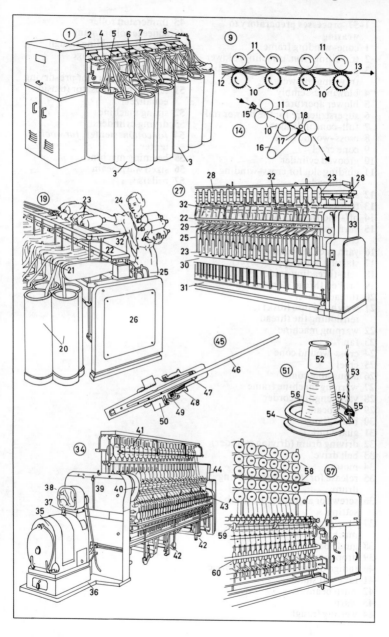

76 Weaving I

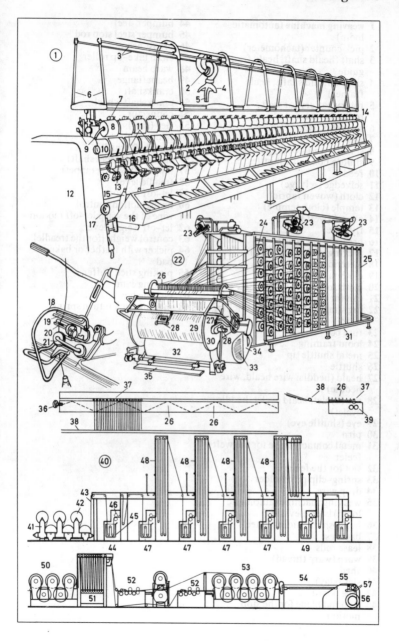

77 Weaving II

1 **weaving machine** (automatic loom)
2 pick counter (tachometer)
3 shaft (heald shaft, heald frame) guide
4 shafts (heald shafts, heald frames)
5 rotary battery for weft replenishment
6 sley (slay) cap
7 weft pirn
8 starting and stopping handle
9 shuttle box, with shuttles
10 reed
11 selvedge (selvage)
12 cloth (woven fabric)
13 temple (cloth temple)
14 electric weft feeler
15 flywheel
16 breast beam board
17 picking stick (pick stick)
18 electric motor
19 cloth take-up motion
20 cloth roller (fabric roller)
21 can for empty pirns
22 lug strap, for moving the picking stick
23 fuse box
24 loom framing
25 metal shuttle tip
26 shuttle
27 heald (heddle, wire heald, wire heddle)
28 eye (eyelet, heald eyelet, heddle eyelet)
29 eye (shuttle eye)
30 pirn
31 metal contact sleeve for the weft feeler
32 slot for the feeler
33 spring-clip pirn holder
34 drop wire
35 weaving machine (automatic loom) [side elevation]
36 heald shaft guiding wheels
37 backrest
38 lease rods
39 warp (warp thread)
40 shed
41 sley (slay)
42 race board
43 stop rod blade for the stop motion
44 bumper steel
45 bumper steel stop rod
46 breast beam
47 cloth take-up roller
48 warp beam
49 beam flange
50 crankshaft
51 crankshaft wheel
52 connector
53 sley (slay)
54 lam rods
55 camshaft wheel
56 camshaft (tappet shaft)
57 tappet (shedding tappet)
58 treadle lever
59 let-off motion
60 beam motion control
61 rope of the warp let-off motion
62 let-off weight lever
63 control weight [for the treadle]
64 picker with leather or bakelite pad
65 picking stick buffer
66 picking cam
67 picking bowl
68 picking stick return spring

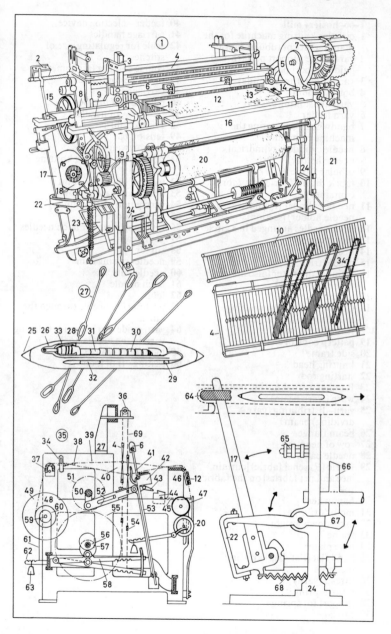

78 Knitting

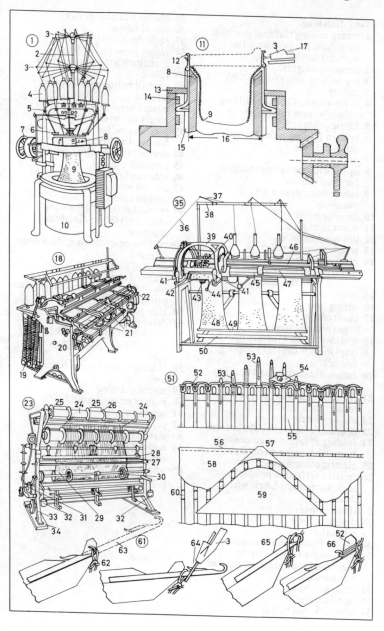

79 Finishing of Textile Fabrics

1–65 finishing

1 rotary milling (fulling) machine for felting the woollen (*Am.* woolen) fabric
2 pressure weights
3 top milling roller (top fulling roller)
4 drive wheel of bottom milling roller (bottom fulling roller)
5 fabric guide roller
6 bottom milling roller (bottom fulling roller)
7 draft board
8 open-width scouring machine for finer fabrics
9 fabric being drawn off the machine
10 drive gearbox
11 water inlet pipe
12 drawing-in roller
13 scroll-opening roller
14 pendulum-type hydro-extractor (centrifuge), for extracting liquors from the fabric
15 machine base
16 casing over suspension
17 outer casing containing rotating cage (rotating basket)
18 hydro-extractor (centrifuge) lid
19 stop-motion device (stopping device)
20 automatic starting and braking device
21 *for cotton:* stenter; *for wool:* tenter
22 air-dry fabric
23 operator's (operative's) platform
24 feeding of fabric by guides onto stenter (tenter) pins or clips
25 electric control panel
26 initial overfeed to produce shrink-resistant fabric when dried
27 thermometer
28 drying section
29 air outlet
30 plaiter (fabric-plaiting device)
31 wire-roller fabric-raising machine for producing raised or nap surface
32 drive gearbox
33 unraised cloth
34 wire-covered rollers
35 plaiter (cuttling device)
36 raised fabric
37 plaiting-down platform
38 rotary press (calendering machine), for press finishing
39 fabric
40 control buttons and control wheels
41 heated press bowl
42 rotary cloth-shearing machine
43 suction slot, for removing loose fibres (*Am.* fibers)
44 doctor blade (cutting cylinder)
45 protective guard
46 rotating brush
47 curved scray entry
48 treadle control
49 [non-shrinking] decatizing (decating) fabric-finishing machine
50 perforated decatizing (decating) cylinder
51 piece of fabric
52 cranked control handle
53 ten-colour (*Am.* ten-color) roller printing machine
54 base of the machine
55 drive motor
56 blanket [of rubber or felt]
57 fabric after printing (printed fabric)
58 electric control panel (control unit)
59 screen printing
60 mobile screen frame
61 squeegee
62 pattern stencil
63 screen table
64 fabric gummed down on table ready for printing
65 screen printing operator (operative)

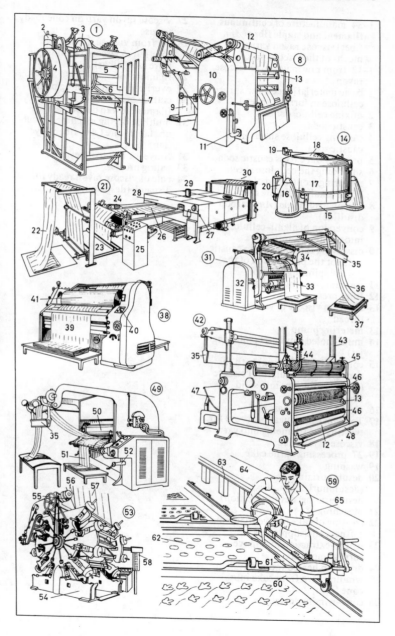

80 Synthetic (Man-made) Fibres (*Am.* Fibers) I

1–34 manufacture of **continuous filament and staple fibre** (*Am.* fiber) **viscose rayon yarns** by means of the viscose process

1–12 from raw material to viscose rayon

1 basic material [beech and spruce cellulose in form of sheets]

2 mixing cellulose sheets

3 caustic soda

4 steeping cellulose sheets in caustic soda

5 pressing out excess caustic soda

6 shredding the cellulose sheets

7 maturing (controlled oxidation) of the alkali–cellulose crumbs

8 carbon disulphide (*Am.* carbon disulfide)

9 conversion of alkali–cellulose into cellulose xanthate

10 dissolving the xanthate in caustic soda for the preparation of the viscose spinning solution

11 vacuum ripening tanks

12 filter press

13–27 from viscose to viscose rayon thread

13 metering pump

14 multi–holed spinneret (spinning jet)

15 coagulating (spinning) bath for converting (coagulating) viscose (viscous solution) into solid filaments

16 Godet wheel, a glass pulley

17 Topham centrifugal pot (box) for twisting the filaments into yarn

18 viscose rayon cake

19–27 processing of the cake

19 washing

20 desulphurizing (desulphurization, *Am.* desulfurizing, desulfurization)

21 bleaching

22 treating of cake to give filaments softness and suppleness

23 hydro–extraction to remove surplus moisture

24 drying in heated room

25 winding yarn from cake into cone form

26 cone-winding machine

27 viscose rayon yarn on cone ready for use

28–34 from viscose spinning solution to viscose rayon staple fibre (*Am.* fiber)

28 filament tow

29 overhead spray washing plant

30 cutting machine for cutting filament tow to desired length

31 multiple drying machine for cut–up staple fibre (*Am.* fiber) layer (lap)

32 conveyor belt (conveyor)

33 baling press

34 bale of viscose rayon ready for dispatch (despatch)

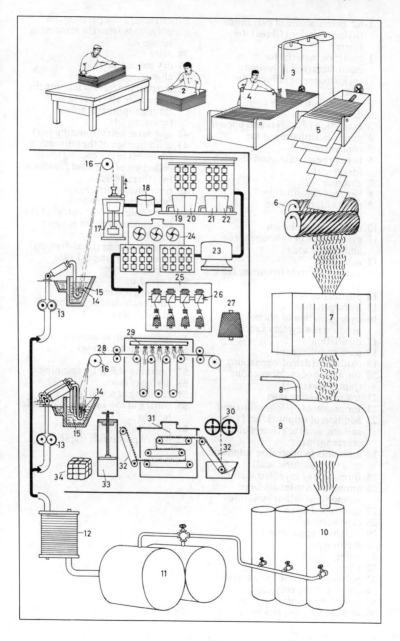

81 Synthetic (Man-made) Fibres (*Am.* Fibers) II

1–62 manufacture of **polyamide** (nylon 6, perlon) **fibres** (*Am.* fibers)

1 coal [raw material for manufacture of polyamide (nylon 6, perlon) fibres (*Am.* fibers)]
2 coking plant for dry coal distillation
3 extraction of coal tar and phenol
4 gradual distillation of tar
5 condenser
6 benzene extraction and dispatch (despatch)
7 chlorine
8 benzene chlorination
9 monochlorobenzene (chlorobenzene)
10 caustic soda solution
11 evaporation of chlorobenzene and caustic soda
12 autoclave
13 sodium chloride (common salt), a by-product
14 phenol (carbolic acid)
15 hydrogen inlet
16 hydrogenation of phenol to produce raw cyclohexanol
17 distillation
18 pure cyclohexanol
19 oxidation (dehydrogenation)
20 formation of cyclohexanone (pimehinketone)
21 hydroxylamine inlet
22 formation of cyclohexanoxime
23 addition of sulphuric acid (*Am.* sulfuric acid) to effect molecular rearrangement
24 ammonia to neutralize sulphuric acid (*Am.* sulfuric acid)
25 formation of caprolactam oil
26 ammonium sulphate (*Am.* ammonium sulfate) solution
27 cooling cylinder
28 caprolactam
29 weighing apparatus
30 melting pot
31 pump
32 filter
33 polymerization in the autoclave
34 cooling of the polyamide
35 solidification of the polyamide
36 vertical lift (*Am.* elevator)
37 extractor for separating the polyamide from the remaining lactam oil
38 drier
39 dry polyamide chips
40 chip container
41 top of spinneret for melting the polyamide and forcing it through spinneret holes (spinning jets)
42 spinneret holes (spinning jets)
43 solidification of the polyamide filaments in the cooling tower
44 collection of extruded filaments into thread form
45 preliminary stretching (preliminary drawing)
46 stretching (cold–drawing) of the polyamide thread to achieve high tensile strength
47 final stretching (final drawing)
48 washing of yarn packages
49 drying chamber
50 rewinding
51 polyamide cone
52 polyamide cone ready for dispatch (despatch)
53 mixer
54 polymerization under vacua
55 stretching (drawing)
56 washing
57 finishing of tow for spinning
58 drying of tow
59 crimping of tow
60 cutting of tow into normal staple lengths
61 polyamide staple
62 bale of polyamide staple

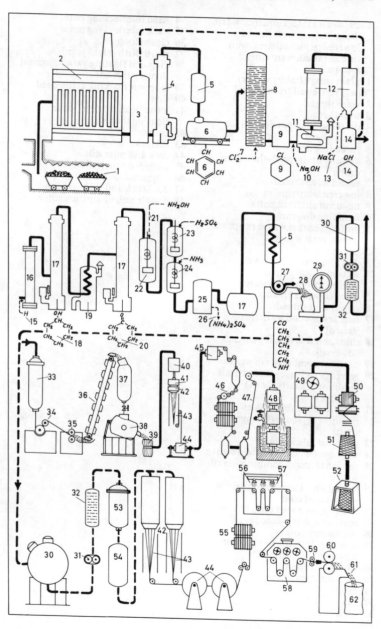

82 Weaves and Knits

1-29 **weaves** [black squares: warp thread raised, weft thread lowered; white squares: weft thread raised, warp thread lowered]
1 plain weave (tabby weave) [weave viewed from above]
2 warp thread
3 weft thread
4 draft (point paper design) for plain weave
5 threading draft
6 denting draft (reed-threading draft)
7 raised warp thread
8 lowered warp thread
9 tie-up of shafts in pairs
10 treadling diagram
11 draft for basket weave (hopsack weave, matt weave)
12 pattern repeat
13 draft for warp rib weave
14 section of warp rib fabric, a section through the warp
15 lowered weft thread
16 raised weft thread
17 first and second warp threads [raised]
18 third and fourth warp threads [lowered]
19 draft for combined rib weave
20 selvedge (selvage) thread draft (additional shafts for the selvedge)
21 draft for the fabric shafts
22 tie-up of selvedge (selvage) shafts
23 tie-up of fabric shafts
24 selvedge (selvage) in plain weave
25 section through combination rib weave
26 thread interlacing of reversible warp-faced cord
27 draft (point paper design) for reversible warp-faced cord
28 interlacing points
29 weaving draft for honeycomb weave in the fabric
30-48 **basic knits**
30 loop, an open loop
31 head
32 side
33 neck
34 head interlocking point
35 neck interlocking point
36 closed loop
37 mesh [with inlaid yarn]
38 diagonal floating yarn (diagonal floating thread)
39 loop interlocking at the head
40 float
41 loose floating yarn (loose floating thread)
42 course
43 inlaid yarn
44 tuck and miss stitch
45 pulled-up tuck stitch
46 staggered tuck stitch
47 2 x 2 tuck and miss stitch
48 double pulled-up tuck stitch

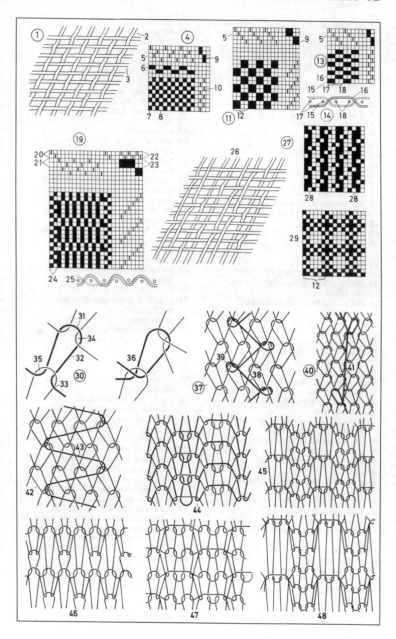

83 Papermaking I

1-52 sulphate (*Am.* sulfate) pulp mill
(kraft pulp mill) [in diagram form]
1 chippers with dust extractor
2 rotary screen (riffler)
3 chip packer (chip distributor)
4 blower
5 disintegrator (crusher, chip
crusher)
6 dust-settling chamber
7 digester
8 liquor preheater
9 control tap
10 swing pipe
11 blow tank (diffuser)
12 blow valve
13 blow pit (diffuser)
14 turpentine separator
15 centralized separator
16 jet condenser (injection condenser)
17 storage tank for condensate
18 hot water tank
19 heat exchanger
20 filter
21 presorter
22 centrifugal screen
23 rotary sorter (rotary strainer)
24 concentrator (thickener, decker)
25 vat (chest)
26 collecting tank for backwater
(low box)
27 conical refiner (cone refiner,
Jordan, Jordan refiner)
28 black liquor filter
29 black liquor storage tank
30 condenser
31 separators
32 heater (heating element)
33 liquor pump
34 heavy liquor pump
35 mixing tank
36 salt cake storage tank (sodium
sulphate storage tank)
37 dissolving tank (dissolver)
38 steam heater
39 electrostatic precipitator
40 air pump
41 storage tank for the uncleared
green liquor
42 concentrator (thickener, decker)
43 green liquor preheater
44 concentrator (thickener, decker)
for the weak wash liquor (wash
water)
45 storage tank for the weak liquor
46 storage tank for the cooking liquor
47 agitator (stirrer)
48 concentrator (thickener, decker)
49 causticizing agitators
(causticizing stirrers)
50 classifier
51 lime slaker

52 reconverted lime
53-65 groundwood mill
(mechanical pulp mill) [diagram]
53 continuous grinder (continuous
chain grinder)
54 strainer (knotter)
55 pulp water pump
56 centrifugal screen
57 screen (sorter)
58 secondary screen (secondary
sorter)
59 rejects chest
60 conical refiner (cone refiner,
Jordan, Jordan refiner)
61 pulp-drying machine (pulp
machine)
62 concentrator (thickener, decker)
63 waste water pump (white water
pump, pulp water pump)
64 steam pipe
65 water pipe
66 continuous grinder (continuous
chain grinder)
67 feed chain
68 groundwood
69 reduction gear for the feed chain
drive
70 stone-dressing device
71 grinding stone (grindstone,
pulpstone)
72 spray pipe
73 conical refiner (cone refiner,
Jordan, Jordan refiner)
74 handwheel for adjusting the
clearance between the knives
(blades)
75 rotating bladed cone (rotating
bladed plug)
76 stationary bladed shell
77 inlet for unrefined cellulose
(chemical wood pulp, chemical
pulp) or groundwood pulp
(mechanical pulp)
78 outlet for refined cellulose
(chemical wood pulp, chemical
pulp) or groundwood pulp
(mechanical pulp)
79-86 stuff (stock) preparation
plant [diagram]
79 conveyor belt (conveyor) for
loading cellulose (chemical wood
pulp, chemical pulp) or groundwood pulp (mechanical pulp)
80 pulper
81 dump chest
82 cone breaker
83 conical refiner (cone refiner,
Jordan, Jordan refiner)
84 refiner
85 stuff chest (stock chest)
86 machine chest (stuff chest)

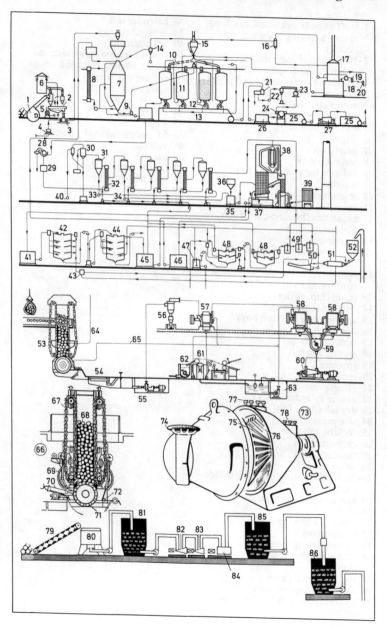

84 Papermaking II

1 stuff chest (stock chest, machine chest), a mixing chest for stuff (stock)

2-10 laboratory apparatus (laboratory equipment) for analysing stuff (stock) and paper

2 Erlenmeyer flask

3 volumetric flask

4 measuring cylinder

5 Bunsen burner

6 tripod

7 petri dish

8 test tube rack

9 balance for measuring basis weight

10 micrometer

11 centrifugal cleaners ahead of the breastbox (headbox, stuff box) of a paper machine

12 standpipe

13-28 paper machine (production line) [diagram]

13 feed-in from the machine chest (stuff chest) with sand table (sand trap, riffler) and knotter

14 wire (machine wire)

15 vacuum box (suction box)

16 suction roll

17 first wet felt

18 second wet felt

19 first press

20 second press

21 offset press

22 drying cylinder (drier)

23 dry felt (drier felt)

24 size press

25 cooling roll

26 calender rolls

27 machine hood

28 delivery reel

29-35 blade coating machine (blade coater)

29 raw paper (body paper)

30 web

31 coater for the top side

32 infrared drier

33 heated drying cylinder

34 coater for the underside (wire side)

35 reel of coated paper

36 calender (Super-calender)

37 hydraulic system for the press rolls

38 calender roll

39 unwind station

40 lift platform

41 rewind station (rewinder, re-reeler, reeling machine, re-reeling machine)

42 roll cutter

43 control panel

44 cutter

45 web

46-51 papermaking by hand

46 vatman

47 vat

48 mould (*Am.* mold)

49 coucher (couchman)

50 post ready for pressing

51 felt

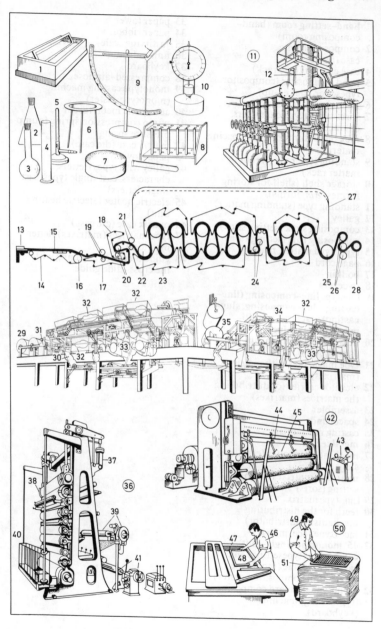

85 Composing Room (Case Room) I

1 **hand-setting room** (hand-composing room)
2 composing frame
3 case (typecase)
4 case cabinet (case rack)
5 hand compositor (compositor, typesetter, maker-up)
6 manuscript (typescript)
7 sorts, types (type characters, characters)
8 rack (case) for furniture (spacing material)
9 standing type rack (standing matter rack)
10 storage shelf (shelf for storing formes, *Am.* forms)
11 standing type (standing matter)
12 galley
13 composing stick (setting stick)
14 composing rule (setting rule)
15 type (type matter, matter)
16 page cord
17 bodkin
18 tweezers
19 **Linotype line-composing (line-casting, slug-composing, slug-casting) machine, a multi-magazine machine**
20 distributing mechanism (distributor)
21 type magazines with matrices (matrixes)
22 elevator carrier for distributing the matrices (matrixes)
23 assembler
24 spacebands
25 casting mechanism
26 metal feeder
27 machine-set matter (cast lines, slugs)
28 matrices (matrixes) for hand-setting (sorts)
29 Linotype matrix
30 teeth for the distributing mechanism (distributor)
31 face (type face, matrix)
32-45 **monotype single-unit composing** (typesetting) **and casting machine** (monotype single-unit composition caster)
32 monotype standard composing (typesetting) machine (keyboard)

33 paper tower
34 paper ribbon
35 justifying scale
36 unit indicator
37 keyboard
38 compressed-air hose
39 monotype casting machine (monotype caster)
40 automatic metal feeder
41 pump compression spring (pump pressure spring)
42 matrix case (die case)
43 paper tower
44 galley with types (letters, characters, cast single types, cast single letters)
45 electric heater (electric heating unit)
46 matrix case (die case)
47 type matrices (matrixes) (letter matrices)
48 guide block for engaging with the cross-slide guide

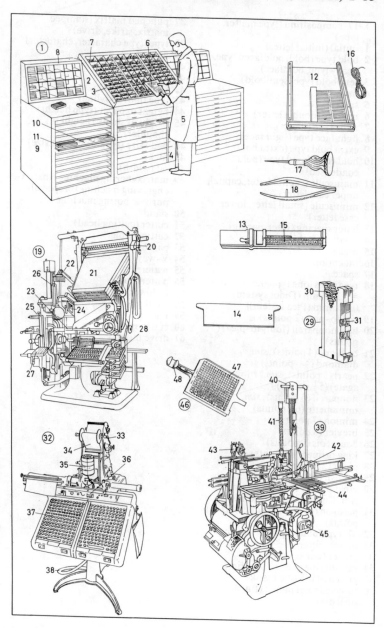

1–17 composition (type matter, type)
1 initial (initial letter)
2 bold type (bold, boldfaced type, heavy type, boldface)
3 semibold type (semibold)
4 line
5 space
6 ligature (double letter)
7 italic type (italics)
8 light face type (light face)
9 extra bold type (extra bold)
10 bold condensed type (bold condensed)
11 majuscule (capital letter, capital, upper case letter)
12 minuscule (small letter, lower case letter)
13 letter spacing (interspacing)
14 small capitals
15 break
16 indention
17 space
18 type sizes [one typographic point = 0.376 mm (Didot system), 0.351 mm (Pica system)]
19 six-to-pica (2 points)
20 half nonpareil (four-to-pica) (3 points)
21 brilliant (4 points); *sim.:* diamond ($4\frac{1}{2}$ points)
22 pearl (5 points); *sim.:* ruby (*Am.* agate) ($5\frac{1}{2}$ points)
23 nonpareil (6 points); *sim.:* minionette ($6\frac{1}{2}$ points)
24 minion (7 points)
25 brevier (8 points)
26 bourgeois (9 points)
27 long primer (10 points)
28 pica (12 points)
29 english (14 points)
30 great primer (two-line brevier, *Am.* Columbian) (16 points)
31 paragon (two-line primer) (20 points)
32–37 typefounding (type casting)
32 punch cutter
33 graver (burin, cutter)
34 magnifying glass (magnifier)
35 punch blank (die blank)
36 finished steel punch (finished steel die)
37 punched matrix (stamped matrix, strike, drive)
38 type (type character, character)
39 head
40 shoulder
41 counter
42 face (type face)
43 type line (bodyline)
44 height to paper (type height)
45 height of shank (height of shoulder)
46 body size (type size, point size)
47 nick
48 set (width)
49 matrix–boring machine (matrix-engraving machine), a special-purpose boring machine
50 stand
51 cutter (cutting head)
52 cutting table
53 pantograph carriage
54 V–way
55 pattern
56 pattern table
57 follower
58 pantograph
59 matrix clamp
60 cutter spindle
61 drive motor

[1] [3] [9] [2]

Alfred **John Dodsley,** essayist and journalist,[4] was born in Wenlock on the 5th August 1841 and died on the 4th October 1920 in Birmingham.[5] His father was a journeyman thatcher and as a boy Dodsley was sent to work in the fields as a bird-scarer. Having taught himself to read and write fluently[8] — for many years the only[6] books he possessed were a Bible and a volume of Tillotson's sermons — he went to Shrewsbury to study. Living in extreme poverty he began to write for the EAST HEREFORDSHIRE GAZETTE and[14] a collection of his essays together with some poems on country life was published in 1868 under the title "Rural Thoughts". Among his most popular works were "The Diary of a Derbyshire Shepherd" (1872),[7] "Rural Verses" (1879), "Leaves from a Country-man's Notebook" (1893) and "Memoirs of Nineteenth Century Shropshire", published posthumously. Dodsley also contributed many articles on country life to London papers and championed[13] the cause of the agricultural worker during the depression of the 1880's. The latter[11] years of his life were embittered by controversy[12] raised by his protests against the unemployment caused by mechanised farming.[15]

[16]— He was for many years president of the **Society for the Protection of the Liberties of the Farm-worker.** [10] [17]

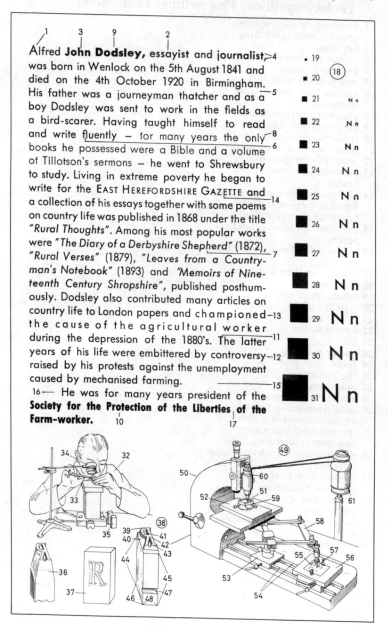

87 Composing Room (Case Room) III (Phototypesetting, Photocomposition, Photosetting, Filmsetting)

1 keyboard console (keyboard unit) for phototypesetting
2 keyboard
3 manuscript (copy)
4 keyboard operator
5 tape punch (perforator)
6 punched tape (punch tape)
7 filmsetter
8 punched tape (punch tape)
9 exposure control device
10 typesetting computer
11 memory unit (storage unit)
12 punched tape (punch tape)
13 punched tape (punch tape) reader
14 photo-unit (photographic unit) for computer-controlled typesetting (composition)
15 punched tape (punch tape) reader
16 type matrices (matrixes) (letter matrices)
17 matrix case (film matrix case)
18 guide block
19 synchronous motor
20 type disc (disk) (matrix disc)
21 mirror assembly
22 optical wedge
23 lens
24 mirror system
25 film
26 flash tubes
27 matrix drum
28 automatic film copier
29 central processing unit of a photocomposition system (photosetting system) for newspaper typesetting
30 punched tape (punch tape) input (input unit)
31 keyboard send-receive teleprinter (Teletype)
32 on-line disc (disk) storage unit
33 alphanumeric (alphameric) disc (disk) store (alphanumeric disc (disk) file)
34 disc (disk) stack (disc pack)

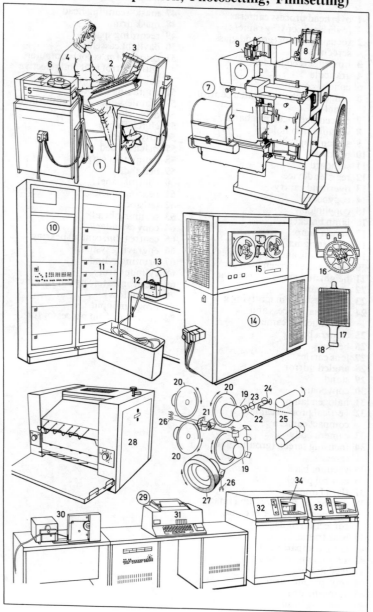

88 Photomechanical Reproduction

1 overhead process camera
   (overhead copying camera)
2 focusing screen (ground glass
   screen)
3 hinged screen holder
4 graticule
5 control console
6 hinged bracket-mounted control
   panel
7 percentage focusing charts
8 vacuum film holder
9 screen magazine
10 bellows
11 standard
12 register device
13 overhead gantry
14 copyboard
15 copyholder
16 lamp bracket
17 xenon lamp
18 copy (original)
19 retouching and stripping desk
20 illuminated screen
21 height and angle adjustment
22 copyboard
23 linen tester, a magnifying glass
24 universal process and
   reproduction camera
25 camera body
26 bellows
27 lens carrier
28 angled mirror
29 stand
30 copyboard
31 halogen lamp
32 vertical process camera, a
   compact camera
33 camera body
34 focusing screen (ground glass
   screen)
35 vacuum back
36 control panel
37 flash lamp
38 mirror for right-reading images
39 scanner (colour, *Am.* color,
   correction unit)
40 base frame
41 lamp compartment
42 xenon lamp housing
43 feed motors
44 transparency arm
45 scanning drum
46 scanning head

47 mask-scanning head
48 mask drum
49 recording space
50 daylight cassette
51 colour (*Am.* color) computer
   with control unit and selective
   colour correction
52 engraving machine
53 seamless engraving adjustment
54 drive clutch
55 clutch flange
56 drive unit
57 machine bed
58 equipment carrier
59 bed slide
60 control panel
61 bearing block
62 tailstock
63 scanning head
64 copy cylinder
65 centre (*Am.* center) bearing
66 engraving system
67 printing cylinder
68 cylinder arm
69 electronics (electronic) cabinet
70 computers
71 program input
72 automatic film processor for
   scanner films

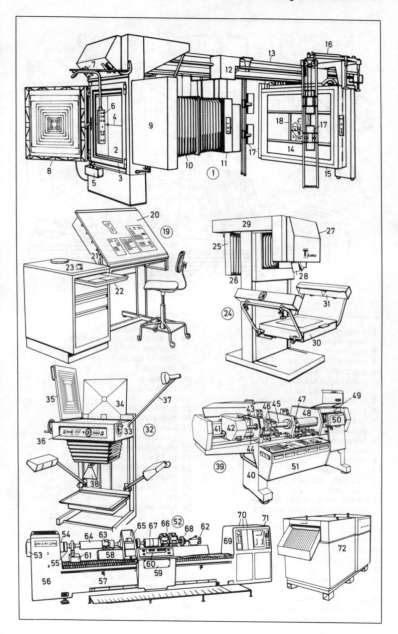

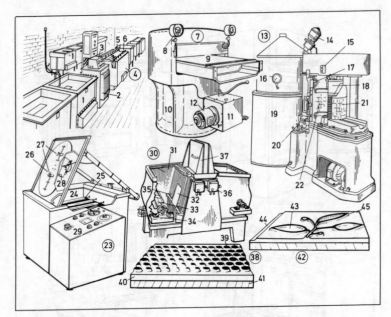

1-6 electrotyping plant
1 cleaning tank
2 rectifier
3 measuring and control unit
4 electroplating tank
  (electroplating bath,
  electroplating vat)
5 anode rod (copper anodes)
6 plate rod (cathode)
**7 hydraulic moulding (*Am.*
  molding) press**
8 pressure gauge (*Am.* gage)
  (manometer)
9 apron
10 round base
11 hydraulic pressure pump
12 drive motor
13 curved plate casting machine
  (curved electrotype casting
  machine)
14 motor
15 control knobs
16 pyrometer
17 mouth piece
18 core
19 melting furnace
20 starting lever
21 cast curved plate (cast curved
  electrotype) for rotary printing
22 fixed mould (*Am.* mold)

23 etching machine
24 etching tank with etching
  solution (etchant, mordant) and
  filming agent (film former)
25 paddles
26 turntable
27 plate clamp
28 drive motor
29 control unit
30 twin etching machine
31 etching tank (etching bath)
  [in section]
32 photoprinted zinc plate
33 paddle
34 outlet cock (drain cock, *Am.* faucet)
35 plate rack
36 control switches
37 lid
38 halftone photoengraving
  (halftone block, halftone plate),
  a block (plate, printing plate)
39 dot (halftone dot), a printing element
40 etched zinc plate
41 block mount (block mounting,
  plate mount, plate mounting)
42 line block (line engraving, line
  etching, line plate, line cut)
43 non-printing, deep-etched areas
44 flange (bevel edge)
45 sidewall

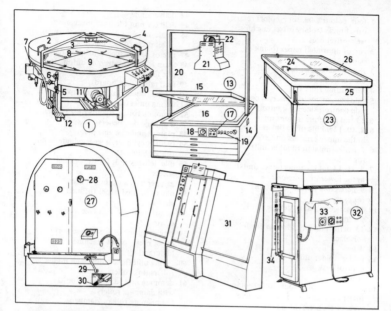

1 plate whirler (whirler, plate-coating machine) for coating offset plates
2 sliding lid
3 electric heater
4 temperature gauge (*Am.* gage)
5 water connection for the spray unit
6 spray unit
7 hand spray
8 plate clamps
9 zinc plate (*also:* magnesium plate, copper plate)
10 control panel
11 drive motor
12 brake pedal
13 vacuum printing frame (vacuum frame, printing-down frame)
14 base of the vacuum printing frame (vacuum frame, printing-down frame)
15 plate glass frame
16 coated offset plate
17 control panel
18 exposure timer
19 vacuum pump switch
20 support
21 point light exposure lamp, a quartz-halogen lamp
22 fan blower
23 stripping table (make-up table) for stripping films
24 crystal glass screen
25 light box
26 straightedge rules
27 vertical plate-drying cabinet
28 hygrometer
29 speed control
30 brake pedal
31 processing machine for presensitized plates
32 burning-in oven for glue-enamel plates (diazo plates)
33 control box (control unit)
34 diazo plate

91 Offset Printing

1 four-colour (*Am.* four-color) rotary offset press (rotary offset machine, web-offset press)
2 roll of unprinted paper (blank paper)
3 reel stand (carrier for the roll of unprinted paper)
4 forwarding rolls
5 side margin control (margin control, side control, side lay control)
6-13 inking units (inker units)
6, 8, 10, 12 inking units (inker units) in the upper printing unit
6-7 perfecting unit (double unit) for yellow
7, 9, 11, 13 inking units (inker units) in the lower printing unit
8-9 perfecting unit (double unit) for cyan
10-11 perfecting unit (double unit) for magenta
12-13 perfecting unit (double unit) for black
14 drier
15 folder (folder unit)
16 control desk
17 sheet
18 four-colour (*Am.* four-color) rotary offset press (rotary offset machine, web-offset press) [diagram]
19 reel stand
20 side margin control (margin control, side control, side lay control)
21 inking rollers (ink rollers, inkers)
22 ink duct (ink fountain)
23 damping rollers (dampening rollers, dampers, dampeners)
24 blanket cylinder
25 plate cylinder
26 route of the paper (of the web)
27 drier
28 chilling rolls (cooling rollers, chill rollers)
29 folder (folder unit)
30 four-colour (*Am.* four-color) sheet-fed offset machine (offset press) [diagram]
31 sheet feeder (feeder)
32 feed table (feed board)
33 route of the sheets through swing-grippers to the feed drum
34 feed drum
35 impression cylinder
36 transfer drums (transfer cylinders)
37 blanket cylinder
38 plate cylinder
39 damping unit (dampening unit)
40 inking units (inker units)
41 printing unit
42 delivery cylinder
43 chain delivery

44 delivery pile
45 delivery unit (delivery mechanism)
46 single-colour (*Am.* single-color) offset press (offset machine)
47 pile of paper (sheets, printing paper)
48 sheet feeder (feeder), an automatic pile feeder
49 feed table (feed board)
50 inking rollers (ink rollers, inkers)
51 inking units (inker units)
52 damping rollers (dampening rollers, dampers, dampeners)
53 plate cylinder, a zinc plate
54 blanket cylinder, a steel cylinder with rubber blanket
55 pile delivery unit for the printed sheets
56 gripper bar, a chain gripper
57 pile of printed paper (printed sheets)
58 guard for the V-belt (vee-belt) drive
59 single-colour (*Am.* single-color) offset press (offset machine) [diagram]
60 inking unit (inker unit) with inking rollers (ink rollers, inkers)
61 damping unit (dampening unit) with damping rollers (dampening rollers, dampers, dampeners)
62 plate cylinder
63 blanket cylinder
64 impression cylinder
65 delivery cylinders with grippers
66 drive wheel
67 feed table (feed board)
68 sheet feeder (feeder)
69 pile of unprinted paper (blank paper, unprinted sheets, blank sheets)
70 small sheet-fed offset press
71 inking unit (inker unit)
72 suction feeder
73 pile feeder
74 instrument panel (control panel) with counter, pressure gauge (*Am.* gage), air regulator, and control switch for the sheet feeder (feeder)
75 flat-bed offset press (offset machine) ('Mailänder' proofing press, proof press)
76 inking unit (inker unit)
77 inking rollers (ink rollers, inkers)
78 bed (press bed, type bed, forme bed, *Am.* form bed)
79 cylinder with rubber blanket
80 starting and stopping lever for the printing unit
81 impression-setting wheel (impression-adjusting wheel)

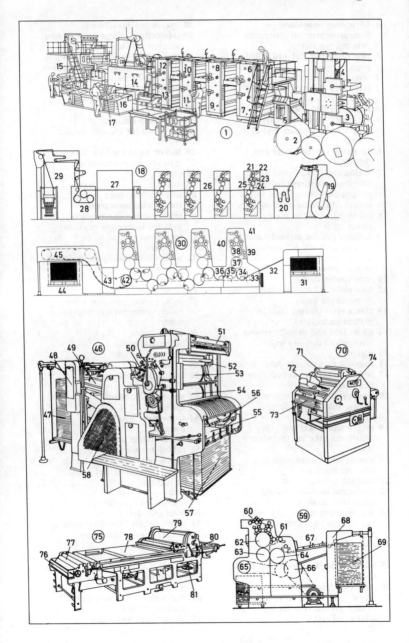

92 Letterpress Printing

1-65 presses (machines) for letterpress printing (letterpress printing machines)

1 two-revolution flat-bed cylinder press

2 impression cylinder

3 lever for raising or lowering the cylinder

4 feed table (feed board)

5 automatic sheet feeder (feeder) [operated by vacuum and air blasts]

6 air pump for the feeder and delivery

7 inking unit (inker unit) with distributing rollers (distributor rollers, distributors) and forme rollers (*Am.* form rollers)

8 ink slab (ink plate) inking unit (inker unit)

9 delivery pile for printed paper

10 sprayer (anti set-off apparatus, anti set-off spray) for dusting the printed sheets

11 interleaving device

12 foot pedal for starting and stopping the press

13 platen press (platen machine, platen) [in section]

14 paper feed and delivery (paper feeding and delivery unit)

15 platen

16 toggle action (toggle-joint action)

17 bed (type bed, press bed, forme bed, *Am.* form bed)

18 forme rollers (*Am.* form rollers) (forme-inking, *Am.* form-inking, rollers)

19 inking unit (inker unit) for distributing the ink (printing ink)

20 stop-cylinder press (stop-cylinder machine)

21 feed table (feed board)

22 feeder mechanism (feeding apparatus, feeder)

23 pile of unprinted paper (blank paper, unprinted sheets, blank sheets)

24 guard for the sheet feeder (feeder)

25 pile of printed paper (printed sheets)

26 control mechanism

27 forme rollers (*Am.* form rollers) (forme-inking, *Am.* form-inking, rollers)

28 inking unit (inker unit)

29 [Heidelberg] platen press (platen machine, platen)

30 feed table (feed board) with pile of unprinted paper (blank paper, unprinted sheets, blank sheets)

31 delivery table

32 starting and stopping lever

33 delivery blower

34 spray gun (sprayer)

35 air pump for vacuum and air blasts

36 locked-up forme (*Am.* form)

37 type (type matter, matter)

38 chase

39 quoin

40 length of furniture

41 rotary letterpress press (rotary letterpress machine, web-fed letterpress machine) for newspapers of up to 16 pages

42 slitters for dividing the width of the web

43 web

44 impression cylinder

45 jockey roller (compensating roller, compensator, tension roller)

46 roll of paper

47 automatic brake

48 first printing unit

49 perfecting unit

50 inking unit (inker unit)

51 plate cylinder

52 second printing unit

53 former

54 tachometer with sheet counter

55 folder (folder unit)

56 folded newspaper

57 inking unit (inker unit) for the rotary press (web-fed press) [in section]

58 web

59 impression cylinder

60 plate cylinder

61 forme rollers (*Am.* form rollers) (forme-inking, *Am.* form-inking, rollers)

62 distributing rollers (distributor rollers, distributors)

63 lifter roller (ductor, ductor roller)

64 duct roller (fountain roller, ink fountain roller)

65 ink duct (ink fountain)

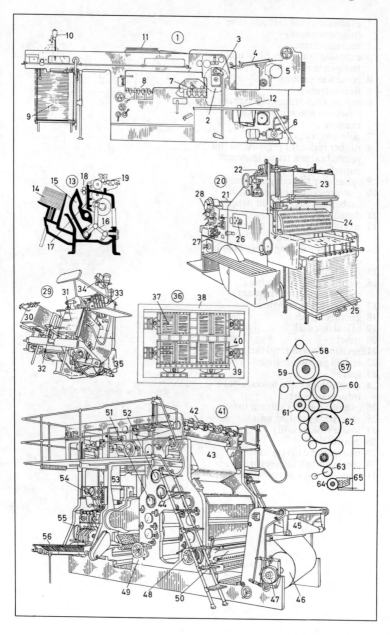

93 Photogravure (Gravure Printing, Intaglio Printing)

1 exposure of the carbon tissue (pigment paper)
2 vacuum frame
3 exposing lamp, a bank of quartz-halogen lamps
4 point source lamp
5 heat extractor
6 carbon tissue transfer machine (laydown machine, laying machine)
7 polished copper cylinder
8 rubber roller for pressing on the printed carbon tissue (pigment paper)
9 cylinder-processing machine
10 gravure cylinder coated with carbon tissue (pigment paper)
11 developing tank
12 staging
13 developed cylinder
14 retoucher painting out (stopping out)
15 etching machine
16 etching tank with etching solution (etchant, mordant)
17 printed gravure cylinder
18 gravure etcher
19 calculator dial
20 timer
21 revising (correcting) the cylinder
22 etched gravure cylinder
23 ledge
24 multicolour (*Am.* multicolor) rotogravure press
25 exhaust pipe for solvent fumes
26 reversible printing unit
27 folder (folder unit)
28 control desk
29 newspaper delivery unit
30 conveyor belt (conveyor)
31 bundled stack of newspapers

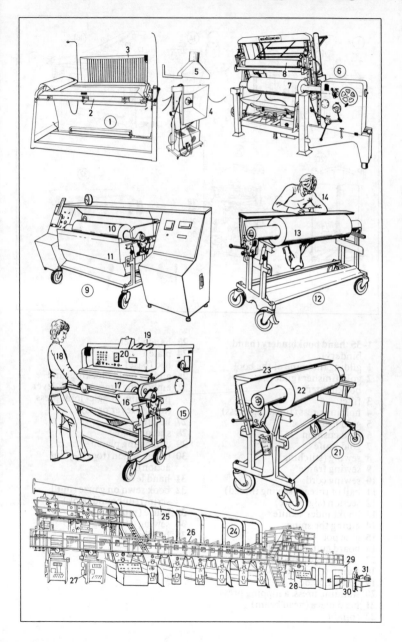

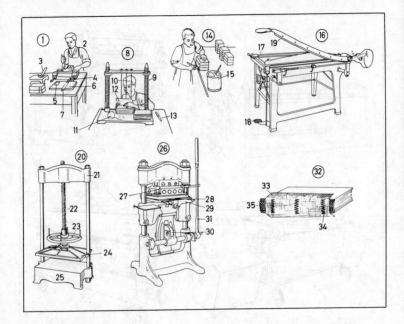

1-35 hand bookbindery (hand bindery)
1 gilding the spine of the book
2 gold finisher (gilder), a bookbinder
3 fillet
4 holding press (finishing press)
5 gold leaf
6 gold cushion
7 gold knife
8 sewing (stitching)
9 sewing frame
10 sewing cord
11 ball of thread (sewing thread)
12 section (signature)
13 bookbinder's knife
14 gluing the spine
15 glue pot
16 board cutter (guillotine)
17 back gauge (*Am.* gage)
18 clamp with foot pedal
19 cutting blade
20 standing press, a nipping press
21 head piece (head beam)
22 spindle

23 handwheel
24 platen
25 bed (base)
26 gilding (gold blocking) and embossing press, a hand-lever press; *sim.*: toggle-joint press (toggle-lever press)
27 heating box
28 sliding plate
29 embossing platen
30 toggle action (toggle-joint action)
31 hand lever
32 book sewn on gauze (mull, scrim) (unbound book)
33 gauze (mull, scrim)
34 sewing (stitching)
35 headband

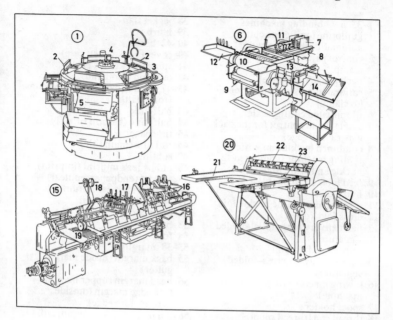

1-23 bookbinding machines
1 **adhesive binder** (perfect binder) for short runs
2 manual feed station
3 cutoff knife and roughing station
4 gluing mechanism
5 delivery (book delivery)
6 **case maker** (case-making machine)
7 board feed hopper
8 pickup sucker
9 glue tank
10 cover cylinder
11 picker head
12 feed table for covering materials [linen, paper, leather]
13 pressing mechanism
14 delivery table
15 **gang stitcher** (gathering and wire-stitching machine, gatherer and wire stitcher)
16 sheet feeder (sheet-feeding station)
17 folder-feeding station
18 stitching wire feed mechanism
19 delivery table
20 **rotary board cutter** (rotary board-cutting machine)
21 feed table with cut-out section
22 rotary cutter
23 feed guide

96 Bookbinding III

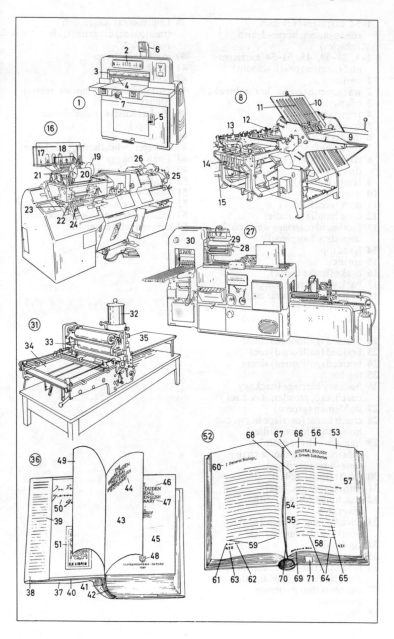

97 Horse-drawn Carriages

1-54 carriages (vehicles, conveyances, horse-drawn vehicles)

1-3, 26-39, 45, 51-54 carriages and coaches (coach wagons)

1 berlin

2 waggonette (*larger:* brake, break)

3 coupé; *sim.:* brougham

4 front wheel

5 coach body

6 dashboard (splashboard)

7 footboard

8 coach box (box, coachman's seat, driver's seat)

9 lamp (lantern)

10 window

11 door (coach door)

12 door handle (handle)

13 footboard (carriage step, coach step, step, footpiece)

14 fixed top

15 spring

16 brake (brake block)

17 back wheel (rear wheel)

18 dogcart, a one-horse carriage

19 shafts (thills, poles)

20 lackey (lacquey, footman)

21 livery

22 braided (gallooned) collar

23 braided (gallooned) coat

24 braided (gallooned) sleeve

25 top hat

26 hackney carriage (hackney coach, cab, growler, *Am.* hack)

27 stableman (groom)

28 coach horse (carriage horse, cab horse, thill horse, thiller)

29 hansom cab (hansom), a cabriolet, a one-horse chaise (one-horse carriage)

30 shafts (thills, poles)

31 reins (rein, *Am.* line)

32 coachman (driver) with inverness

33 covered char-a-banc (brake, break), a pleasure vehicle

34 gig (chaise)

35 barouche

36 landau, a two-horse carriage; *sim.:* landaulet, landaulette

37 omnibus (horse-drawn omnibus)

38 phaeton

39 Continental stagecoach (mailcoach, diligence); *also:* road coach

40 mailcoach driver

41 posthorn

42 hood

43 post horses (relay horses, relays)

44 tilbury

45 troika (Russian three-horse carriage)

46 leader

47 wheeler (wheelhorse, pole horse)

48 English buggy

49 American buggy

50 tandem

51 vis-à-vis

52 collapsible hood (collapsible top)

53 mailcoach (English stagecoach)

54 covered (closed) chaise

98 Bicycle

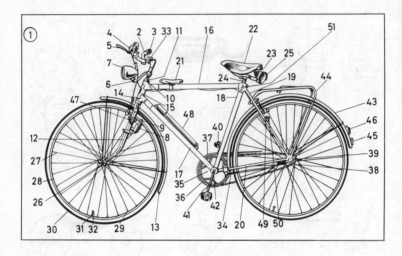

1 **bicycle** (cycle, *coll.* bike, *Am.* wheel), a gent's bicycle, a touring bicycle (touring cycle, roadster)
2 **handlebar** (handlebars), a touring cycle handlebar
3 **handlebar grip** (handgrip, grip)
4 **bicycle bell**
5 **hand brake** (front brake), a rim brake
6 **lamp bracket**
7 **headlamp** (bicycle lamp)
8 **dynamo**
9 **pulley**
10-12 **front forks**
10 **handlebar stem**
11 **steering head**
12 **fork blades** (fork ends)
13 **front mudguard** (*Am.* front fender)
14-20 **bicycle frame**
14 **steering tube** (fork column)
15 **head badge**
16 **crossbar** (top tube)
17 **down tube**
18 **seat tube**
19 **seat stays**
20 **chain stays**
21 **child's seat** (child carrier seat)

22 **bicycle saddle**
23 **saddle springs**
24 **seat pillar**
25 **saddle bag** (tool bag)
26-32 **wheel** (front wheel)
26 **hub**
27 **spoke**
28 **rim** (wheel rim)
29 **spoke nipple** (spoke flange, spoke end)
30 **tyres** (*Am.* tires) (tyre, pneumatic tyre, high–pressure tyre); *inside:* tube (inner tube), *outside:* tyre (outer case, cover)
31 **valve**, a tube valve with valve tube or a patent valve with ball
32 **valve sealing cap**
33 **bicycle speedometer** with milometer
34 **kick stand** (prop stand)
35-42 **bicycle drive** (chain drive)
35-39 **chain transmission**
35 **chain wheel**
36 **chain**, a roller chain
37 **chain guard**
38 **sprocket wheel** (sprocket)
39 **wing nut** (fly nut, butterfly nut)
40 **pedal**

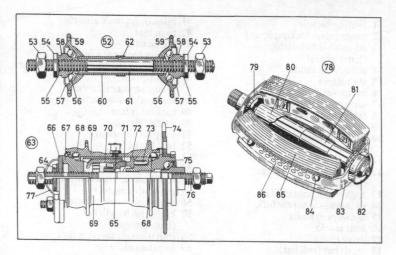

41 crank
42 bottom bracket bearing
43 rear mudguard (*Am.* rear fender)
44 luggage carrier (carrier)
45 reflector
46 rear light (rear lamp)
47 footrest
48 bicycle pump
49 bicycle lock, a wheel lock
50 patent key
51 cycle serial number (factory number, frame number)
52 front hub (front hub assembly)
53 wheel nut
54 locknut (locking nut)
55 washer (slotted cone adjusting washer)
56 ball bearing
57 dust cap
58 cone (adjusting cone)
59 centre (*Am.* center) hub
60 spindle
61 axle
62 clip covering lubrication hole (lubricator)
63 free-wheel hub with back-pedal brake (with coaster brake)
64 safety nut

65 lubricator
66 brake arm
67 brake arm cone
68 bearing cup with ball bearings in ball race
69 hub shell (hub body, hub barrel)
70 brake casing
71 brake cone
72 driver
73 driving barrel
74 sprocket
75 thread head
76 axle
77 bracket
78 bicycle pedal (pedal, reflector pedal)
79 cup
80 spindle
81 axle
82 dust cap
83 pedal frame
84 rubber stud
85 rubber block (rubber tread)
86 glass reflector

99 Motorcycles, Bicycles, Scooters, Mopeds

1 folding bicycle
2 hinge (*also*: locking lever)
3 adjustable handlebar (handlebars)
4 adjustable saddle
5 stabilizers
6 motor–assisted bicycle
7 air–cooled two–stroke engine
8 telescopic forks
9 tubular frame
10 fuel tank (petrol tank, *Am.* gasoline tank)
11 semi–rise handlebars
12 two–speed gear–change (gearshift)
13 high–back polo saddle
14 swinging–arm rear fork
15 upswept exhaust
16 heat shield
17 drive chain
18 crash bar (roll bar)
19 speedometer (*coll.* speedo)
20 battery–powered moped, an electrically–powered vehicle
21 swivel saddle
22 battery compartment
23 wire basket
24 touring moped (moped)
25 pedal crank (pedal drive, starter pedal)
26 single–cylinder two–stroke engine
27 spark–plug cap
28 fuel tank (petrol tank, *Am.* gasoline tank)
29 moped headlamp (front lamp)
30–35 handlebar fittings
30 twist grip throttle control (throttle twist grip)
31 twist grip (gear–change, gearshift)
32 clutch lever
33 hand brake lever
34 speedometer (*coll.* speedo)
35 rear–view mirror (mirror)
36 front wheel drum brake (drum brake)
37 Bowden cables (brake cables)
38 stop and tail light unit
39 light motorcycle with kickstarter
40 housing for instruments with speedometer and electronic rev counter (revolution counter)
41 telescopic shock absorber
42 twin seat
43 kickstarter
44 pillion footrest, a footrest
45 handlebar (handlebars)
46 chain guard
47 motor scooter (scooter)
48 removable side panel
49 tubular frame
50 metal fairings
51 prop stand (stand)
52 foot brake
53 horn (hooter)
54 hook for handbag or briefcase
55 foot gear–change control (foot gearshift control)
56 high–riser; *sim.*: Chopper
57 high–rise handlebar (handlebars)
58 imitation motorcycle fork
59 banana saddle
60 chrome bracket

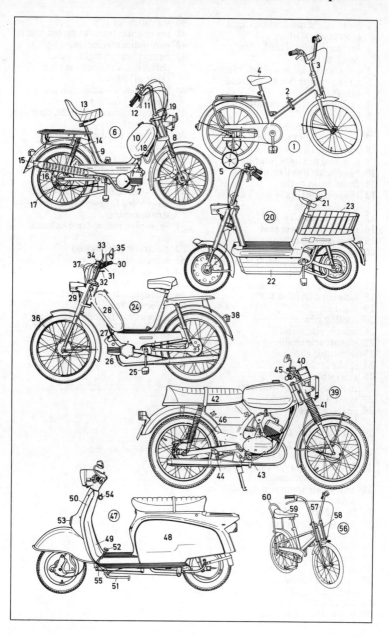

100 Motorcycle

1 lightweight motorcycle (light motorcycle) [50 cc]
2 fuel tank (petrol tank, *Am.* gasoline tank)
3 air-cooled single-cylinder four-stroke engine (with overhead camshaft)
4 carburettor (*Am.* carburetor)
5 intake pipe
6 five-speed gearbox
7 swinging-arm rear fork
8 number plate (*Am.* license plate)
9 stop and tail light (rear light)
10 headlight (headlamp)
11 front drum brake
12 brake cable (brake line), a Bowden cable
13 rear drum brake
14 racing-style twin seat
15 upswept exhaust
16 scrambling motorcycle (cross-country motorcycle) [125 cc], a light motorcycle
17 lightweight cradle frame
18 number disc (disk)
19 solo seat
20 cooling ribs
21 motorcycle stand
22 motorcycle chain
23 telescopic shock absorber
24 spokes
25 rim (wheel rim)
26 motorcycle tyre (*Am.* tire)
27 tyre (*Am.* tire) tread
28 gear-change lever (gearshift lever)
29 twist grip throttle control (throttle twist grip)
30 rear-view mirror (mirror)
31-58 heavy (heavyweight, large-capacity) motorcycles
31 heavyweight motorcycle with water-cooled engine
32 front disc (disk) brake
33 disc (disk) brake calliper (caliper)
34 floating axle
35 water cooler
36 oil tank
37 indicator (indicator light, turn indicator light)
38 kickstarter
39 water-cooled engine
40 speedometer
41 rev counter (revolution counter)
42 rear indicator (indicator light)
43 heavy (heavyweight, high-performance) machine with fairing [1000 cc]
44 integrated streamlining, an integrated fairing
45 indicator (indicator light, turn indicator light)
46 anti-mist windscreen (*Am.* windshield)
47 horizontally-opposed twin engine with cardan transmission
48 light alloy wheel
49 four-cylinder machine [400 cc]
50 air-cooled four-cylinder four-stroke engine
51 four-pipe megaphone exhaust pipe
52 electric starter button
53 sidecar machine
54 sidecar body
55 sidecar crash bar
56 sidelight (*Am.* sidemarker lamp)
57 sidecar wheel
58 sidecar windscreen (*Am.* windshield)

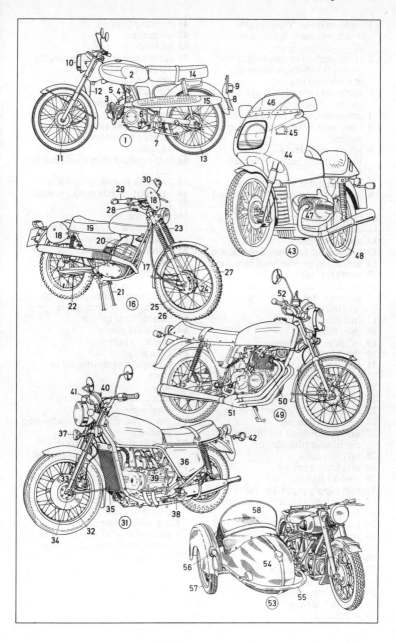

101 Internal Combustion Engines

1 eight–cylinder V (vee) fuel–injection spark–ignition engine (Otto–cycle engine)
2 cross–section of spark–ignition engine (Otto–cycle internal combustion engine)
3 sectional view of five–cylinder in–line diesel engine
4 cross–section of diesel engine
5 two–rotor Wankel engine (rotary engine)
6 single–cylinder two–stroke internal combustion engine
7 fan
8 fan clutch for viscous drive
9 ignition distributor (distributor) with vacuum timing control
10 double roller chain
11 camshaft bearing
12 air–bleed duct
13 oil pipe for camshaft lubrication
14 camshaft, an overhead camshaft
15 venturi throat
16 intake silencer (absorption silencer, *Am.* absorption muffler)
17 fuel pressure regulator
18 inlet manifold
19 cylinder crankcase
20 flywheel
21 connecting rod (piston rod)
22 cover of crankshaft bearing
23 crankshaft
24 oil bleeder screw (oil drain plug)
25 roller chain of oil pump drive
26 vibration damper
27 distributor shaft for the ignition distributor (distributor)
28 oil filler neck
29 diaphragm spring
30 control linkage
31 fuel supply pipe (*Am.* fuel line)
32 fuel injector (injection nozzle)
33 rocker arm
34 rocker arm mounting
35 spark plug (sparking plug) with suppressor
36 exhaust manifold
37 piston with piston rings and oil scraper ring
38 engine mounting
39 dog flange (dog)
40 crankcase

41 oil sump (sump)
42 oil pump
43 oil filter
44 starter motor (starting motor)
45 cylinder head
46 exhaust valve
47 dipstick
48 cylinder head gasket
49 double bushing chain
50 warm–up regulator
51 tapered needle for idling adjustment
52 fuel pressure pipe (fuel pressure line)
53 fuel leak line (drip fuel line)
54 injection nozzle (spray nozzle)
55 heater plug
56 thrust washer
57 intermediate gear shaft for the injection pump drive
58 injection timer unit
59 vacuum pump (low–pressure regulator)
60 cam for vacuum pump
61 water pump (coolant pump)
62 cooling water thermostat
63 thermo time switch
64 fuel hand pump
65 injection pump
66 glow plug
67 oil pressure limiting valve
68 rotor
69 seal
70 torque converter
71 single–plate clutch
72 multi–speed gearing (multi–step gearing)
73 port liners in the exhaust manifold for emission control
74 disc (disk) brake
75 differential gear (differential)
76 generator
77 foot gear–change control (foot gearshift control)
78 dry multi–plate clutch
79 cross–draught (*Am.* cross–draft) carburettor (*Am.* carburetor)
80 cooling ribs

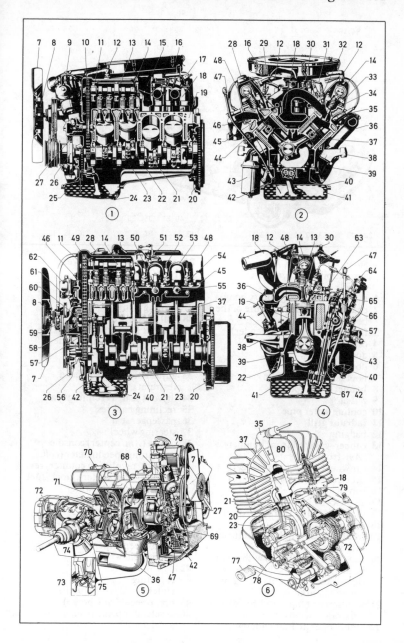

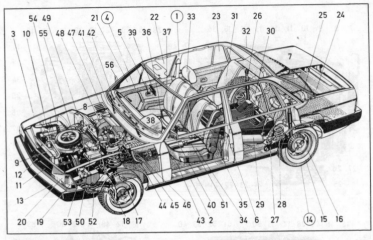

1-56 motor car (car, *Am*. automobile, auto), a passenger vehicle
1 monocoque body (unitary body)
2 chassis, the understructure of the body
3 front wing (*Am*. front fender)
4 car door
5 door handle
6 door lock
7 boot lid (*Am*. trunk lid)
8 bonnet (*Am*. hood)
9 radiator
10 cooling water pipe
11 radiator grill
12 badging
13 rubber-covered front bumper (*Am*. front fender)
14 car wheel, a disc (disk) wheel
15 car tyre (*Am*. automobile tire)
16 rim (wheel rim)
17-18 disc (disk) brake
17 brake disc (disk) (braking disc)
18 calliper (caliper)
19 front indicator light (front turn indicator light)
20 headlight (headlamp) with main beam (high beam), dipped beam (low beam), sidelight (side lamp, *Am*. sidemarker lamp)
21 windscreen (*Am*. windshield), a panoramic windscreen
22 crank-operated car window

23 quarter light (quarter vent)
24 boot (*Am*. trunk)
25 spare wheel
26 damper (shock absorber)
27 trailing arm
28 coil spring
29 silencer (*Am*. muffler)
30 automatic ventilation system
31 rear seats
32 rear window
33 adjustable headrest (head restraint)
34 driver's seat, a reclining seat
35 reclining backrest
36 passenger seat
37 steering wheel
38 centre (*Am*. center) console containing speedometer (*coll*. speedo), revolution counter (rev counter, tachometer), clock, fuel gauge (*Am*. gage), water temperature gauge, oil temperature gauge
39 inside rear-view mirror
40 left-hand wing mirror
41 windscreen wiper (*Am*. windshield wiper)
42 defroster vents
43 carpeting
44 clutch pedal (*coll*. clutch)
45 brake pedal (*coll*. brake)
46 accelerator pedal (*coll*. accelerator)

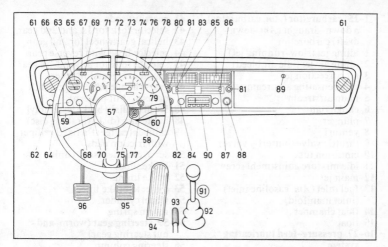

47 inlet vent
48 blower fan
49 brake fluid reservoir
50 battery
51 exhaust pipe
52 front running gear with front wheel drive
53 engine mounting
54 intake silencer (*Am.* intake muffler)
55 air filter (air cleaner)
56 right–hand wing mirror
57–90 dashboard (fascia panel)
57 controlled–collapse steering column
58 steering wheel spoke
59 indicator and dimming switch
60 wiper/washer switch and horn
61 side window blower
62 sidelight, headlight, and parking light switch
63 fog lamp warning light
64 fog headlamp and rear lamp switch
65 fuel gauge (*Am.* gage)
66 water temperature gauge (*Am.* gage)
67 warning light for rear fog lamp
68 hazard flasher switch
69 main beam warning light
70 electric rev counter (revolution counter)
71 fuel warning light

72 warning light for the hand brake and dual–circuit brake system
73 oil pressure warning light
74 speedometer (*coll.* speedo) with trip mileage recorder
75 starter and steering lock
76 warning lights for turn indicators and hazard flashers
77 switch for the courtesy light and reset button for the trip mileage recorder
78 ammeter
79 electric clock
80 warning light for heated rear window
81 switch for the leg space ventilation
82 rear window heating switch
83 ventilation switch
84 temperature regulator
85 fresh–air inlet and control
86 fresh–air regulator
87 warm–air regulator
88 cigar lighter
89 glove compartment (glove box) lock
90 car radio
91 gear lever (gearshift lever, floor-type gear–change)
92 leather gaiter
93 hand brake lever
94 accelerator pedal
95 brake pedal
96 clutch pedal

103 Motor Car (*Am.* Automobile) II

1–15 carburettor (*Am.* carburetor),
a down–draught (*Am.* down–
draft) carburettor
1 idling jet (slow–running jet)
2 idling air jet (idle air bleed)
3 air correction jet
4 compensating airstream
5 main airstream
6 choke flap
7 plunger
8 venturi
9 throttle valve (butterfly valve)
10 emulsion tube
11 idle mixture adjustment screw
12 main jet
13 fuel inlet (*Am.* gasoline inlet)
(inlet manifold)
14 float chamber
15 float
**16–27 pressure–feed lubricating
system**
16 oil pump
17 oil sump
18 sump filter
19 oil cooler
20 oil filter
21 main oil gallery (drilled gallery)
22 crankshaft drilling (crankshaft
tributary, crankshaft bleed)
23 crankshaft bearing (main
bearing)
24 camshaft bearing
25 connecting–rod bearing
26 gudgeon pin (piston pin)
27 bleed
**28–47 four–speed synchromesh
gearbox**
28 clutch pedal
29 crankshaft
30 drive shaft (propeller shaft)
31 starting gear ring
32 sliding sleeve for 3rd and 4th
gear
33 synchronizing cone
34 helical gear wheel for 3rd gear
35 sliding sleeve for 1st and 2nd
gear
36 helical gear wheel for 1st gear
37 lay shaft
38 speedometer drive
39 helical gear wheel for
speedometer drive
40 main shaft

41 gearshift rods
42 selector fork for 1st and 2nd gear
43 helical gear wheel for 2nd gear
44 selector head with reverse gear
45 selector fork for 3rd and 4th gear
46 gear lever (gearshift lever)
47 gear–change pattern (gearshift
pattern, shift pattern)
48–55 disc (disk) brake [assembly]
48 brake disc (disk) (braking disc)
49 calliper (caliper), a fixed calliper
with friction pads
50 servo cylinder (servo unit)
51 brake shoes
52 brake lining
53 outlet to brake line
54 wheel cylinder
55 return spring
56–59 steering gear (worm–and–
nut steering gear)
56 steering column
57 worm gear sector
58 steering drop arm
59 worm
60–64 water–controlled heater
60 air intake
61 heat exchanger (heater box)
62 blower fan
63 flap valve
64 defroster vent
65–71 live axle (rigid axle)
65 propeller shaft
66 trailing arm
67 rubber bush
68 coil spring
69 damper (shock absorber)
70 Panhard rod
71 stabilizer bar
72–84 MacPherson strut unit
72 body–fixing plate
73 upper bearing
74 suspension spring
75 piston rod
76 suspension damper
77 rim (wheel rim)
78 stub axle
79 steering arm
80 track–rod ball–joint
81 trailing link arm
82 bump rubber (rubber bonding)
83 lower bearing
84 lower suspension arm

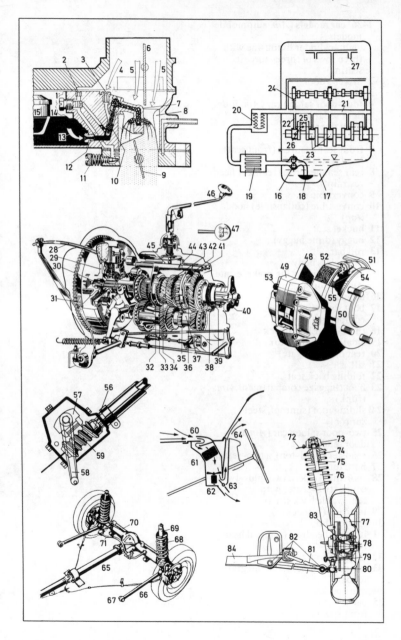

1–36 car models (*Am.* automobile models)

1 eight–cylinder limousine with three rows of three–abreast seating
2 driver's door
3 rear door
4 four–door saloon car (*Am.* four–door sedan)
5 front door
6 rear door
7 front seat headrest (front seat head restraint)
8 rear seat headrest (rear seat head restraint)
9 convertible
10 convertible (collapsible) hood (top)
11 bucket seat
12 buggy (dune buggy)
13 roll bar
14 fibre glass body
15 estate car (shooting brake, estate, *Am.* station wagon)
16 tailgate
17 boot space (luggage compartment)
18 three–door hatchback
19 small three–door car
20 rear door (tailgate)
21 sill
22 folding back seat
23 boot (luggage compartment, *Am.* trunk)
24 sliding roof (sunroof, steel sunroof)
25 two–door saloon car (*Am.* two–door sedan)
26 roadster (hard–top), a two–seater
27 hard top
28 sporting coupé, a two–plus–two coupé (two–seater with removable back seats)
29 fastback (liftback)
30 spoiler rim
31 integral headrest (integral head restraint)
32 GT car (gran turismo car)
33 integral bumper (*Am.* integral fender)
34 rear spoiler
35 back
36 front spoiler

105 Lorries (*Am.* Trucks), Vans, Buses

1 light cross–country lorry (light truck, pickup truck) with all–wheel drive (four–wheel drive)
2 cab (driver's cab)
3 loading platform (body)
4 spare tyre (*Am.* spare tire), a cross–country tyre
5 light lorry (light truck, pickup truck)
6 platform truck
7 medium van
8 sliding side door [for loading and unloading]
9 minibus
10 folding top (sliding roof)
11 rear door
12 hinged side door
13 luggage compartment
14 passenger seat
15 cab (driver's cab)
16 air inlet
17 motor coach (coach, bus)
18 luggage locker
19 hand luggage (suitcase, case)
20 heavy lorry (heavy truck, heavy motor truck)
21 tractive unit (tractor, towing vehicle)
22 trailer (drawbar trailer)
23 swop platform (body)
24 three–way tipper (three–way dump truck)
25 tipping body (dump body)
26 hydraulic cylinder
27 supported container platform
28 articulated vehicle, a vehicle tanker
29 tractive unit (tractor, towing vehicle)
30–33 semi–trailer (skeletal)
30 tank
31 turntable
32 undercarriage
33 spare wheel
34 midi bus [for short–route town operations]
35 outward–opening doors
36 double–deck bus (double–decker bus)
37 lower deck (lower saloon)
38 upper deck (upper saloon)
39 boarding platform
40 trolley bus
41 current collector
42 trolley (trolley shoe)
43 overhead wires
44 trolley bus trailer
45 pneumatically sprung rubber connection

1–55 agent's garage (distributor's garage, *Am*. specialty shop)
1–23 diagnostic test bay
1 computer
2 main computer plug
3 computer harness (computer cable)
4 switch from automatic to manual
5 slot for program cards
6 print-out machine (printer)
7 condition report (data print-out)
8 master selector (hand control)
9 light read-out [green: OK; red: not OK]
10 rack for program cards
11 mains button
12 switch for fast readout
13 firing sequence insert
14 shelf for used cards
15 cable boom
16 oil temperature sensor
17 test equipment for wheel and steering alignment
18 right-hand optic plate
19 actuating transistors
20 projector switch
21 check light for wheel alignment, a row of photocells
22 check light for steering alignment, a row of photocells
23 power screwdriver
24 beam setter
25 hydraulic lift
26 adjustable arm of hydraulic lift
27 hydraulic lift pad
28 excavation
29 pressure gauge (*Am*. gage)
30 grease gun
31 odds-and-ends box
32 wall chart [of spare parts]
33 automatic computer test
34 motor car (car, *Am*. automobile, auto), a passenger vehicle
35 engine compartment
36 bonnet (*Am*. hood)
37 bonnet support (*Am*. hood support)
38 computer harness (computer cable)

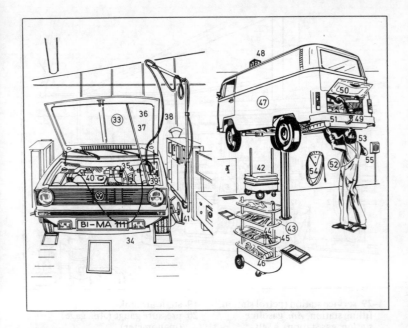

39 main computer socket; *also:*
multi-outlet socket
40 oil temperature sensor
41 wheel mirror for visual wheel
and steering alignment
42 tool trolley
43 tools
44 impact wrench
45 torque wrench
46 body hammer (roughing-out
hammer)
47 vehicle under repair, a minibus
48 car location number
49 rear engine
50 tailgate
51 exhaust system
52 exhaust repair
53 motor car mechanic (motor
vehicle mechanic, *Am.*
automotive mechanic)
54 air hose
55 intercom

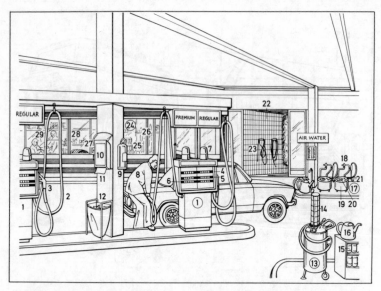

1-29 service station (petrol station, filling station, *Am.* gasoline station, gas station), a self-service station
1 petrol (*Am.* gasoline) pump (blending pump) for regular and premium grade petrol (*Am.* gasoline) (*sim.:* for derv)
2 hose (petrol pump, *Am.* gasoline pump, hose)
3 nozzle
4 cash readout
5 volume read-out
6 price display
7 indicator light
8 driver using self-service petrol pump (*Am.* gasoline pump)
9 fire extinguisher
10 paper-towel dispenser
11 paper towel
12 litter receptacle
13 two-stroke blending pump
14 meter
15 engine oil
16 oil can
17 tyre pressure gauge (*Am.* tire pressure gage)
18 air hose
19 static air tank
20 pressure gauge (*Am.* gage) (manometer)
21 air filler neck
22 repair bay (repair shop)
23 car-wash hose, a hose (hosepipe)
24 accessory shop
25 petrol can (*Am.* gasoline can)
26 rain cape
27 car tyres (*Am.* automobile tires)
28 car accessories
29 cash desk (console)

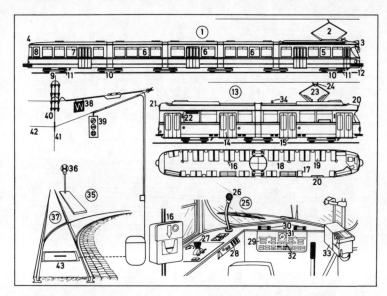

1 twelve-axle articulated railcar for interurban rail service
2 current collector
3 head of the railcar
4 rear of the railcar
5 carriage A containing the motor
6 carriage B (*also:* carriages C and D)
7 carriage E containing the motor
8 rear controller
9 bogie
10 carrying bogie
11 wheel guard
12 bumper (*Am.* fender)
13 six-axle articulated railcar ('Mannheim' type) for tram (*Am.* streetcar, trolley) and urban rail services
14 entrance and exit door, a double folding door
15 step
16 ticket-cancelling machine
17 single seat
18 standing room portion
19 double seat
20 route (number) and destination sign
21 route sign (number sign)
22 indicator (indicator light)
23 pantograph (current collector)

24 carbon or aluminium (*Am.* aluminum) alloy trolley shoes
25 driver's position
26 microphone
27 controller
28 radio equipment (radio communication set)
29 dashboard
30 dashboard lighting
31 speedometer
32 buttons controlling doors, windscreen wipers, internal and external lighting
33 ticket counter with change machine
34 radio antenna
35 tram stop (*Am.* streetcar stop, trolley stop)
36 tram stop sign (*Am.* streetcar stop sign, trolley stop sign)
37 electric change points
38 points signal (switch signal)
39 points change indicator
40 trolley wire contact point
41 trolley wire (overhead contact wire)
42 overhead cross wire
43 electric (*also:* electrohydraulic, electromechanical) points mechanism

109 Cross-section of a Street

1–5 road layers
1 anti–frost layer
2 bituminous sub–base course
3 base course
4 binder course
5 bituminous surface
6 kerb (curb)
7 kerbstone (curbstone)
8 paving (pavement)
9 pavement (*Am.* sidewalk, walkway)
10 gutter
11 pedestrian crossing (zebra crossing, *Am.* crosswalk)
12 street corner
13 street
14 electricity cables
15 telephone cables
16 telephone cable pipeline
17 cable manhole with cover (with manhole cover)
18 lamp post with lamp
19 electricity cables for technical installations
20 subscribers' (*Am.* customers') telephone lines

21 gas main
22 water main
23 drain
24 drain cover
25 drain pipe
26 waste pipe
27 combined sewer
28 district heating main
29 underground tunnel

Refuse Disposal (*Am.* Garbage Disposition), 110
Street Cleaning

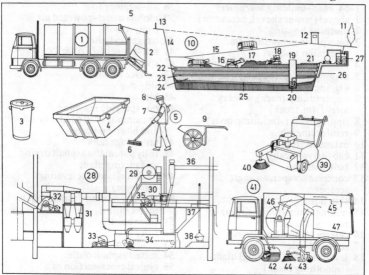

1 refuse collection vehicle (*Am.*
  garbage truck)
2 dustbin–tipping device (*Am.*
  garbage can dumping device), a
  dust–free emptying system
3 dustbin (*Am.* garbage can, trash can)
4 refuse container (*Am.* garbage
  container)
5 road sweeper (*Am.* street
  sweeper)
6 broom
7 fluorescent armband
8 cap with fluorescent band
9 road sweeper's (*Am.* street
  sweeper's) barrow
10 controlled tip (*Am.* sanitary
  landfill, sanitary fill)
11 screen
12 weigh office
13 fence
14 embankment
15 access ramp
16 bulldozer
17 refuse (*Am.* garbage)
18 bulldozer for dumping and
  compacting
19 pump shaft
20 waste water pump
21 porous cover

22 compacted and decomposed refuse
23 gravel filter layer
24 morainic filter layer
25 drainage layer
26 drain pipe
27 water tank
28 refuse (*Am.* garbage)
  incineration unit
29 furnace
30 oil–firing system
31 separation plant
32 extraction fan
33 low–pressure fan for the grate
34 continuous feed grate
35 fan for the oil–firing system
36 conveyor for separately
  incinerated material
37 coal feed conveyor
38 truck for carrying fuller's earth
39 mechanical sweeper
40 circular broom
41 road–sweeping lorry (street–
  cleaning lorry, street cleaner)
42 cylinder broom
43 suction port
44 feeder broom
45 air flow
46 fan
47 dust collector

1-54 road-building machinery
1 shovel (power shovel, excavator)
2 machine housing
3 caterpillar mounting (*Am.* caterpillar tractor)
4 digging bucket arm (dipper stick)
5 digging bucket (bucket)
6 digging bucket (bucket) teeth
7 tipper (dump truck), a heavy lorry (*Am.* truck)
8 tipping body (*Am.* dump body)
9 reinforcing rib
10 extended front
11 cab (driver's cab)
12 bulk material
13 concrete scraper, an aggregate scraper
14 skip hoist
15 mixing drum (mixer drum), a mixing machine
16 caterpillar hauling scraper
17 scraper blade
18 levelling (*Am.* leveling) blade (smoothing blade)
19 grader (motor grader)
20 scarifier (ripper, road ripper, rooter)
21 grader levelling (*Am.* leveling) blade (grader ploughshare, *Am.* plowshare)
22 blade-slewing gear (slew turntable)
23 light railway (narrow-gauge, *Am.* narrow-gage, railway)
24 light railway (narrow-gauge, *Am.* narrow-gage) diesel locomotive
25 trailer wagon (wagon truck, skip)
26 tamper (rammer); *heavier:* frog
27 guide rods
28 bulldozer
29 bulldozer blade
30 pushing frame
31 road-metal spreading machine (macadam spreader, stone spreader)
32 tamping beam
33 sole-plate
34 side stop
35 side of storage bin
36 three-wheeled roller, a road roller
37 roller

38 all-weather roof
39 mobile diesel-powered air compressor
40 oxygen cylinder
41 self-propelled gritter
42 spreading flap
43 surface finisher
44 side stop
45 bin
46 tar-spraying machine (bituminous distributor) with tar and bitumen heater
47 tar storage tank
48 fully automatic asphalt drying and mixing plant
49 bucket elevator (elevating conveyor)
50 asphalt-mixing drum (asphalt mixer drum)
51 filler hoist
52 filler opening
53 binder injector
54 mixed asphalt outlet
55 typical cross-section of a bituminous road
56 grass verge
57 crossfall
58 asphalt surface (bituminous layer, bituminous coating)
59 base (base course)
60 gravel sub-base course (hardcore sub-base course, Telford base), an anti-frost layer
61 sub-drainage
62 perforated cement pipe
63 drainage ditch
64 soil covering

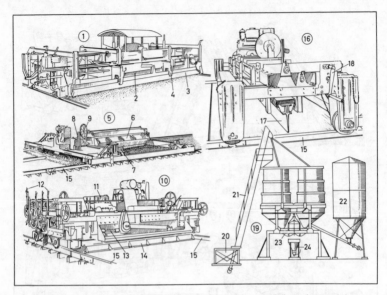

1-24 concrete road construction
(highway construction)
1 subgrade grader
2 tamping beam (consolidating beam)
3 levelling (*Am.* leveling) beam
4 roller guides for the levelling (*Am.* leveling) beam
5 concrete spreader
6 concrete spreader box
7 cable guides
8 control levers
9 handwheel for emptying the boxes
10 concrete-vibrating compactor
11 gearing (gears)
12 control levers (operating levers)
13 axle drive shaft to vibrators (tampers) of vibrating beam
14 screeding board (screeding beam)
15 road form
16 joint cutter
17 joint-cutting blade
18 crank for propelling machine

19 concrete-mixing plant, a stationary central mixing plant, an automatic batching and mixing plant
20 collecting bin
21 bucket elevator
22 cement store
23 concrete mixer
24 concrete pump hopper

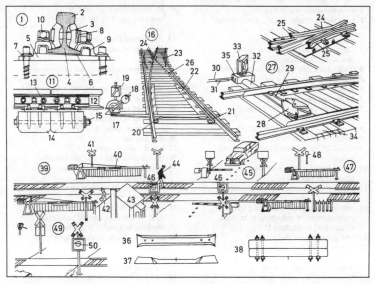

1-38 **line** (track)
1 rail
2 rail head
3 web (rail web)
4 rail foot (rail bottom)
5 sole-plate (base plate)
6 cushion
7 coach screw (coach bolt)
8 lock washers (spring washers)
9 rail clip (clip)
10 T-head bolt
11 rail joint (joint)
12 fishplate
13 fishbolt
14 coupled sleeper (*Am*. coupled tie, coupled crosstie)
15 coupling bolt
16 manually-operated points (switch)
17 switch stand
18 weight
19 points signal (switch signal, points signal lamp, switch signal lamp)
20 pull rod
21 switch blade (switch tongue)
22 slide chair
23 check rail (guard rail)
24 frog
25 wing rail
26 closure rail
27 remote-controlled points (switch)
28 point lock (switch lock)
29 stretcher bar

30 point wire
31 turnbuckle
32 channel
33 electrically illuminated points signal (switch signal)
34 trough
35 points motor with protective casing
36 steel sleeper (*Am*. steel tie, steel crosstie)
37 concrete sleeper (*Am*. concrete tie, concrete crosstie)
38 coupled sleeper (*Am*. coupled tie, coupled crosstie)
39-50 **level crossings** (*Am*. grade crossings)
39 protected level crossing (*Am*. protected grade crossing)
40 barrier (gate)
41 warning cross (*Am*. crossbuck)
42 crossing keeper (*Am*. gateman)
43 crossing keeper's box (*Am*. gateman's box)
44 linesman (*Am*. trackwalker)
45 half-barrier crossing
46 warning light
47 intercom controlled crossing; *sim.:* telephone-controlled crossing
48 intercom system
49 unprotected level crossing (*Am*. unprotected grade crossing)
50 warning light

114 Railway Line (*Am.* Railroad Track) II (Signalling Equipment)

1-6 stop signals (main signals)
1 stop signal (main signal), a semaphore signal in 'stop' position
2 signal arm (semaphore arm)
3 electric stop signal (colour light, *Am.* color light, signal) at 'stop'
4 signal position: 'proceed at low speed'
5 signal position: 'proceed'
6 substitute signal
7-24 distant signals
7 semaphore signal at 'be prepared to stop at next signal'
8 supplementary semaphore arm
9 colour light (*Am.* color light) distant signal at 'be prepared to stop at next signal'
10 signal position: 'be prepared to proceed at low speed'
11 signal position: 'proceed main signal ahead'
12 semaphore signal with indicator plate showing a reduction in braking distance of more than 5%
13 triangle (triangle sign)
14 colour light (*Am.* color light) distant signal with indicator light for showing reduced braking distance
15 supplementary white light
16 distant signal indicating 'be prepared to stop at next signal' (yellow light)
17 second distant signal (distant signal with supplementary light, without indicator plate)
18 distant signal with speed indicator
19 distant speed indicator
20 distant signal with route indicator
21 route indicator
22 distant signal without supplementary arm in position: 'be prepared to stop at next signal'
23 distant signal without supplementary arm in 'be prepared to proceed' position
24 distant signal identification plate
25-44 supplementary signals
25 stop board for indicating the stopping point at a control point
26-29 approach signs
26 approach sign 100 m from distant signal
27 approach sign 175 m from distant signal
28 approach sign 250 m from distant signal
29 approach sign at a distance of 5% less than the braking distance on the section
30 chequered sign indicating stop signals (main signals) not positioned immediately to the right of or over the line (track)

31-32 stop boards to indicate the stopping point of the front of the train
33 stop board (be prepared to stop)
34-35 snow plough (*Am.* snowplow) signs
34 'raise snow-plough (*Am.* snowplow)' sign
35 'lower snow-plough (*Am.* snowplow)' sign
36-44 speed restriction signs
36-38 speed restriction sign [maximum speed 3 × 10 = 30 kph]
36 sign for day running
37 speed code number
38 illuminated sign for night running
39 commencement of temporary speed restriction
40 termination of temporary speed restriction
41 speed restriction sign for a section with a permanent speed restriction [maximum speed 5 × 10 = 50 kph]
42 commencement of permanent speed restriction
43 speed restriction warning sign [only on main lines]
44 speed restriction sign [only on main lines]
45-52 points signals (switch signals)
45-48 single points (single switches)
45 route straight ahead (main line)
46 [right] branch
47 [left] branch
48 branch [seen from the frog]
49-52 double crossover
49 route straight ahead from left to right
50 route straight ahead from right to left
51 turnout to the left from the left
52 turnout to the right from the right
53 manually-operated signal box (*Am.* signal tower, switch tower)
54 lever mechanism
55 points lever (switch lever) [blue], a lock lever
56 signal lever [red]
57 catch
58 route lever
59 block instruments
60 block section panel
61 **electrically-operated signal box** (*Am.* signal tower, switch tower)
62 points (switch) and signal knobs
63 lock indicator panel
64 track and signal indicator
65 **track diagram control layout**
66 track diagram control panel (domino panel)
67 push buttons
68 routes
69 intercom system

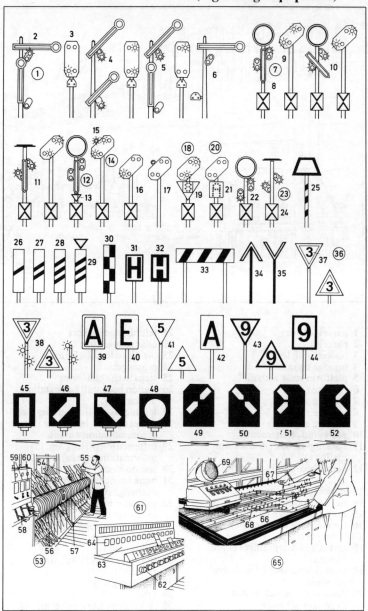

1 parcels office
2 parcels
3 basket [with lock]
4 luggage counter
5 platform scale with dial
6 suitcase (case)
7 luggage sticker
8 luggage receipt
9 luggage clerk
10 poster (advertisement)
11 station post box (*Am.* station mailbox)
12 notice board indicating train delays
13 station restaurant
14 waiting room
15 map of the town (street map)
16 timetable (*Am.* schedule)
17 hotel porter
18 arrivals and departures board (timetable)
19 arrival timetable (*Am.* arrival schedule)
20 departure timetable (*Am.* departure schedule)

21 left luggage lockers
22 change machine
23 tunnel to the platforms
24 passengers
25 steps to the platforms
26 station bookstall (*Am.* station bookstand)
27 left luggage office (left luggage)
28 travel centre (*Am.* center); *also:* accommodation bureau
29 information office (*Am.* information bureau)
30 station clock
31 bank branch with foreign exchange counter
32 indicator board showing exchange rates
33 railway map (*Am.* railroad map)
34 ticket office
35 ticket counter
36 ticket (railway ticket, *Am.* railroad ticket)
37 revolving tray
38 grill
39 ticket clerk (*Am.* ticket agent)

40 ticket–printing machine (ticket–stamping machine)
41 hand–operated ticket printer
42 pocket timetable (*Am.* pocket train schedule)
43 luggage rest
44 first aid station
45 Travellers' (*Am.* Travelers') Aid
46 telephone box (telephone booth, telephone kiosk, call box)
47 cigarettes and tobacco kiosk
48 flower stand
49 railway information clerk
50 official timetable (official railway guide, *Am.* train schedule)

1 platform
2 steps to the platform
3 bridge to the platforms
4 platform number
5 platform roofing
6 passengers
7–12 luggage
7 suitcase (case)
8 luggage label
9 hotel sticker
10 travelling (*Am*. traveling) bag
11 hat box
12 umbrella, a walking–stick umbrella
13 main building; *also*: offices
14 platform
15 crossing
16 news trolley
17 news vendor (*Am*. news dealer)
18 reading matter for the journey
19 edge of the platform
20 railway policeman (*Am*. railroad policeman)
21 destination board

22 destination indicator
23 departure time indicator
24 delay indicator
25 suburban train, a railcar
26 special compartment
27 platform loudspeaker
28 station sign
29 electric trolley (electric truck)
30 loading foreman
31 porter (*Am*. redcap)
32 barrow
33 drinking fountain
34 electric Trans–Europe Express; *also*: Intercity train
35 electric locomotive, an express locomotive
36 collector bow (sliding bow)
37 secretarial compartment
38 destination board
39 wheel tapper
40 wheel–tapping hammer
41 station foreman
42 signal
43 red cap

44 inspector
45 pocket timetable (*Am.* pocket train schedule)
46 platform clock
47 starting signal
48 platform lighting
49 refreshment kiosk
50 beer bottle
51 newspaper
52 parting kiss
53 embrace
54 platform seat
55 litter bin (*Am.* litter basket)
56 platform post box (*Am.* platform mailbox)
57 platform telephone
58 trolley wire (overhead contact wire)
59–61 track
59 rail
60 sleeper (*Am.* tie, crosstie)
61 ballast (bed)

117 Goods Station (Freight Depot)

1 ramp (vehicle ramp); *sim.:*
   livestock ramp
2 electric truck
3 trailer
4 part loads (*Am.* package freight,
   less–than–carload freight); *in
   general traffic:* general goods in
   general consignments (in mixed
   consignments)
5 crate
6 goods van (*Am.* freight car)
7 goods shed (*Am.* freight house)
8 loading strip
9 loading dock
10 bale of peat
11 bale of linen (of linen cloth)
12 fastening (cord)
13 wicker bottle (wickered bottle,
    demijohn)
14 trolley
15 goods lorry (*Am.* freight truck)
16 forklift truck (fork truck,
    forklift)
17 loading siding
18 bulky goods
19 small railway–owned (*Am.*
    railroad–owned) container
20 showman's caravan (*sim.:* circus
    caravan)
21 flat wagon (*Am.* flat freight car)
22 loading gauge (*Am.* gage)
23 bale of straw
24 flat wagon (*Am.* flatcar) with
    side stakes
25 fleet of lorries (*Am.* trucks)
26–39 **goods shed** (*Am.* freight
    house)
26 goods office (forwarding office,
    Am. freight office)
27 part–load goods (*Am.* package
    freight)
28 forwarding agent (*Am.* freight
    agent, shipper)
29 loading foreman
30 consignment note (waybill)
31 weighing machine
32 pallet
33 porter
34 electric cart (electric truck)
35 trailer
36 loading supervisor
37 goods shed door (*Am.* freight
    house door)

38 rail (slide rail)
39 roller
40 weighbridge office
41 weighbridge
42 marshalling yard (*Am.*
    classification yard, switch yard)
43 shunting engine (shunting
    locomotive, shunter, *Am.* switch
    engine, switcher)
44 marshalling yard signal box
    (*Am.* classification yard switch
    tower)
45 yardmaster
46 hump
47 sorting siding (classification
    siding, classification track)
48 rail brake (retarder)
49 slipper brake (slipper)
50 storage siding (siding)
51 buffer (buffers, *Am.* bumper)
52 wagon load (*Am.* carload)
53 warehouse
54 container station
55 gantry crane
56 lifting gear (hoisting gear)
57 container
58 container wagon (*Am.* container
    car)
59 semi–trailer

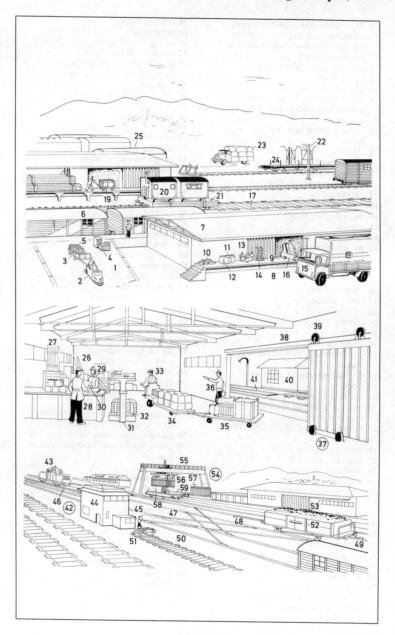

118 Railway Vehicles (Rolling Stock) I

1-21 express train coach (express train carriage, express train car, corridor compartment coach), a passenger coach
1 side elevation (side view)
2 coach body
3 underframe (frame)
4 bogie (truck) with steel and rubber suspension and shock absorbers
5 battery containers (battery boxes)
6 steam and electric heat exchanger for the heating system
7 sliding window
8 rubber connecting seal
9 ventilator
10-21 plan
10 second-class section
11 corridor
12 folding seat (tip-up seat)
13 passenger compartment (compartment)
14 compartment door
15 washroom
16 toilet (lavatory, WC)
17 first-class section
18 swing door
19 sliding connecting door
20 door
21 vestibule
22-32 dining car (restaurant car, diner)
22-25 side elevation (side view)
22 door
23 loading door
24 current collector for supplying power during stops
25 battery boxes (battery containers)
26-32 plan
26 staff washroom
27 storage cupboard
28 washing-up area
29 kitchen
30 electric oven with eight hotplates
31 counter
32 dining compartment
33 dining car kitchen
34 chef (head cook)
35 kitchen cabinet
36 sleeping car (sleeper)
37 side elevation (side view)
38-42 plan
38 two-seat twin-berth compartment (two-seat two-berth compartment, *Am.* bedroom)

39 folding doors
40 washstand
41 office
42 toilet (lavatory, WC)
43 express train compartment
44 upholstered reclining seat
45 armrest
46 ashtray in the armrest
47 adjustable headrest
48 antimacassar
49 mirror
50 coat hook
51 luggage rack
52 compartment window
53 fold-away table (pull-down table)
54 heating regulator
55 litter receptacle
56 curtain
57 footrest
58 corner seat
59 open car
60 side elevation (side view)
61-72 plan
61 open carriage
62 row of single seats
63 row of double seats
64 reclining seat
65 seat upholstery
66 backrest
67 headrest
68 down-filled headrest cushion with nylon cover
69 armrest with ashtray
70 cloakroom
71 luggage compartment
72 toilet (lavatory, WC)
73 buffet car (quick-service buffet car), a self-service restaurant car
74 side elevation (side view)
75 current collector for supplying power
76 plan
77 dining compartment
78-79 buffet (buffet compartment)
78 customer area
79 serving area
80 kitchen
81 staff compartment
82 staff toilet (staff lavatory, staff WC)
83 food compartments
84 plates
85 cutlery
86 till (cash register)

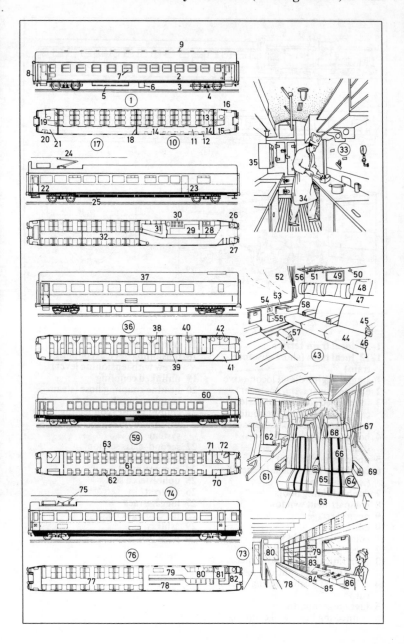

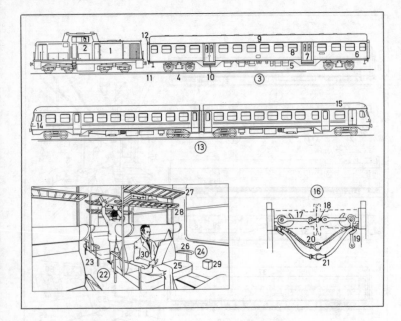

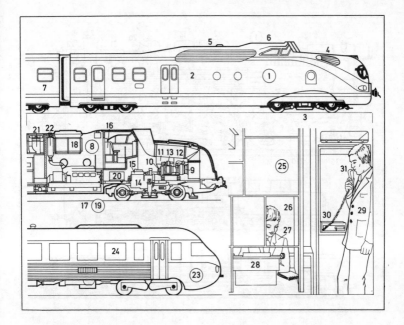

1–22 Trans-Europe Express
1 German Federal Railway trainset, a diesel trainset or gas turbine trainset
2 driving unit
3 drive wheel unit
4 main engine
5 diesel generator unit
6 cab (driver's cab, *Am.* engineer's cab)
7 second coach
8 gas turbine driving unit [diagram]
9 gas turbine
10 turbine transmission
11 air intake
12 exhaust with silencers (*Am.* mufflers)
13 dynastarter
14 Voith transmission
15 heat exchanger for the transmission oil
16 gas turbine controller
17 gas turbine fuel tank

18 oil-to-air cooling unit for transmission and turbine
19 auxiliary diesel engine
20 fuel tank
21 cooling unit
22 exhaust with silencers (*Am.* mufflers)
23 **Société Nationale des Chemins de Fer Français** (SNCF) experimental trainset with six-cylinder underfloor diesel engine and twin-shaft gas turbine
24 turbine unit with silencers (*Am.* mufflers)
25 secretarial compartment
26 typing compartment
27 secretary
28 typewriter
29 travelling (*Am.* traveling) salesman
30 dictating machine
31 microphone

121 Railway Vehicles (Rolling Stock) IV

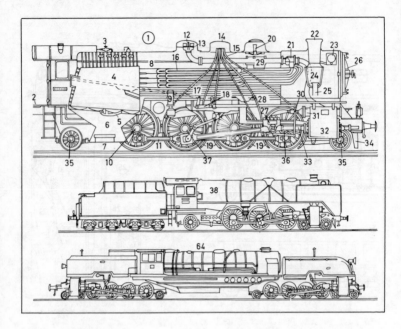

1–69 steam locomotives
2–37 locomotive boiler and driving gear

2 tender platform with coupling
3 safety valve for excess boiler pressure
4 firebox
5 drop grate
6 ashpan with damper doors
7 bottom door of the ashpan
8 smoke tubes (flue tubes)
9 feed pump
10 axle bearing
11 connecting rod
12 steam dome
13 regulator valve (regulator main valve)
14 sand dome
15 sand pipes (sand tubes)
16 boiler (boiler barrel)
17 fire tubes or steam tubes
18 reversing gear (steam reversing gear)
19 sand pipes
20 feed valve

21 steam collector
22 chimney (smokestack, smoke outlet and waste steam exhaust)
23 feedwater preheater (feedwater heater, economizer)
24 spark arrester
25 blast pipe
26 smokebox door
27 cross head
28 mud drum
29 top feedwater tray
30 combination lever
31 steam chest
32 cylinder
33 piston rod with stuffing box (packing box)
34 guard iron (rail guard, *Am*. pilot, cowcatcher)
35 carrying axle (running axle, dead axle)
36 coupled axle
37 driving axle
38 express locomotive with tender

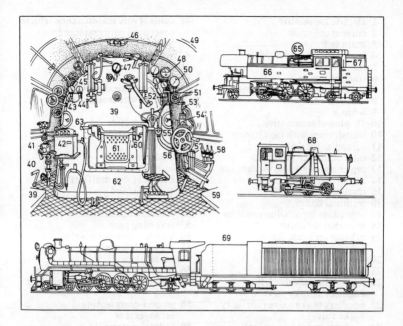

39–63 cab (driver's cab, *Am.* engineer's cab)
39 fireman's seat
40 drop grate lever
41 line steam injector
42 automatic lubricant pump (automatic lubricator)
43 preheater pressure gauge (*Am.* gage)
44 carriage heating pressure gauge (*Am.* gage)
45 water gauge (*Am.* gage)
46 light
47 boiler pressure gauge (*Am.* gage)
48 distant–reading temperature gauge (*Am.* gage)
49 cab (driver's cab, *Am.* engineer's cab)
50 brake pressure gauge (*Am.* gage)
51 whistle valve handle
52 driver's timetable (*Am.* engineer's schedule)
53 driver's brake valve (*Am.* engineer's brake valve)
54 speed recorder (tachograph)
55 sanding valve
56 reversing wheel
57 emergency brake valve
58 release valve
59 driver's seat (*Am.* engineer's seat)
60 firehole shield
61 firehole door
62 vertical boiler
63 firedoor handle handgrip
64 articulated locomotive (Garratt locomotive)
65 tank locomotive
66 water tank
67 fuel tender
68 steam storage locomotive (fireless locomotive)
69 condensing locomotive (locomotive with condensing tender)

122 Railway Vehicles (Rolling Stock) V

1 electric locomotive
2 current collector
3 main switch
4 high-tension transformer
5 roof cable
6 traction motor
7 inductive train control system
8 main air reservoir
9 whistle
10-18 plan of locomotive
10 transformer with tap changer
11 oil cooler with blower
12 oil-circulating pump
13 tap changer driving mechanism
14 air compressor
15 traction motor blower
16 terminal box
17 capacitors for auxiliary motors
18 commutator cover
19 cab (driver's cab, *Am.* engineer's cab)
20 controller handwheel
21 dead man's handle
22 driver's brake valve (*Am.* engineer's brake valve)
23 ancillary brake valve (auxiliary brake valve)
24 pressure gauge (*Am.* gage)
25 bypass switch for the dead man's handle
26 tractive effort indicator
27 train heating voltage indicator
28 contact wire voltage indicator (overhead wire voltage indicator)
29 high-tension voltage indicator
30 on/off switch for the current collector
31 main switch
32 sander switch (sander control)
33 anti-skid brake switch
34 visual display for the ancillary systems
35 speedometer
36 running step indicator
37 clock
38 controls for the inductive train control system
39 cab heating switch
40 whistle lever

41 contact wire maintenance vehicle (overhead wire maintenance vehicle), a diesel railcar
42 work platform (working platform)
43 ladder
44-54 mechanical equipment of the contact wire maintenance vehicle
44 air compressor
45 blower oil pump
46 generator
47 diesel engine
48 injection pump
49 silencer (*Am.* muffler)
50 change-speed gear
51 cardan shaft
52 wheel flange lubricator
53 reversing gear
54 torque converter bearing
55 accumulator railcar (battery railcar)
56 battery box (battery container)
57 cab (driver's cab, *Am.* engineer's cab)
58 second-class seating arrangement
59 toilet (lavatory, WC)
60 fast electric multiple-unit train
61 front railcar
62 driving trailer car

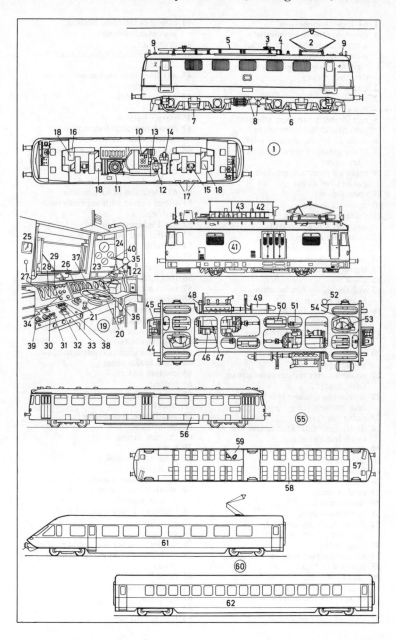

123 Railway Vehicles (Rolling Stock) VI

1-84 diesel locomotives
1 diesel-hydraulic locomotive,
a mainline locomotive (diesel
locomotive) for medium
passenger and goods service
(freight service)
2 bogie (truck)
3 wheel and axle set
4 main fuel tank
5 cab (driver's cab, *Am.* engineer's
cab) of a diesel locomotive
6 main air pressure gauge (*Am.* gage)
7 brake cylinder pressure gauge
(*Am.* gage)
8 main air reservoir pressure
gauge (*Am.* gage)
9 speedometer
10 auxiliary brake
11 driver's brake valve (*Am.*
engineer's brake valve)
12 controller handwheel
13 dead man's handle
14 inductive train control system
15 signal lights
16 clock
17 voltage meter for the train
heating system
18 current meter for the train
heating system
19 engine oil temperature gauge
(*Am.* gage)
20 transmission oil temperature
gauge (*Am.* gage)
21 cooling water temperature gauge
(*Am.* gage)
22 revolution counter (rev counter,
tachometer)
23 radio telephone
24 diesel-hydraulic locomotive
[plan and elevation]
25 diesel engine
26 cooling unit
27 fluid transmission
28 wheel and axle drive
29 cardan shaft
30 starter motor
31 instrument panel
32 driver's control desk (*Am.*
engineer's control desk)
33 hand brake
34 air compressor with electric motor
35 equipment locker
36 heat exchanger for transmission oil
37 engine room ventilator
38 magnet for the inductive train
control system
39 train heating generator

40 casing of the train heating
system transformer
41 preheater
42 exhaust silencer (*Am.* exhaust
muffler)
43 auxiliary heat exchanger for the
transmission oil
44 hydraulic brake
45 tool box
46 starter battery
47 diesel-hydraulic locomotive for
light and medium shunting service
48 exhaust silencer (*Am.* exhaust
muffler)
49 bell and whistle
50 yard radio
51-67 elevation of locomotive
51 diesel engine with supercharged
turbine
52 fluid transmission
53 output gear box
54 radiator
55 heat exchanger for the engine
lubricating oil
56 fuel tank
57 main air reservoir
58 air compressor
59 sand boxes
60 reserve fuel tank
61 auxiliary air reservoir
62 hydrostatic fan drive
63 seat with clothes compartment
64 hand brake wheel
65 cooling water
66 ballast
67 engine and transmission control
wheel
68 small diesel locomotive for
shunting service
69 exhaust casing
70 horn
71 main air reservoir
72 air compressor
73 eight–cylinder diesel engine
74 Voith transmission with
reversing gear
75 heating oil tank (fuel oil tank)
76 sand box
77 cooling unit
78 header tank for the cooling water
79 oil bath air cleaner (oil bath air
filter)
80 hand brake wheel
81 control wheel
82 coupling
83 cardan shaft
84 louvred shutter

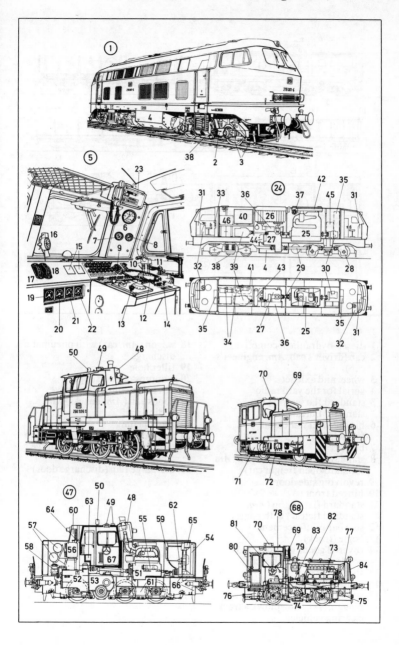

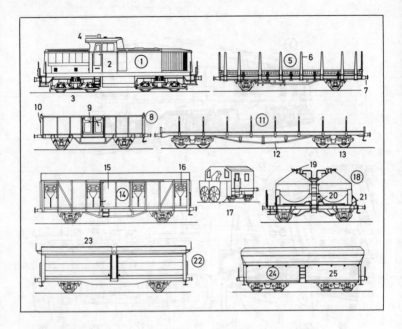

1 diesel–hydraulic locomotive
2 cab (driver's cab, *Am.* engineer's cab)
3 wheel and axle set
4 aerial for the yard radio
5 standard flat wagon (*Am.* standard flatcar)
6 hinged steel stanchion (stanchion)
7 buffers
8 standard open goods wagon (*Am.* standard open freight car)
9 revolving side doors
10 hinged front
11 standard flat wagon (*Am.* standard flatcar) with bogies
12 sole bar reinforcement
13 bogie (truck)
14 covered goods van (covered goods wagon, *Am.* boxcar)
15 sliding door
16 ventilation flap
17 snow blower (rotary snow plough, *Am.* snowplow), a track-clearing vehicle

18 wagon (*Am.* car) with pneumatic discharge
19 filler hole
20 compressed–air supply
21 discharge connection valve
22 goods van (*Am.* boxcar) with sliding roof
23 roof opening
24 bogie open self-discharge wagon (*Am.* bogie open self-discharge freight car)
25 discharge flap (discharge door)

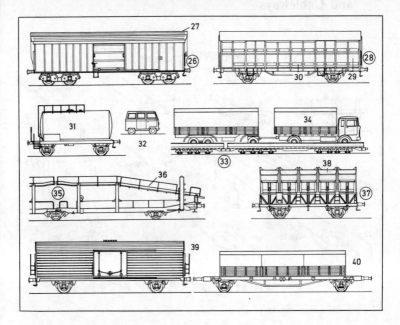

26 bogie wagon with swivelling
   (*Am.* swiveling) roof
27 swivelling (*Am.* swiveling) roof
28 large–capacity wagon (*Am.*
   large–capacity car) for small
   livestock
29 sidewall with ventilation flaps
   (slatted wall)
30 ventilation flap
31 tank wagon (*Am.* tank car)
32 track inspection railcar
33 open special wagons (*Am.* open
   special freight cars)
34 lorry (*Am.* truck) with trailer
35 two–tier car carrier (double–
   deck car carrier)
36 hinged upper deck
37 tipper wagon (*Am.* dump car)
   with skips
38 skip
39 general–purpose refrigerator
   wagon (refrigerator van, *Am.*
   refrigerator car)
40 interchangeable bodies for flat
   wagons (*Am.* flatcars)

125 Mountain Railways (*Am.* Mountain Railroads) and Cableways

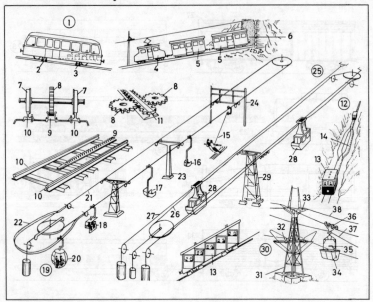

37 haulage cable
38 suspension cable (supporting cable)
39 **valley station** (lower station)
40 tension weight shaft
41 tension weight for the suspension cable (supporting cable)
42 tension weight for the haulage cable
43 tension cable pulley
44 suspension cable (supporting cable)
45 haulage cable
46 balance cable (lower cable)
47 auxiliary cable (emergency cable)
48 auxiliary-cable tensioning mechanism (emergency-cable tensioning mechanism)
49 haulage cable rollers
50 spring buffer (*Am.* spring bumper)
51 valley station platform (lower station platform)
52 cabin (cableway gondola, ropeway gondola, suspension line gondola), a large-capacity cabin
53 pulley cradle
54 suspension gear
55 stabilizer
56 guide rail
57 **top station** (upper station)
58 suspension cable guide (supporting cable guide)
59 suspension cable anchorage (supporting cable anchorage)
60 haulage cable rollers
61 haulage cable guide wheel
62 haulage cable driving pulley
63 main drive
64 standby drive
65 control room
66 **cabin pulley cradle**
67 main pulley cradle
68 double cradle
69 two-wheel cradle
70 running wheels
71 suspension cable brake (supporting cable brake), an emergency brake in case of haulage cable failure
72 suspension gear bolt
73 haulage cable sleeve
74 balance cable sleeve (lower cable sleeve)
75 derailment guard
76 **cable supports** (ropeway supports, suspension line supports, intermediate supports)
77 pylon, a framework support
78 tubular steel pylon, a tubular steel support
79 suspension cable guide rail (supporting cable guide rail, support guide rail)
80 support truss, a frame for work on the cable
81 base of the support

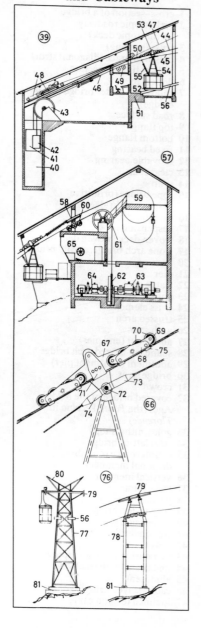

126 Bridges

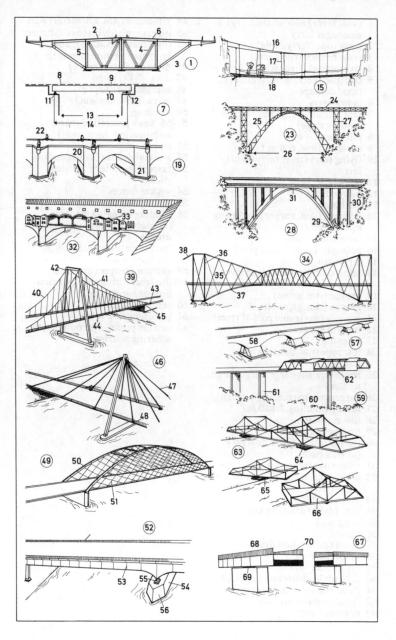

127 Rivers and River Engineering

1 **cable ferry** (*also:* chain ferry), a passenger ferry
2 ferry rope (ferry cable)
3 river branch (river arm)
4 river island (river islet)
5 collapsed section of riverbank, flood damage
6 **motor ferry**
7 ferry landing stage (motorboat landing stage)
8 pile foundations
9 current (flow, course)
10 **flying ferry** (river ferry), a car ferry
11 ferry boat
12 buoy (float)
13 anchorage
14 harbour (*Am.* harbor) for laying up river craft
15 **ferry boat** (punt)
16 pole (punt pole, quant pole)
17 ferryman
18 blind river branch (blind river arm)
19 groyne (*Am.* groin)
20 groyne (*Am.* groin) head
21 fairway (navigable part of river)
22 **train of barges**
23 river tug
24 tow rope (tow line, towing hawser)
25 barge (freight barge, cargo barge, lighter)
26 bargeman (bargee, lighterman)
27 **towing** (hauling, haulage)
28 towing mast
29 towing engine
30 towing track; *form.:* tow path (towing path)
31 river after river training
32 **dike** (dyke, main dike, flood wall, winter dike)
33 drainage ditch
34 dike (dyke) drainage sluice
35 wing wall
36 outfall
37 drain (infiltration drain)
38 berm (berme)
39 top of dike (dyke)
40 dike (dyke) batter (dike slope)
41 flood bed (inundation area)
42 flood containment area
43 current meter

44 kilometre (*Am.* kilometer) sign
45 dikereeve's (dykereeve's) house (dikereeve's cottage); *also:* ferryman's house (cottage)
46 dikereeve (dykereeve)
47 dike (dyke) ramp
48 summer dike (dyke)
49 levee (embankment)
50 sandbags
51-55 **bank protection** (bank stabilization, revetment)
51 riprap
52 alluvial deposit (sand deposit)
53 fascine (bundle of wooden sticks)
54 wicker fences
55 stone pitching
56 **floating dredging machine** (dredger), a multi-bucket ladder dredge
57 bucket elevator chain
58 dredging bucket
59 **suction dredger** (hydraulic dredger) with trailing suction pipe or barge sucker
60 centrifugal pump
61 back scouring valve
62 suction pump, a jet pump with scouring nozzles

128 Waterway and Hydraulic Engineering

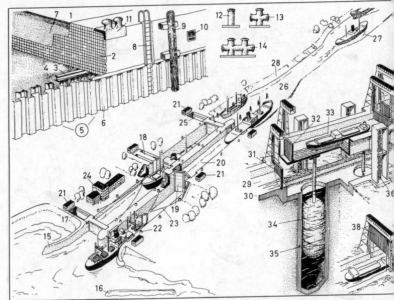

1–14 quay wall
1 road surface
2 body of wall
3 steel sleeper
4 steel pile
5 sheet pile wall (sheet pile bulkhead, sheetpiling)
6 box pile
7 backfilling (filling)
8 ladder
9 fender (fender pile)
10 recessed bollard
11 double bollard
12 bollard
13 cross-shaped bollard (cross-shaped mooring bitt)
14 double cross-shaped bollard (double cross-shaped mooring bitt)
15–28 canal
15–16 canal entrance
15 mole
16 breakwater
17–25 staircase of locks
17 lower level
18 lock gate, a sliding gate
19 mitre (*Am.* miter) gate

20 lock (lock chamber)
21 power house
22 warping capstan (hauling capstan), a capstan
23 warp
24 offices (e.g. canal administration, river police, customs)
25 upper level (head)
26 lock approach
27 lay-by
28 bank slope
29–38 boat lift (*Am.* boat elevator)
29 lower pound (lower reach)
30 canal bed
31 pound lock gate, a vertical gate
32 lock gate
33 boat tank (caisson)
34 float
35 float shaft
36 lifting spindle
37 upper pound (upper reach)
38 vertical gate
39–46 pumping plant and reservoir
39 forebay
40 surge tank
41 pressure pipeline

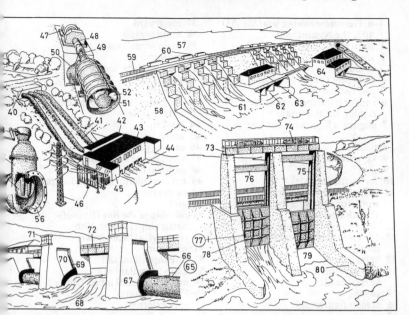

42 valve house (valve control house)
43 turbine house (pumping station)
44 discharge structure (outlet structure)
45 control station
46 transformer station
47–52 axial-flow pump (propeller pump)
47 drive motor
48 gear
49 drive shaft
50 pressure pipe
51 suction head
52 impeller wheel
53–56 sluice valve (sluice gate)
53 crank drive
54 valve housing
55 sliding valve (sliding gate)
56 discharge opening
57–64 dam (barrage)
57 reservoir (storage reservoir, impounding reservoir, impounded reservoir)
58 masonry dam
59 crest of dam
60 spillway (overflow spillway)

61 stilling basin (stilling box, stilling pool)
62 scouring tunnel (outlet tunnel, waste water outlet)
63 valve house (valve control house)
64 power station
65–72 rolling dam (weir), a barrage; *other system:* shutter weir
65 roller, a barrier
66 roller top
67 flange
68 submersible roller
69 rack track
70 recess
71 hoisting gear cabin
72 service bridge (walkway)
73–80 sluice dam
73 hoisting gear bridge
74 hoisting gear (winding gear)
75 guide groove
76 counterweight (counterpoise)
77 sluice gate (floodgate)
78 reinforcing rib
79 dam sill (weir sill)
80 wing wall

129 Types of Historical Ship

1–6 Germanic rowing boat [ca. AD 400], the Nydam boat
1 stern post
2 steersman
3 oarsman
4 stem post (stem)
5 oar, for rowing
6 rudder (steering oar), a side rudder, for steering
7 **dugout**, a hollowed–out tree trunk
8 paddle
9–12 trireme, a Roman warship
9 ram
10 forecastle (fo'c'sle)
11 grapple (grapnel, grappling iron), for fastening the enemy ship alongside
12 three banks (tiers) of oars
13–17 Viking ship (longship, dragon ship) [Norse]
13 helm (tiller)
14 awning crutch with carved horses' heads
15 awning
16 dragon figurehead
17 shield
18–26 cog (Hansa cog, Hansa ship)
18 anchor cable (anchor rope, anchor hawser)
19 forecastle (fo'c'sle)
20 bowsprit
21 furled (brailed–up) square sail
22 town banner (city banner)
23 aftercastle (sterncastle)
24 rudder, a stem rudder
25 elliptical stern (round stern)
26 wooden fender
27–43 caravel (carvel) ['Santa Maria' 1492]
27 admiral's cabin
28 spanker boom
29 mizzen (mizen, mutton spanker, lateen spanker), a lateen sail
30 lateen yard
31 mizzen (mizen) mast
32 lashing
33 mainsail (main course), a square sail
34 bonnet, a removable strip of canvas
35 bowline
36 bunt line (martinet)

37 main yard
38 main topsail
39 main topsail yard
40 mainmast
41 foresail (fore course)
42 foremast
43 spritsail
44–50 galley [15th to 18th century], a slave galley
44 lantern
45 cabin
46 central gangway
47 slave driver with whip
48 galley slaves
49 covered platform in the forepart of the ship
50 gun
51–60 ship of the line (line–of–battle ship) [18th to 19th century], a three–decker
51 jib boom
52 fore topgallant sail
53 main topgallant sail
54 mizzen (mizen) topgallant sail
55–57 gilded stern
55 upper stern
56 stern gallery
57 quarter gallery, a projecting balcony with ornamental portholes
58 lower stern
59 gunports for broadside fire
60 gunport shutter

130 Sailing Ship I

1–72 rigging (rig, tackle) and sails of a bark (barque)

1–9 masts
1 bowsprit with jib boom
2–4 foremast
2 lower foremast
3 fore topmast
4 fore topgallant mast
5–7 mainmast
5 lower mainmast
6 main topmast
7 main topgallant mast
8–9 mizzen (mizen) mast
8 lower mizzen (lower mizen)
9 mizzen (mizen) topmast
10–19 standing rigging
10 stay
11 topmast stay
12 topgallant stay
13 royal stay
14 jib stay
15 bobstay
16 shrouds
17 fore topmast rigging (main topmast rigging, mizzen (mizen) topmast rigging)
18 fore topgallant rigging (main topgallant rigging)
19 backstays
20–31 fore-and-aft sails
20 fore topmast staysail
21 inner jib
22 outer jib
23 flying jib
24 main topmast staysail
25 main topgallant staysail
26 main royal staysail
27 mizzen (mizen) staysail
28 mizzen (mizen) topmast staysail
29 mizzen (mizen) topgallant staysail
30 mizzen (mizen, spanker, driver)
31 gaff topsail
32–45 spars
32 foreyard
33 lower fore topsail yard
34 upper fore topsail yard
35 lower fore topgallant yard
36 upper fore topgallant yard
37 fore royal yard
38 main yard
39 lower main topsail yard
40 upper main topsail yard
41 lower main topgallant yard
42 upper main topgallant yard
43 main royal yard
44 spanker boom
45 spanker gaff
46 footrope
47 lifts
48 spanker boom topping lift
49 spanker peak halyard
50 foretop
51 fore topmast crosstrees
52 maintop
53 main topmast crosstrees
54 mizzen (mizen) top
55–66 square sails
55 foresail (fore course)
56 lower fore topsail
57 upper fore topsail
58 lower fore topgallant sail
59 upper fore topgallant sail
60 fore royal
61 mainsail (main course)
62 lower main topsail
63 upper main topsail
64 lower main topgallant sail
65 upper main topgallant sail
66 main royal sail
67–71 running rigging
67 braces
68 sheets
69 spanker sheet
70 spanker vangs
71 bunt line
72 reef

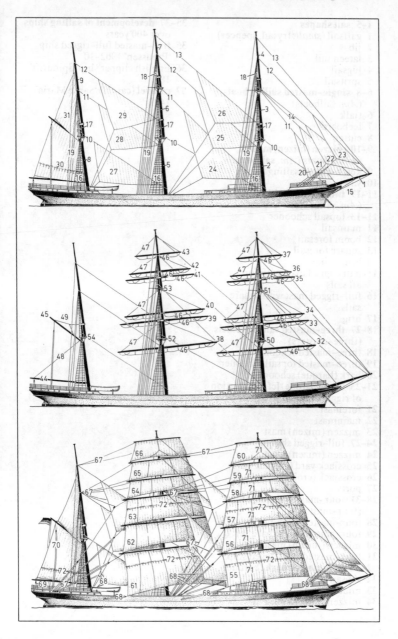

131 Sailing Ship II

1–5 sail shapes
1 gaffsail (*small:* trysail, spencer)
2 jib
3 lateen sail
4 lugsail
5 spritsail
6–8 single-masted sailing boats
(*Am.* sailboats)
6 tjalk
7 leeboard
8 cutter
**9–10 mizzen (mizen) masted
sailing boats (*Am.* sailboats)**
9 ketch-rigged sailing barge
10 yawl
11–17 two-masted sailing boats
(*Am.* sailboats)
11–13 topsail schooner
11 mainsail
12 boom foresail
13 square foresail
14 brigantine
15 half-rigged mast with fore-and-
aft sails
16 full-rigged mast with square
sails
17 brig
18–27 three-masted sailing vessels
(three-masters)
18 three-masted schooner
19 three-masted topsail schooner
20 bark (barque) schooner
21–23 bark (barque) [cf. illustration
of rigging and sails in plate 219]
21 foremast
22 mainmast
23 mizzen (mizen) mast
24–27 full-rigged ship
24 mizzen (mizen) mast
25 crossjack yard (crojack yard)
26 crossjack (crojack)
27 ports
28–31 four-masted sailing ships
(four-masters)
28 four-masted schooner
29 four-masted bark (barque)
30 mizzen (mizen) mast
31 four-masted full-rigged ship
32–34 five-masted bark (barque)
32 skysail
33 middle mast
34 mizzen (mizen) mast

35–37 development of sailing ships
over 400 years
35 five-masted full-rigged ship
'Preussen' 1902–10
36 English clipper ship 'Spindrift'
1867
37 caravel (carvel) 'Santa Maria'
1492

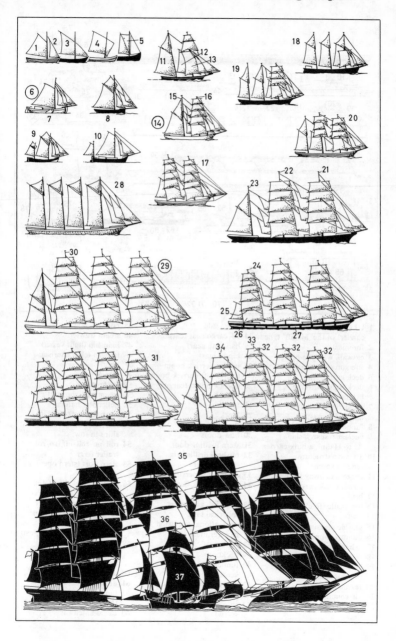

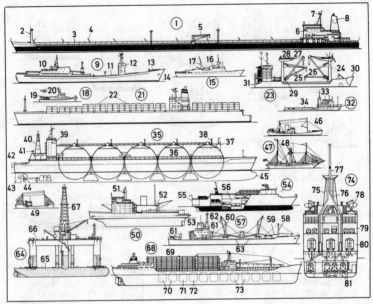

1 **ULCC** (ultra large crude carrier) of the 'all-aft' type
2 foremast
3 catwalk with the pipes
4 fire gun (fire nozzle)
5 deck crane
6 deckhouse with the bridge
7 aft signal (signalling) and radar mast
8 funnel
9 **nuclear research ship** 'Otto Hahn', a bulk carrier
10 aft superstructure (engine room)
11 cargo hatchway for bulk goods (bulk cargoes)
12 bridge
13 forecastle (fo'c'sle)
14 stem
15 **seaside pleasure boat**
16 dummy funnel
17 exhaust mast
18 **rescue cruiser**
19 helicopter platform (working deck)
20 rescue helicopter
21 **all-container ship**
22 containers stowed on deck

23 **cargo ship**
24-29 cargo gear (cargo-handling gear)
24 bipod mast
25 jumbo derrick boom (heavy-lift derrick boom)
26 derrick boom (cargo boom)
27 tackle
28 block
29 thrust bearing
30 bow doors
31 stern loading door
32 **offshore drilling rig supply vessel**
33 compact superstructure
34 loading deck (working deck)
35 **liquefied-gas tanker**
36 spherical tank
37 navigational television receiver mast
38 vent mast
39 deckhouse
40 funnel
41 ventilator
42 transom stern (transom)
43 rudder blade (rudder)
44 ship's propeller (ship's screw)

45 bulbous bow
46 steam trawler
47 **lightship** (light vessel)
48 lantern (characteristic light)
49 smack
50 **ice breaker**
51 steaming light mast
52 helicopter hangar
53 stern towing point, for gripping the bow of ships in tow
54 **roll-on-roll-off (ro-ro) trailer ferry**
55 stern port (stern opening) with ramp
56 stern vehicle lifts (*Am.* heavy vehicle elevators)
57 **multi-purpose freighter**
58 ventilator-type samson (sampson) post (ventilator-type king post)
59 derrick boom (cargo boom, cargo gear, cargo-handling gear)
60 derrick mast
61 deck crane
62 jumbo derrick boom (heavy-lift derrick boom)
63 cargo hatchway

133 Shipbuilding

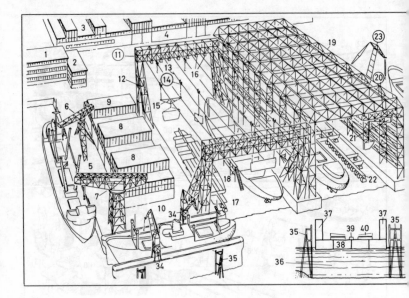

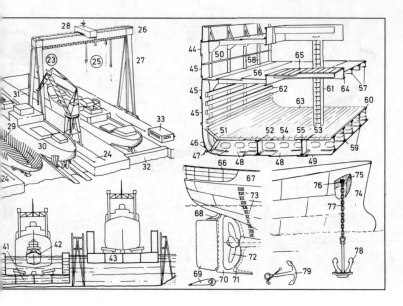

40 bilge block (bilge shore, side
     support)
41-43 docking a ship
41 flooded floating dock
42 tug towing the ship
43 emptied (pumped-out) dock
44-61 **structural parts of the ship**
44-56 longitudinal structure
44-49 shell (shell plating, skin)
44 sheer strake
45 side strake
46 bilge strake
47 bilge keel
48 bottom plating
49 flat plate keel (keel plate)
50 stringer (side stringer)
51 tank margin plate
52 longitudinal side girder
53 centre (*Am.* center) plate girder
     (centre girder, kelson, keelson,
     vertical keel)
54 tank top plating (tank top, inner
     bottom plating)
55 centre (*Am.* center) strake
56 deck plating
57 deck beam
58 frame (rib)
59 floor plate

60 cellular double bottom
61 hold pillar (pillar)
61, 63 dunnage
62 side battens (side ceiling, spar
     ceiling)
63 ceiling (floor ceiling)
64-65 hatchway
64 hatch coaming
65 hatch cover (hatchboard)
66-72 stern
66 guard rail
67 bulwark
68 rudder stock
69-70 Oertz rudder
69 rudder blade (rudder)
70-71 stern frame
70 rudder post
71 propeller post (screw post)
72 ship's propeller (ship's screw)
73 draught (draft) marks
74-79 bow
74 stem, a bulbous stem (bulbous
     bow)
75 hawse
76 hawse pipe
77 anchor cable (chain cable)
78 stockless anchor (patent anchor)
79 stocked anchor

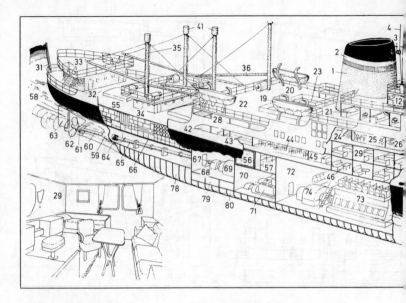

**1–71 combined cargo and
passenger ship** [of the older type]
1 funnel
2 funnel marking
3 siren (fog horn)
4–11 compass platform (compass
bridge, compass flat, monkey
bridge)
4 antenna lead-in (antenna down–
lead)
5 radio direction finder (RDF)
antenna (direction finder
antenna, rotatable loop antenna,
aural null loop antenna)
6 magnetic compass (mariner's
compass)
7 morse lamp (signalling, *Am*.
signaling, lamp)
8 radar antenna (radar scanner)
9 code flag signal
10 code flag halyards
11 triatic stay (signal stay)
12–18 bridge deck (bridge)
12 radio room
13 captain's cabin
14 navigating bridge
15 starboard sidelight [green; port
sidelight red]
16 wing of bridge
17 shelter (weather cloth, dodger)
18 wheelhouse
19–21 boat deck
19 ship's lifeboat
20 davit
21 officer's cabin
22–27 promenade deck
22 sun deck (lido deck)
23 swimming pool
24 companion ladder
(companionway)
25 library (ship's library)
26 lounge
27 promenade
28–30 A–deck
28 semi-enclosed deck space
29 double–berth cabin, a cabin
30 de luxe cabin
31 ensign staff
32–42 B–deck (main deck)
32 after deck
33 poop
34 deckhouse
35 samson (sampson) post (king
post)
36 derrick boom (cargo boom)

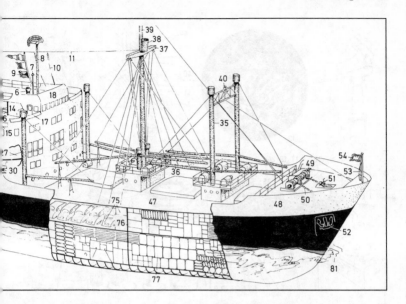

37 crosstrees (spreader)
38 crow's nest
39 topmast
40 forward steaming light
41 ventilator lead
42 galley (caboose, cookroom, ship's kitchen)
43 ship's pantry
44 dining room
45 purser's office
46 single–berth cabin
47 foredeck
48 forecastle (fo'c'sle)
49–51 ground tackle
49 windlass
50 anchor cable (chain cable)
51 compressor (chain compressor)
52 anchor
53 jackstaff
54 jack
55 after holds
56 cold storage room (insulated hold)
57 store room
58 wake
59 shell bossing (shaft bossing)
60 tail shaft (tail end shaft)

61 shaft strut (strut, spectacle frame, propeller strut, propeller bracket)
62 three–blade ship's propeller (ship's screw)
63 rudder blade (rudder)
64 stuffing box
65 propeller shaft
66 shaft alley (shaft tunnel)
67 thrust block
68–74 diesel–electric drive
68 electric engine room
69 electric motor
70 auxiliary engine room
71 auxiliary engines
72 main engine room
73 main engine, a diesel engine
74 generator
75 forward holds
76 tween deck
77 cargo
78 ballast tank (deep tank) for water ballast
79 fresh water tank
80 fuel tank
81 bow wave

135 Navigation

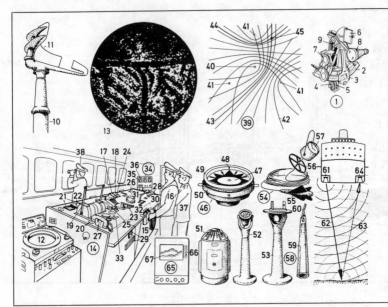

1 **sextant**
2 graduated arc
3 index bar (index arm)
4 decimal micrometer
5 vernier
6 index mirror
7 horizon glass (horizon mirror)
8 telescope
9 grip (handgrip)
10-13 **radar equipment** (radar apparatus)
10 radar pedestal
11 revolving radar reflector
12 radar display unit (radar screen)
13 radar image (radar picture)
14-38 **wheelhouse**
14 steering and control position
15 ship's wheel for controlling the rudder mechanism
16 helmsman (*Am.* wheelsman)
17 rudder angle indicator
18 automatic pilot (autopilot)
19 control lever for the variable-pitch propeller (reversible propeller, feathering propeller, feathering screw)

20 propeller pitch indicator
21 main engine revolution indicator
22 ship's speedometer (log)
23 control switch for bow thruster (bow-manoeuvring, *Am.* maneuvering, propeller)
24 echo recorder (depth recorder, echograph)
25 engine telegraph (engine order telegraph)
26 controls for the anti-rolling system (for the stabilizers)
27 local-battery telephone
28 shipping traffic radio telephone
29 navigation light indicator panel (running light indicator panel)
30 microphone for ship's address system
31 gyro compass (gyroscopic compass), a compass repeater
32 control button for the ship's siren (ship's fog horn)
33 main engine overload indicator
34 detector indicator unit for fixing the ship's position

35 rough focusing indicator
36 fine focusing indicator
37 navigating officer
38 captain
39 **Decca navigation system**
40 master station
41 slave station
42 null hyperbola
43 hyperbolic position line 1
44 hyperbolic position line 2
45 position (fix, ship fix)
46-53 **compasses**
46 liquid compass (fluid compass, spirit compass, wet compass), a magnetic compass
47 compass card
48 lubber's line (lubber's mark, lubber's point)
49 compass bowl
50 gimbal ring
51-53 gyro compass (gyroscopic compass, gyro compass unit)
51 master compass (master gyro compass)
52 compass repeater (gyro repeater)
53 compass repeater with pelorus
54 **patent log** (screw log, mechanical log, towing log, taffrail log, speedometer)

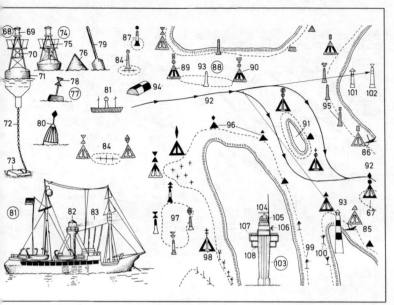

55 rotator
56 governor
57 log clock
58-67 leads
58 hand lead
59 lead (lead sinker)
60 leadline
61-67 echo sounder (echo sounding machine)
61 sound transmitter
62 sound wave (sound impulse)
63 echo (sound echo, echo signal)
64 echo receiver (hydrophone)
65 echograph (echo sounding machine recorder)
66 depth scale
67 echogram (depth recording, depth reading)
68-108 sea marks (floating navigational marks) **for buoyage and lighting systems**
68-83 fairway marks (channel marks)
68 light and whistle buoy
69 light (warning light)
70 whistle
71 buoy
72 mooring chain
73 sinker (mooring sinker)
74 light and bell buoy
75 bell
76 conical buoy
77 can buoy
78 topmark
79 spar buoy
80 topmark buoy
81 lightship (light vessel)
82 lantern mast (lantern tower)
83 beam of light
84-102 fairway markings (channel markings)
84 wreck [green buoys]
85 wreck to starboard
86 wreck to port
87 shoals (shallows, shallow water, *Am.* flats)
88 middle ground to port
89 division (bifurcation) [beginning of the middle ground; topmark: red cylinder above red ball]
90 convergence (confluence) [end of the middle ground; topmark: red St. Antony's cross above red ball]
91 middle ground
92 main fairway (main navigable channel)
93 secondary fairway (secondary navigable channel)
94 can buoy
95 port hand buoys (port hand marks) [red]
96 starboard hand buoys (starboard hand marks) [black]
97 shoals (shallows, shallow water, *Am.* flats) outside the fairway
98 middle of the fairway (mid-channel)
99 starboard markers (inverted broom)
100 port markers [upward-pointing broom]
101-102 range lights (leading lights)
101 lower range light (lower leading light)
102 higher range light (higher leading light)
103 lighthouse
104 radar antenna (radar scanner)
105 lantern (characteristic light)
106 radio direction finder (RDF) antenna
107 machinery and observation platform (machinery and observation deck)
108 living quarters

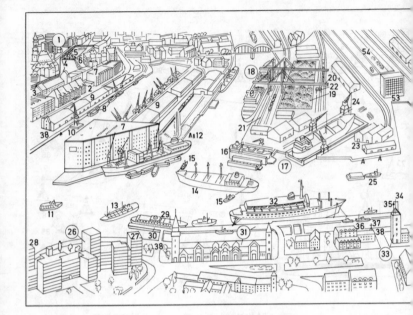

1 dock area
2 free port (foreign trade zone)
3 free zone frontier (free zone enclosure)
4 customs barrier
5 customs entrance
6 port custom house
7 entrepôt
8 barge (dumb barge, lighter)
9 break–bulk cargo transit shed (general cargo transit shed, package cargo transit shed)
10 floating crane
11 harbour (*Am.* harbor) ferry (ferryboat)
12 fender (dolphin)
13 bunkering boat
14 break–bulk carrier (general cargo ship)
15 tug
16 floating dock (pontoon dock)
17 dry dock
18 coal wharf
19 coal bunker
20 transporter loading bridge

21 quayside railway
22 weighing bunker
23 warehouse
24 quayside crane
25 launch and lighter
26 port hospital
27 quarantine wing
28 Institute of Tropical Medicine
29 excursion steamer (pleasure steamer)
30 jetty
31 passenger terminal
32 liner (passenger liner, ocean liner)
33 meteorological office, a weather station
34 signal mast (signalling mast)
35 storm signal
36 port administration offices
37 tide level indicator
38 quayside road (quayside roadway)
39 roll-on roll-off (ro-ro) system (roll-on roll-off operation)
40 gantry

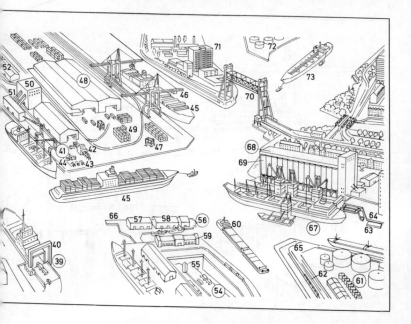

41 truck–to–truck system (truck–to–truck operation)
42 foil-wrapped unit loads
43 pallets
44 forklift truck (fork truck, forklift)
45 container ship
46 transporter container–loading bridge
47 container carrier truck
48 container terminal (container berth)
49 unit load
50 cold store
51 conveyor belt (conveyor)
52 fruit storage shed (fruit warehouse)
53 office building
54 urban motorway (*Am.* freeway)
55 harbour (*Am.* harbor) tunnels
56 fish dock
57 fish market
58 auction room
59 fish-canning factory
60 push tow

61 tank farm
62 railway siding
63 landing pontoon (landing stage)
64 quay
65 breakwater (mole)
66 pier (jetty), a quay extension
67 bulk carrier
68 silo
69 silo cylinder
70 lift bridge
71 industrial plant
72 storage tanks
73 tanker

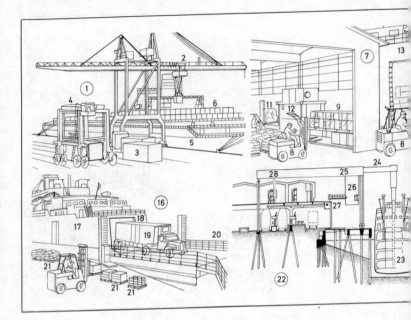

1 container terminal (container berth), a modern cargo–handling berth
2 transporter container-loading bridge (loading bridge); *sim.:* transtainer crane (transtainer)
3 container
4 truck (carrier)
5 all-container ship
6 containers stowed on deck
7 truck-to-truck handling (horizontal cargo handling with pallets)
8 forklift truck (fork truck, forklift)
9 unitized foil-wrapped load (unit load)
10 flat pallet, a standard pallet
11 unitized break-bulk cargo
12 heat sealing machine
13 break-bulk carrier (general cargo ship)
14 cargo hatchway
15 receiving truck on board ship
16 multi-purpose terminal

17 roll-on roll-off ship (ro-ro-ship)
18 stern port (stern opening)
19 driven load, a lorry (*Am.* truck)
20 ro-ro depot
21 unitized load (unitized package)
22 banana-handling terminal [section]
23 seaward tumbler
24 jib
25 elevator bridge
26 chain sling
27 lighting station
28 shore-side tumbler for loading trains and lorries (*Am.* trucks)
29 bulk cargo handling
30 bulk carrier
31 floating bulk-cargo elevator
32 suction pipes
33 receiver
34 delivery pipe
35 bulk transporter barge
36 floating pile driver
37 pile driver frame
38 pile hammer

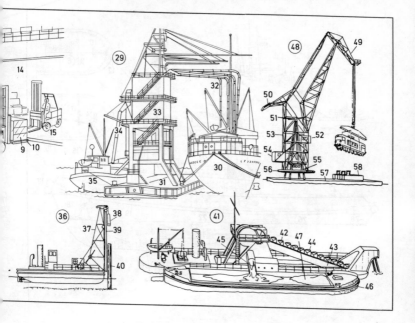

39 driving guide rail
40 pile
41 bucket dredger, a dredger
42 bucket chain
43 bucket ladder
44 dredger bucket
45 chute
46 hopper barge
47 spoil
48 floating crane
49 jib (boom)
50 counterweight (counterpoise)
51 adjusting spindle
52 crane driver's cabin (crane driver's cage)
53 crane framework
54 winch house
55 control platform
56 turntable
57 pontoon, a pram
58 engine superstructure (engine mounting)

138 Salvage (Salving) and Towage

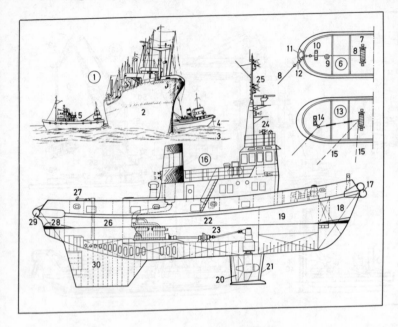

1 salvaging (salving) of a ship run aground
2 ship run aground (damaged vessel)
3 sandbank; *also*: quicksand
4 open sea
5 tug (salvage tug)
6–15 towing gear
6 towing gear for towing at sea
7 towing winch (towing machine, towing engine)
8 tow rope (tow line, towing hawser)
9 tow rope guide
10 cross–shaped bollard
11 hawse hole
12 anchor cable (chain cable)
13 towing gear for work in harbours (*Am.* harbors)
14 guest rope
15 position of the tow rope (tow line, towing hawser)
16 tug (salvage tug) [vertical elevation]
17 bow fender (pudding fender)

18 forepeak
19 living quarters
20 Schottel propeller
21 Kort vent
22 engine and propeller room
23 clutch coupling
24 compass platform (compass bridge, compass flat, monkey bridge)
25 fire-fighting equipment
26 stowage
27 tow hook
28 afterpeak
29 stern fender
30 main manoeuvring (*Am.* maneuvering) keel

230

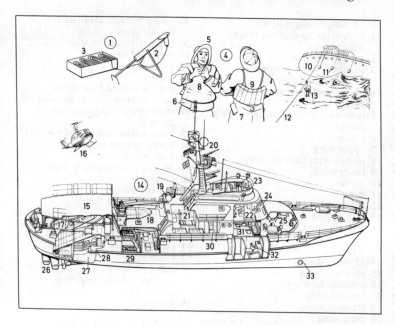

1 rocket apparatus (rocket gun,
   line–throwing gun)
2 life rocket (rocket)
3 rocket line (whip line)
4 oilskins
5 sou'wester (southwester)
6 oilskin jacket
7 oilskin coat
8 inflatable life jacket
9 cork life jacket (cork life
   preserver)
10 stranded ship (damaged vessel)
11 oil bag, for trickling oil on the
   water surface
12 lifeline
13 breeches buoy
14 rescue cruiser
15 helicopter landing deck
16 rescue helicopter
17 daughter boat
18 inflatable boat (inflatable
   dinghy)
19 life raft
20 fire–fighting equipment for fires
   at sea

21 hospital unit with operating
   cabin and exposure bath
22 navigating bridge
23 upper tier of navigating bridge
24 lower tier of navigating bridge
25 messroom
26 rudders and propeller (screw)
27 stowage
28 foam can
29 side engines
30 shower
31 coxswain's cabin
32 crew member's single–berth
   cabin
33 bow propeller

140 Aircraft I

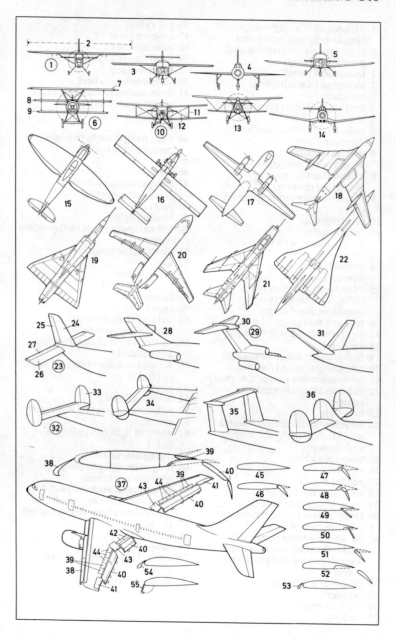

1-31 cockpit of a single-engine (single-engined) racing and passenger aircraft (racing and passenger plane)
1 instrument panel
2 air-speed (*Am.* airspeed) indicator
3 artificial horizon (gyro horizon)
4 altimeter
5 radio compass (automatic direction finder)
6 magnetic compass
7 boost gauge (*Am.* gage)
8 tachometer (rev counter, revolution counter)
9 cylinder temperature gauge (*Am.* gage)
10 accelerometer
11 chronometer
12 turn indicator with ball
13 directional gyro
14 vertical speed indicator (rate-of-climb indicator, variometer)
15 VOR radio direction finder [*VOR: very high frequency omnidirectional range*]
16 left tank fuel gauge (*Am.* gage)
17 right tank fuel gauge (*Am.* gage)
18 ammeter
19 fuel pressure gauge (*Am.* gage)
20 oil pressure gauge (*Am.* gage)
21 oil temperature gauge (*Am.* gage)
22 radio and radio navigation equipment
23 map light
24 wheel (control column, control stick) for operating the ailerons and elevators
25 co-pilot's wheel
26 switches
27 rudder pedals
28 co-pilot's rudder pedals
29 microphone for the radio
30 throttle lever (throttle control)
31 mixture control
32-66 single-engine (single-engined) racing and passenger aircraft (racing and passenger plane)
32 propeller (airscrew)
33 spinner
34 flat four engine
35 cockpit
36 pilot's seat
37 co-pilot's seat
38 passenger seats
39 hood (canopy, cockpit hood, cockpit canopy)
40 steerable nose wheel
41 main undercarriage unit (main landing gear unit)
42 step
43 wing
44 right navigation light (right position light)
45 spar
46 rib
47 stringer (longitudinal reinforcing member)
48 fuel tank
49 landing light
50 left navigation light (left position light)
51 electrostatic conductor
52 aileron
53 landing flap
54 fuselage (body)
55 frame (former)
56 chord
57 stringer (longitudinal reinforcing member)
58 vertical tail (vertical stabilizer and rudder)
59 vertical stabilizer (vertical fin, tail fin)
60 rudder
61 horizontal tail
62 tailplane (horizontal stabilizer)
63 elevator
64 warning light (anticollision light)
65 dipole antenna
66 long-wire antenna (long-conductor antenna)
67-72 principal manoeuvres (*Am.* maneuvers) of the aircraft (aeroplane, plane, *Am.* airplane)
67 pitching
68 lateral axis
69 yawing
70 vertical axis (normal axis)
71 rolling
72 longitudinal axis

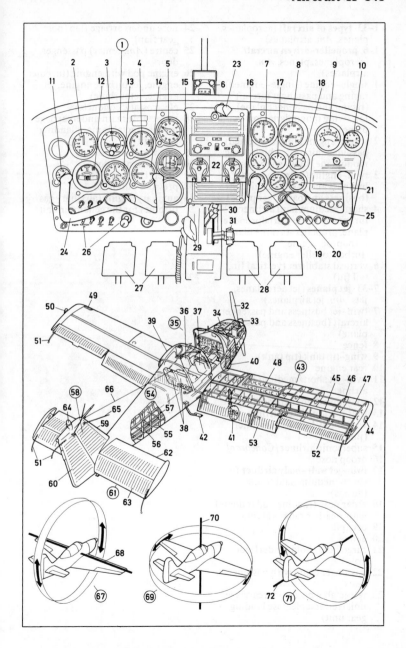

1–33 types of aircraft (aeroplanes, planes, *Am.* airplanes)

1–6 propeller–driven aircraft (aeroplanes, planes, *Am.* airplanes)

1 single–engine (single–engined) racing and passenger aircraft (racing and passenger plane), a low–wing monoplane (low–wing plane)

2 single–engine (single–engined) passenger aircraft, a high–wing monoplane (high–wing plane)

3 twin–engine (twin–engined) business and passenger aircraft (business and passenger plane)

4 short/medium haul airliner, a turboprop plane (turbopropeller plane, propeller–turbine plane)

5 turboprop engine (turbopropeller engine)

6 vertical stabilizer (vertical fin, tail fin)

7–33 jet planes (jet aeroplanes, jets, *Am.* jet airplanes)

7 twin–jet business and passenger aircraft (business and passenger plane)

8 fence

9 wing–tip tank (tip tank)

10 rear engine

11 twin–jet short/medium haul airliner

12 tri–jet medium haul airliner

13 four–jet long haul airliner

14 wide–body long haul airliner (jumbo jet)

15 supersonic airliner *[Concorde]*

16 droop nose

17 **twin–jet wide–body airliner** for short/medium haul routes (airbus)

18 radar nose (radome, radar dome) with weather radar antenna

19 cockpit

20 galley

21 cargo hold (hold, underfloor hold)

22 passenger cabin with passenger seats

23 retractable nose undercarriage unit (retractable nose landing gear unit)

24 nose undercarriage flap (nose gear flap)

25 centre (*Am.* center) passenger door

26 engine pod with engine (turbojet engine, jet turbine engine, jet engine, jet turbine)

27 electrostatic conductors

28 retractable main undercarriage unit (retractable main landing gear unit)

29 side window

30 rear passenger door

31 toilet (lavatory, WC)

32 pressure bulkhead

33 auxiliary engine (auxiliary gas turbine) for the generator unit

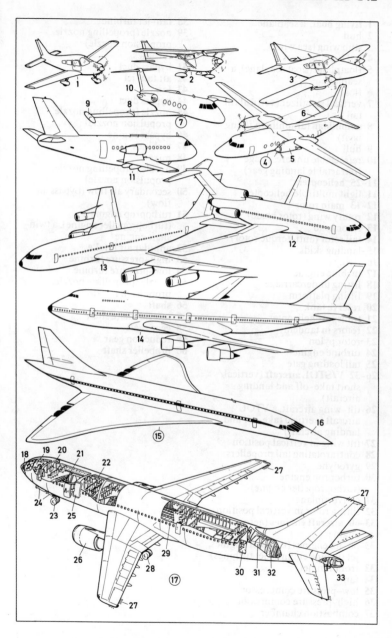

1 flying boat, a seaplane
2 hull
3 stub wing (sea wing)
4 tail bracing wires
5 floatplane (float seaplane), a seaplane
6 float
7 vertical stabilizer (vertical fin, tail fin)
8 amphibian (amphibian flying boat)
9 hull
10 retractable undercarriage (retractable landing gear)
11-25 helicopters
11 light multirole helicopter
12-13 main rotor
12 rotary wing (rotor blade)
13 rotor head
14 tail rotor (anti-torque rotor)
15 landing skids
16 flying crane
17 turbine engines
18 lifting undercarriage
19 lifting platform
20 reserve tank
21 transport helicopter
22 rotors in tandem
23 rotor pylon
24 turbine engine
25 tail loading gate
26-32 V/STOL aircraft (vertical/short take-off and landing aircraft)
26 tilt-wing aircraft, a VTOL aircraft (vertical take-off and landing aircraft)
27 tilt wing in vertical position
28 contrarotating tail propellers
29 gyrodyne
30 turboprop engine (turbopropeller engine)
31 convertiplane
32 tilting rotor in vertical position
33-60 aircraft engines (aero engines)
33-50 jet engines (turbojet engines, jet turbine engines, jet turbines)
33 front fan-jet
34 fan
35 low-pressure compressor
36 high-pressure compressor
37 combustion chamber

38 fan-jet turbine
39 nozzle (propelling nozzle, propulsion nozzle)
40 turbines
41 bypass duct
42 aft fan-jet
43 fan
44 bypass duct
45 nozzle (propelling nozzle, propulsion nozzle)
46 bypass engine
47 turbines
48 mixer
49 nozzle (propelling nozzle, propulsion nozzle)
50 secondary air flow (bypass air flow)
51 turboprop engine (turbopropeller engine), a twin-shaft engine
52 annular air intake
53 high-pressure turbine
54 low-pressure turbine
55 nozzle (propelling nozzle, propulsion nozzle)
56 shaft
57 intermediate shaft
58 gear shaft
59 reduction gear
60 propeller shaft

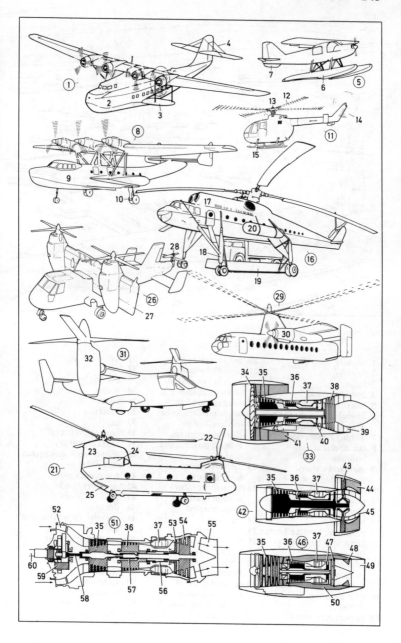

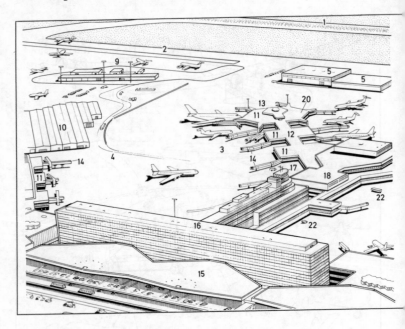

1 runway
2 taxiway
3 apron
4 apron taxiway
5 baggage terminal
6 tunnel entrance to the baggage terminal
7 airport fire service
8 fire appliance building
9 mail and cargo terminal
10 cargo warehouse
11 assembly point
12 pier
13 pierhead
14 passenger loading bridge
15 departure building (terminal)
16 administration building
17 control tower (tower)
18 waiting room (lounge)
19 airport restaurant

20 spectators' terrace
21 aircraft in loading position (nosed in)
22 service vehicles, e.g. baggage loaders, water tankers, galley loaders, toilet-cleaning vehicles, ground power units, tankers
23 aircraft tractor (aircraft tug)
24-53 airport information symbols (pictographs)
24 'airport'
25 'departures'
26 'arrivals'
27 'transit passengers'
28 'waiting room' ('lounge')
29 'assembly point' ('meeting point', 'rendezvous point')
30 'spectators' terrace'

31 'information'
32 'taxis'
33 'car hire'
34 'trains'
35 'buses'
36 'entrance'
37 'exit'
38 'baggage retrieval'
39 'luggage lockers'
40 'telephone – emergency calls only'
41 'emergency exit'
42 'passport check'
43 'press facilities'
44 'doctor'
45 'chemist' (*Am.* 'druggist')
46 'showers'
47 'gentlemen's toilet' ('gentlemen')
48 'ladies toilet' ('ladies')
49 'chapel'
50 'restaurant'
51 'change'
52 'duty free shop'
53 'hairdresser'

145 Space Flight I

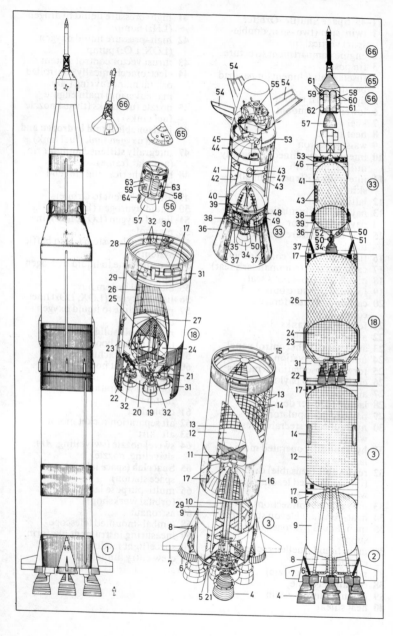

146 Space Flight II

1–45 Space Shuttle–Orbiter

1 twin–spar (two–spar, double–spar) vertical fin
2 engine compartment structure
3 fin post
4 fuselage attachment [of payload bay doors]
5 upper thrust mount
6 lower thrust mount
7 keel
8 heat shield
9 waist longeron
10 integrally machined (integrally milled) main rib
11 integrally stiffened light alloy skin
12 lattice girder
13 payload bay insulation
14 payload bay door
15 low–temperature surface insulation
16 flight deck (crew compartment)
17 captain's seat (commander's seat)
18 pilot's seat (co-pilot's seat)
19 forward pressure bulkhead
20 carbon fibre reinforced nose cone
21 forward fuel tanks
22 avionics consoles
23 automatic flight control panel
24 upward observation windows
25 forward observation windows
26 entry hatch to payload bay
27 air lock
28 ladder to lower deck
29 payload manipulator arm
30 hydraulically steerable nose wheel
31 hydraulically operated main landing gear
32 removable (reusable) carbon fibre reinforced leading edge [of wing]
33 movable elevon sections
34 heat–resistant elevon structure
35 main liquid hydrogen (LH$_2$) supply
36 main liquid-fuelled rocket engine
37 nozzle (thrust nozzle)
38 coolant feed line
39 engine control system
40 heat shield
41 high-pressure liquid hydrogen (LH$_2$) pump
42 high-pressure liquid oxygen (LOX, LO$_2$) pump
43 thrust vector control system
44 electromechanically controlled orbital manoeuvring (*Am.* maneuvering) main engine
45 nozzle fuel tanks (thrust nozzle fuel tanks)
46 **jettisonable liquid hydrogen and liquid oxygen tank** (fuel tank)
47 integrally stiffened annular rib (annular frame)
48 hemispherical end rib (end frame)
49 aft attachment to Orbiter
50 liquid hydrogen (LH$_2$) line
51 liquid oxygen (LOX, LO$_2$) line
52 manhole
53 surge baffle system (slosh baffle system)
54 pressure line to liquid hydrogen tank
55 electrical system bus
56 liquid oxygen (LOX, LO$_2$) line
57 pressure line to liquid oxygen tank
58 **recoverable solid–fuel rocket** (solid rocket booster)
59 auxiliary parachute bay
60 compartment housing the recovery parachutes and the forward separation rocket motors
61 cable duct
62 aft separation rocket motors
63 aft skirt
64 swivel nozzle (swivelling, *Am.* swiveling, nozzle)
65 **Spacelab** (space laboratory, space station)
66 multi-purpose laboratory (orbital workshop)
67 astronaut
68 gimbal–mounted telescope
69 measuring instrument platform
70 spaceflight module
71 crew entry tunnel

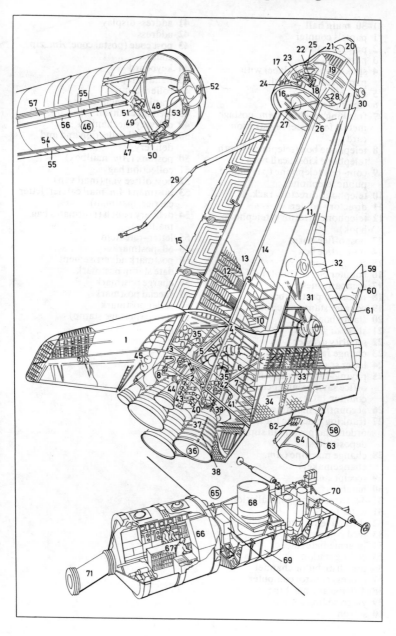

147 Post Office I

148 Post Office II (Telephones and Telegraphy)

1 **telephone box** (telephone booth, telephone kiosk, call box), a public telephone

2 telephone user (*with own telephone:* telephone subscriber, telephone customer)

3 coin–box telephone (pay phone, public telephone) for local and long–distance calls (trunk calls)

4 emergency telephone

5 telephone directory (telephone book)

6–26 telephone instruments (telephones)

6 standard table telephone

7 telephone receiver (handset)

8 earpiece

9 mouthpiece (microphone)

10 dial (push–button keyboard)

11 finger plate (dial finger plate, dial wind–up plate)

12 finger stop (dial finger stop)

13 cradle (handset cradle, cradle switch)

14 receiver cord (handset cord)

15 telephone casing (telephone cover)

16 subscriber's (customer's) private meter

17 switchboard (exchange) for a system of extensions

18 push button for connecting main exchange lines

19 push buttons for calling extensions

20 push–button telephone

21 earthing button for the extensions

22–26 switchboard with extensions

22 exchange

23 switchboard operator's set

24 main exchange line

25 switching box (automatic switching system, automatic connecting system, switching centre, *Am.* center)

26 extension

27–41 telephone exchange

27 fault repair service

28 maintenance technician

29 testing board (testing desk)

30 telegraphy

31 teleprinter (teletypewriter)

32 paper tape

33 directory enquiries

34 information position (operator's position)

35 operator

36 microfilm reader

37 microfilm file

38 microfilm card with telephone numbers

39 date indicator display

40 testing and control station

41 switching centre (*Am.* center) for telephone, telex, and data transmission services

42 **selector**, a motor uniselector made of noble metals; *sim.:* electronic selector

43 contact arc (bank)

44 contact arm (wiper)

45 contact field

46 contact arm tag

47 electromagnet

48 selector motor

49 restoring spring (resetting spring)

50 **communication links**

51–52 satellite radio link

51 earth station with directional antenna

52 communications satellite with directional antenna

53 coastal station

54–55 intercontinental radio link

54 short–wave station

55 ionosphere

56 submarine cable (deep–sea cable)

57 underwater amplifier

58 **data transmission** (data services)

59 input/output device for data carriers

60 data processor

61 teleprinter

62–64 data carriers

62 punched tape (punch tape)

63 magnetic tape

64 punched card (punch card)

65 telex link

66 teleprinter (page printer)

67 dialling (*Am.* dialing) unit

68 telex tape (punched tape, punch tape) for transmitting the text at maximum speed

69 telex message

70 keyboard

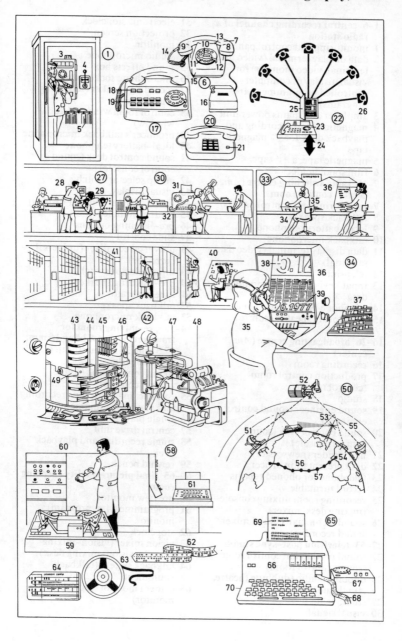

149 Broadcasting (Radio and Television) I

1–6 central recording channel of a radio station
1 monitoring and control panel
2 data display terminal (video data terminal, video monitor) for visual display of computer-controlled programmes (*Am.* programs)
3 amplifier and mains power unit
4 magnetic sound recording and playback deck for $\frac{1}{4}''$ magnetic tape
5 magnetic tape, a $\frac{1}{4}''$ tape
6 film spool holder
7–15 radio switching centre (*Am.* center) control room
7 monitoring and control panel
8 talkback speaker
9 local–battery telephone
10 talkback microphone
11 data display terminal (video data terminal)
12 teleprinter
13 input keyboard for computer data
14 telephone switchboard panel
15 monitoring speaker (control speaker)
16–26 broadcasting centre (*Am.* center)
16 recording room
17 production control room (control room)
18 studio
19 sound engineer (sound control engineer)
20 sound control desk (sound control console)
21 newsreader (newscaster)
22 duty presentation officer
23 telephone for phoned reports
24 record turntable
25 recording room mixing console (mixing desk, mixer)
26 sound technician (sound mixer, sound recordist)
27–53 television post–sync studio
27 sound production control room (sound control room)
28 dubbing studio (dubbing theatre, *Am* theater)
29 studio table
30 visual signal

31 electronic stopclock
32 projection screen
33 monitor
34 studio microphone
35 sound effects box
36 microphone socket panel
37 recording speaker (recording loudspeaker)
38 control room window (studio window)
39 producer's talkback microphone
40 local–battery telephone
41 sound control desk (sound control console)
42 group selector switch
43 visual display
44 limiter display (clipper display)
45 control modules
46 pre-listening buttons
47 slide control
48 universal equalizer (universal corrector)
49 input selector switch
50 pre-listening speaker
51 tone generator
52 talkback speaker
53 talkback microphone
54–59 pre-mixing room for transferring and mixing 16 mm, 17.5 mm, 35 mm perforated magnetic film
54 sound control desk (sound control console)
55 compact magnetic tape recording and playback equipment
56 single playback deck
57 central drive unit
58 single recording and playback deck
59 rewind bench
60–65 final picture quality checking room
60 preview monitor
61 programme (*Am.* program) monitor
62 stopclock
63 vision mixer (vision–mixing console, vision–mixing desk)
64 talkback system (talkback equipment)
65 camera monitor (picture monitor)

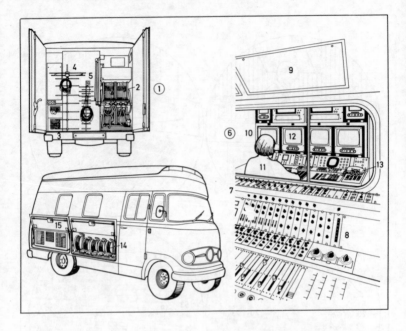

1–15 outside broadcast (OB) vehicle (television OB van; *also:* sound OB van, radio OB van)
1 rear equipment section of the OB vehicle
2 camera cable
3 cable connection panel
4 television (TV) reception aerial (receiving aerial) for Channel I
5 television (TV) reception aerial (receiving aerial) for Channel II
6 interior equipment (on-board equipment) of the OB vehicle
7 sound production control room (sound control room)
8 sound control desk (sound control console)
9 monitoring loudspeaker
10 vision control room (video control room)
11 video controller (vision controller)
12 camera monitor (picture monitor)
13 on-board telephone (intercommunication telephone)
14 microphone cable
15 air-conditioning equipment

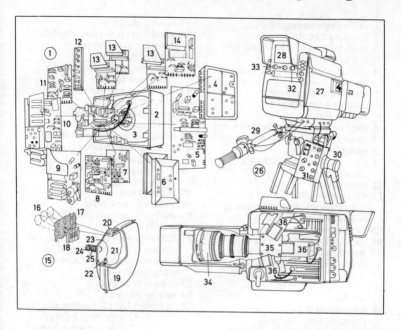

1 **colour** (*Am.* **color**) **television (TV) receiver** (colour television set) of modular design
2 television cabinet
3 television tube (picture tube)
4 IF (intermediate frequency) amplifier module
5 colour (*Am.* color) decoder module
6 VHF and UHF tuner
7 horizontal synchronizing module
8 vertical deflection module
9 horizontal linearity control module
10 horizontal deflection module
11 control module
12 convergence module
13 colour (*Am.* color) output stage module
14 sound module
15 colour (*Am.* color) picture tube
16 electron beams
17 shadow mask with elongated holes
18 strip of fluorescent (luminescent, phosphorescent) material
19 coating (film) of fluorescent material
20 inner magnetic screen (screening)
21 vacuum
22 temperature-compensated shadow mask mount
23 centring (centering) ring for the deflection system
24 electron gun assembly
25 rapid heat-up cathode
26 **television (TV) camera**
27 camera head
28 camera monitor
29 control arm (control lever)
30 focusing adjustment
31 control panel
32 contrast control
33 brightness control
34 zoom lens
35 beam–splitting prism (beam splitter)
36 pickup unit (colour, *Am.* color, pickup tube)

1 **radio cassette recorder**
2 carrying handle
3 push buttons for the cassette recorder unit
4 station selector buttons (station preset buttons)
5 built-in microphone
6 cassette compartment
7 tuning dial
8 slide control [for volume or tone]
9 tuning knob (tuning control, tuner)
10 **compact cassette**
11 cassette box (cassette holder, cassette cabinet)
12 cassette tape
13-48 **stereo system** (*also:* quadraphonic system) made up of Hi-Fi components
13-14 **stereo speakers**
14 speaker (loudspeaker), a three-way speaker with crossover (crossover network)
15 tweeter
16 mid-range speaker
17 woofer
18 **record player** (automatic record changer, auto changer)
19 record player housing (record player base)
20 turntable
21 tone arm
22 counterbalance (counterweight)
23 gimbal suspension
24 stylus pressure control (stylus force control)
25 anti-skate control
26 magnetic cartridge with (conical or elliptical) stylus, a diamond
27 tone arm lock
28 tone arm lift
29 speed selector (speed changer)
30 starter switch
31 treble control
32 dust cover
33 **stereo cassette deck**
34 cassette compartment
35-36 recording level meters (volume unit meters, VU meters)
35 left-channel recording level meter
36 right-channel recording level meter
37 **tuner**
38 VHF (FM) station selector buttons

39 tuning meter
40 **amplifier;** *tuner and amplifier together:* receiver (control unit)
41 volume control
42 four-channel balance control (level control)
43 treble and bass tuning
44 input selector
45 **four-channel demodulator** for CD4 records
46 quadra/stereo converter
47 cassette box (cassette holder, cassette cabinet)
48 record storage slots (record storage compartments)
49 **microphone**
50 microphone screen
51 microphone base (microphone stand)
52 **three-in-one stereo component system** (automatic record changer, cassette deck, and stereo receiver)
53 tone arm balance
54 tuning meters
55 indicator light for automatic FeO/CrO$_2$ tape switch-over
56 **open-reel-type recorder**, a two or four-track unit
57 tape reel (open tape reel)
58 open-reel tape (recording tape, $\frac{1}{4}''$ tape)
59 sound head housing with erasing head (erase head), recording head, and reproducing head (*or:* combined head)
60 tape deflector roller and end switch (limit switch)
61 recording level meter (VU meter)
62 tape speed selector
63 on/off switch
64 tape counter
65 stereo microphone sockets (stereo microphone jacks)
66 **headphones** (headset)
67 padded headband (padded headpiece)
68 membrane
69 earcups (earphones)
70 headphone cable plug, a standard multi-pin plug
71 headphone cable (headphone cord)

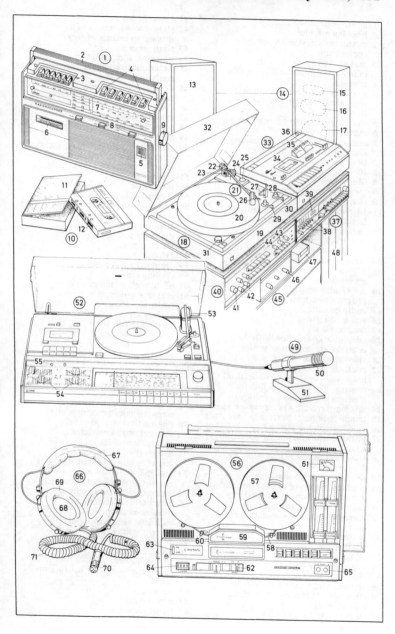

153 Teaching Equipment and Information Technology

1 group instruction using a **teaching machine**
2 instructor's desk with central control unit
3 master control panel with individual diplays and cross total counters
4 student input device (student response device) in the hand of a student
5 study step counter (progress counter)
6 overhead projector
7 apparatus for producing audio-visual learning programmes (*Am.* programs)
8-10 frame coding device
8 film viewer
9 memory unit (storage unit)
10 film perforator
11-14 audio coding equipment (sound coding equipment)
11 coding keyboard
12 two-track tape recorder
13 four-track tape recorder
14 recording level meter
15 PIP (programmed individual presentation) system
16 AV (audio-visual) projector for programmed instruction
17 audio cassette
18 video cassette
19 data terminal
20 telephone connection with the central data collection station
21 **video telephone**
22 conference circuit (conference hook-up, conference connection)
23 camera tube switch (switch for transmitting speaker's picture)
24 talk button (talk key, speaking key)
25 touch-tone buttons (touch-tone pad)
26 video telephone screen
27 infrared transmission of television sound
28 television receiver (television set, TV set)
29 infrared sound transmitter
30 cordless battery-powered infrared sound headphones (headset)
31 **microfilming system** [diagram]
32 magnetic tape station (data storage unit)
33 buffer storage
34 adapter unit
35 digital control
36 camera control
37 character storage
38 analogue (*Am.* analog) control
39 correction (adjustment) of picture tube geometry
40 cathode ray tube (CRT)
41 optical system
42 slide (transparency) of a form for mixing-in images of forms
43 flash lamp
44 universal film cassettes
45-84 **demonstration and teaching equipment**
45 demonstration model of a four-stroke engine
46 piston
47 cylinder head
48 spark plug (sparking plug)
49 contact breaker
50 crankshaft with balance weights (counterbalance weights) (counterbalanced crankshaft)
51 crankcase
52 inlet valve
53 exhaust valve
54 coolant bores (cooling water bores)
55 demonstration model of a two-stroke engine
56 deflector piston
57 transfer port
58 exhaust port
59 crankcase scavenging
60 cooling ribs
61-67 models of molecules
61 ethylene molecule
62 hydrogen atom
63 carbon atom
64 formaldehyde atom
65 oxygen molecule
66 benzene ring
67 water molecule
68-72 electronic circuits made up of modular elements
68 logic element (logic module), an integrated circuit
69 plugboard for electronic elements (electronic modules)
70 linking (link-up, joining, connection) of modules
71 magnetic contact
72 assembly (construction) of a circuit, using magnetic modules
73 multiple meter for measuring current, voltage and resistance
74 measurement range selector
75 measurement scale (measurement dial)
76 indicator needle (pointer)
77 current/voltage meter
78 adjusting screw
79 optical bench
80 triangular rail
81 laser (teaching laser, instruction laser)
82 diaphragm
83 lens system
84 target (screen)

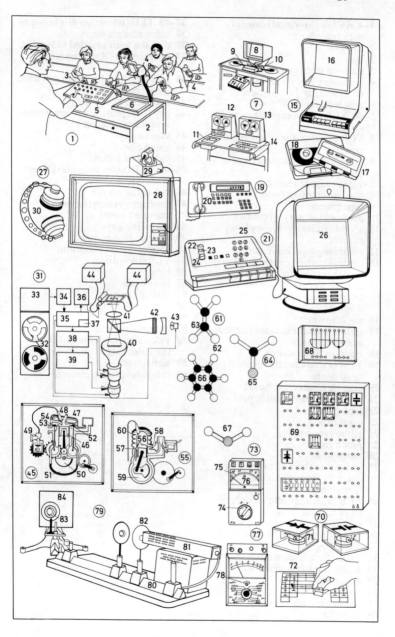

1-4 **AV** (audio–visual) camera
   with recorder
1 camera
2 lens
3 built–in microphone
4 portable video (videotape)
   recorder (for $\frac{1}{4}''$ open–reel
   magnetic tape
5-36 **VCR (video cassette recorder)
   system**
5 VCR cassette (for $\frac{1}{2}''$ magnetic
   tape)
6 domestic television receiver
   (*also:* monitor)
7 video cassette recorder
8 cassette compartment
9 tape counter
10 centring (centering) control
11 sound (audio) recording level
   control
12 recording level indicator
13 control buttons (operating keys)
14 tape threading indicator light
15 changeover switch for selecting
   audio or video recording level
   display
16 on/off switch
17 station selector buttons (station
   preset buttons)
18 built–in timer switch
19 VCR (video cassette recorder)
   head drum
20 erasing head (erase head)
21 stationary guide (guide pin)
22 tape guide
23 capstan
24 audio sync head
25 pinch roller
26 video head
27 grooves in the wall of the head
   drum to promote air cushion
   formation
28 VCR (video cassette recorder)
   track format
29 tape feed
30 direction of video head
   movement
31 video track, a slant track
32 sound track (audio track)
33 sync track
34 sync head
35 sound head (audio head)
36 video head

37-45 **TED (television disc) system**
37 video disc player
38 disc slot with inserted video disc
39 programme (*Am.* program)
   selector
40 programme (*Am.* program) scale
   (programme dial)
41 operating key ('play')
42 key for repeating a scene (scene–
   repeat key, 'select')
43 stop key
44 video disc
45 video disc jacket
46-60 **VLP (video long play) video
   disc system**
46 video disc player
47 cover projection (*below it:*
   scanning zone)
48 operating keys
49 slow motion control
50 optical system [diagram]
51 VLP video disc
52 lens
53 laser beam
54 rotating mirror
55 semi–reflecting mirror
56 photodiode
57 helium–neon laser
58 video signals on the surface of
   the video disc
59 signal track
60 individual signal element ('pit')

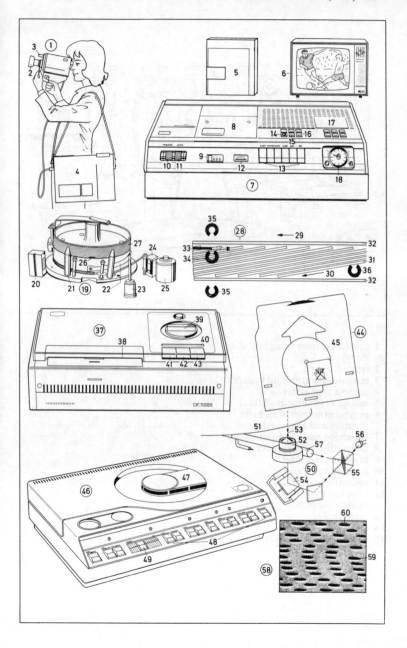

155 Computer Centre (*Am.* Center)

1 disc (disk) store (magnetic disc store)
2 magnetic tape
3 console operator (chief operator)
4 console typewriter
5 intercom (intercom system)
6 central processor with main memory and arithmetic unit
7 operation and error indicators
8 floppy disc (disk) reader
9 magnetic tape unit
10 magnetic tape reel
11 operating indicators
12 punched card (punch card) reader and punch
13 card stacker
14 operator
15 operating instructions

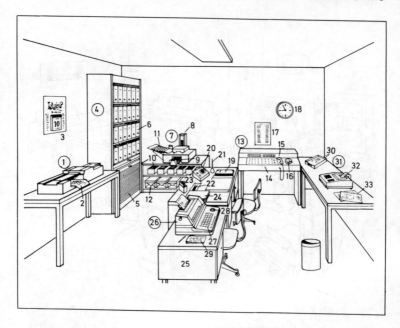

1–33 receptionist's office
(secretary's office)
1 facsimile telegraph
2 transmitted copy (received copy)
3 wall calendar
4 filing cabinet
5 tambour door (roll-up door)
6 file (document file)
7 transfer-type addressing machine
8 vertical stencil magazine
9 stencil ejection
10 stencil storage drawer
11 paper feed
12 stock of notepaper
13 switchboard (internal telephone exchange)
14 push-button keyboard for internal connections
15 handset
16 dial
17 internal telephone list
18 master clock (main clock)
19 folder containing documents, correspondence, etc. for signing (to be signed)
20 intercom (office intercom)
21 pen
22 pen and pencil tray
23 card index
24 stack (set) of forms
25 typing desk
26 memory typewriter
27 keyboard
28 rotary switch for the main memory and the magnetic tape loop
29 shorthand pad (*Am.* steno pad)
30 letter tray
31 office calculator
32 printer
33 business letter

1–36 executive's office
1 swivel chair
2 desk
3 writing surface (desk top)
4 desk drawer
5 cupboard (storage area) with door
6 desk mat (blotter)
7 business letter
8 appointments diary
9 desk set
10 intercom (office intercom)
11 desk lamp
12 pocket calculator (electronic calculator)
13 telephone, an executive-secretary system
14 dial; *also:* push-button keyboard
15 call buttons
16 receiver (telephone receiver)
17 dictating machine
18 position indicator
19 control buttons (operating keys)
20 cabinet

21 visitor's chair
22 safe
23 bolts (locking mechanism)
24 armour (*Am.* armor) plating
25 confidential documents
26 patent
27 petty cash
28 picture
29 bar (drinks cabinet)
30 bar set
31–36 conference grouping
31 conference table
32 pocket-sized dictating machine (micro cassette recorder)
33 ashtray
34 corner table
35 table lamp
36 two-seater sofa [part of the conference grouping]

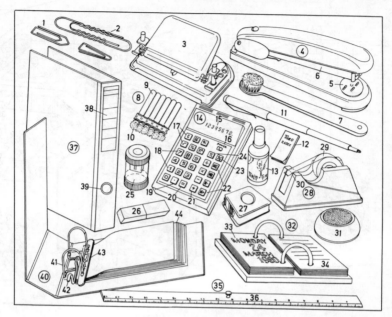

1-44 office equipment (office supplies, office materials)

1, 2 paper clips
3 punch
4 stapler (stapling machine)
5 anvil
6 spring-loaded magazine
7 type-cleaning brush for typewriters
8 type cleaner (type-cleaning kit)
9 fluid container (fluid reservoir)
10 cleaning brush
11 felt tip pen
12 correcting paper [for typing errors]
13 correcting fluid [for typing errors]
14 electronic pocket calculator
15 eight-digit fluorescent display
16 on/off switch
17 function keys
18 number keys
19 decimal key
20 'equals' key
21 instruction keys (command keys)
22 memory keys
23 percent key (percentage key)
24 π-key (pi-key) for mensuration of circles
25 pencil sharpener
26 typewriter rubber
27 adhesive tape dispenser
28 adhesive tape holder (roller-type adhesive tape dispenser)
29 roll of adhesive tape
30 tear-off edge
31 moistener
32 desk diary
33 date sheet (calendar sheet)
34 memo sheet
35 ruler
36 centimetre and millimetre (*Am.* centimeter and millimeter) graduations
37 file (document file)
38 spine label (spine tag)
39 finger hole
40 arch board file
41 arch unit
42 release lever (locking lever, release/lock lever)
43 compressor
44 bank statement (statement of account)

1–48 open plan office
1 partition wall (partition screen)
2 filing drawer with suspension file system
3 suspension file
4 file tab
5 file (document file)
6 filing clerk
7 clerical assistant
8 note for the files
9 telephone
10 filing shelves
11 clerical assistant's desk
12 office cupboard
13 plant stand (planter)
14 indoor plants (houseplants)
15 programmer
16 data display terminal (visual display unit)
17 customer service representative
18 customer
19 computer-generated design (computer-generated art)
20 sound-absorbing partition

21 typist
22 typewriter
23 filing drawer
24 customer card index
25 office chair, a swivel chair
26 typing desk
27 card index box
28 multi-purpose shelving
29 proprietor
30 business letter
31 proprietor's secretary
32 shorthand pad (*Am.* steno pad)
33 audio typist
34 dictating machine
35 earphone
36 statistics chart
37 pedestal containing a cupboard or drawers
38 sliding-door cupboard
39 office furniture arranged in an angular configuration
40 wall-mounted shelf
41 letter tray

42 wall calendar
43 data centre (*Am.* center)
44 calling up information on the
    data display terminal (visual
    display unit)
45 waste paper basket
46 sales statistics
47 EDP print-out, a continuous
    fan-fold sheet
48 connecting element

160 Office V (Office Machinery)

1 **electric typewriter**, a golf ball typewriter
2–6 keyboard
2 space bar
3 shift key
4 line space and carrier return key
5 shift lock
6 margin release key
7 tabulator key
8 tabulator clear key
9 on/off switch
10 striking force control (impression control)
11 ribbon selector
12 margin scale
13 left margin stop
14 right margin stop
15 golf ball (spherical typing element) bearing the types
16 ribbon cassette
17 paper bail with rollers
18 platen
19 typing opening (typing window)
20 paper release lever
21 carrier return lever
22 platen knob
23 line space adjuster
24 variable platen action lever
25 push-in platen variable
26 erasing table
27 transparent cover
28 exchange golf ball (exchange typing element)
29 type
30 golf ball cap (cap of typing element)
31 teeth
32 **web-fed automatic copier**
33 magazine for paper roll
34 paper size selection (format selection)
35 print quantity selection
36 contrast control
37 main switch (on/off switch)
38 start print button
39 document glass
40 transfer blanket
41 toner roll
42 exposure system
43 print delivery (copy delivery)
44 **letter-folding machine**
45 paper feed
46 folding mechanism

47 receiving tray
48 **small offset press**
49 paper feed
50 lever for inking the plate cylinder
51–52 inking unit (inker unit)
51 distributing roller (distributor)
52 ink roller (inking roller, fountain roller)
53 pressure adjustment
54 sheet delivery (receiving table)
55 printing speed adjustment
56 jogger for aligning the piles of sheets
57 pile of paper (pile of sheets)
58 folding machine
59 gathering machine (collating machine, assembling machine) for short runs
60 gathering station (collating station, assembling station)
61 adhesive binder (perfect binder) for hot adhesives
62 **magnetic tape dictating machine**
63 headphones (headset, earphones)
64 on/off switch
65 microphone cradle
66 foot control socket
67 telephone adapter socket
68 headphone socket (earphone socket, headset socket)
69 microphone socket
70 built-in loudspeaker
71 indicator lamp (indicator light)
72 cassette compartment
73 forward wind, rewind, and stop buttons
74 time scale with indexing marks
75 time scale stop

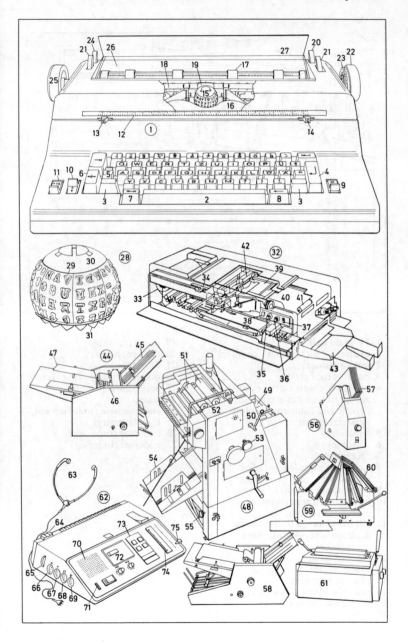

161 Bank

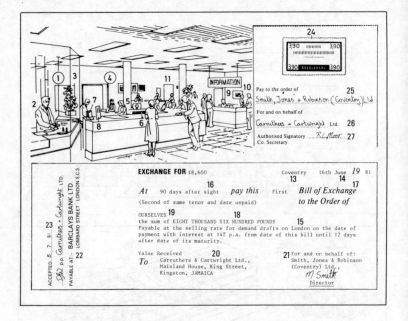

24	
390 IIIIIIII 390	
IIIIIIIIIIIIIIIIIIIII	
390 IIIIIIII 390	

Pay to the order of   **25**
Smith, Jones & Robinson (Coventry) Ltd

For and on behalf of   **26**
Carruthers & Cartwright Ltd.

Authorised Signatory   ..... *B.L.Moor* **27**
Co. Secretary

EXCHANGE FOR £8,600   Coventry   16th June   *19* 81
                    13   **14**   **17**

At   90 days after sight   *pay this*   First   *Bill of Exchange*
       16   *to the Order of*
(Second of same tenor and date unpaid)

OURSELVES **19**   **18**
the sum of EIGHT THOUSAND SIX HUNDRED POUNDS   **15**
Payable at the selling rate for demand drafts on London on the date of
payment with interest at 14% p.a. from date of this bill until 12 days
after date of its maturity.

Value Received   **20**   **21** For and on behalf of:
To   Carruthers & Cartwright Ltd.,   Smith, Jones & Robinson
      Mainland House, King Street,   (Coventry) Ltd.,
      Kingston, JAMAICA   *M Smith*
                                     Director

(left margin vertical text)
ACCEPTED 5. 7. 81   **23**
p.p. Carruthers & Cartwright LTD.
PAYABLE AT: BARCLAYS BANK LTD.
LOMBARD STREET LONDON E.C.3.   **22**

1-11 **main hall**
1 cashier's desk (cashier's counter)
2 teller (cashier)
3 bullet-proof glass
4 service counters (service and
   advice for savings accounts,
   private and company accounts,
   personal loans)
5 bank clerk
6 customer
7 brochures
8 stock list (price list, list of
   quotations)
9 information counter
10 foreign exchange counter
11 entrance to strong room
12 **bill of exchange** (bill); *here:* a
   draft, an acceptance (a bank
   acceptance)
13 place of issue
14 date of issue
15 place of payment
16 date of maturity (due date)
17 bill clause (draft clause)
18 value

19 payee (remittee)
20 drawee (payer)
21 drawer
22 domicilation (paying agent)
23 acceptance
24 stamp
25 endorsement (indorsement,
   transfer entry)
26 endorsee (indorsee)
27 endorser (indorser)

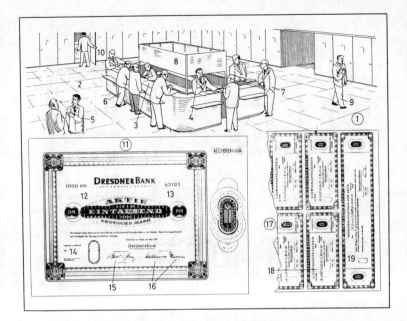

1–10 stock exchange (exchange for the sale of securities, stocks, and bonds)
1 exchange hall (exchange floor)
2 market for securities
3 broker's post
4 sworn stockbroker (exchange broker, stockbroker, *Am.* specialist), an inside broker
5 kerbstone broker (kerbstoner, curbstone broker, curbstoner, outside broker), a commercial broker dealing in unlisted securities
6 member of the stock exchange (stockjobber, *Am.* floor trader, room trader)
7 stock exchange agent (boardman), a bank employee
8 quotation board
9 stock exchange attendant (waiter)
10 telephone box (telephone booth, telephone kiosk, call box)

11–19 securities; *kinds:* share (*Am.* stock), fixed–income security, annuity, bond, debenture bond, municipal bond (corporation stock), industrial bond, convertible bond
11 share certificate (*Am.* stock certificate); *here:* bearer share (share warrant)
12 par (par value, nominal par, face par) of the share
13 serial number
14 page number of entry in bank's share register (bank's stock ledger)
15 signature of the chairman of the board of governors
16 signature of the chairman of the board of directors
17 sheet of coupons (coupon sheet, dividend coupon sheet)
18 dividend warrant (dividend coupon)
19 talon

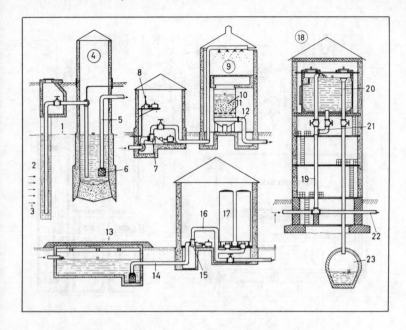

1–66 drinking water supply
1 water table (groundwater level)
2 water–bearing stratum (aquifer, aquafer)
3 groundwater stream (underground stream)
4 collector well for raw water
5 suction pipe
6 pump strainer (with foot valve)
7 bucket pump with motor
8 vacuum pump with motor
9 rapid–filter plant
10 filter gravel (filter bed)
11 filter bottom, a grid
12 filtered water outlet
13 purified water tank
14 suction pipe with pump strainer and foot valve
15 main pump with motor
16 delivery pipe
17 compressed–air vessel (air vessel, air receiver)
18 water tower
19 riser pipe (riser)
20 overflow pipe
21 outlet
22 distribution main
23 excess water conduit
24–39 tapping a spring
24 chamber
25 chamber wall
26 manhole
27 ventilator
28 step irons
29 filling (backing)
30 outlet control valve
31 outlet valve
32 strainer
33 overflow pipe (overflow)
34 bottom outlet
35 earthenware pipes
36 impervious stratum (impermeable stratum)
37 rough rubble
38 water–bearing stratum (aquifer, aquafer)
39 loam seal (clay seal)
40–52 individual water supply
40 well
41 suction pipe

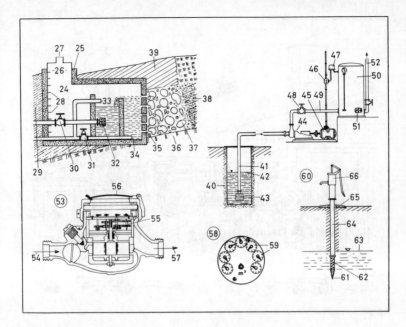

42 water table (groundwater level)
43 pump strainer with foot valve
44 centrifugal pump
45 motor
46 motor safety switch
47 manostat, a switching device
48 stop valve
49 delivery pipe
50 compressed–air vessel (air vessel,
    air receiver)
51 manhole
52 delivery pipe
53 water meter, a rotary meter
54 water inlet
55 counter gear assembly
56 cover with glass lid
57 water outlet
58 water–meter dial
59 counters
60 driven well (tube well, drive
    well)
61 pile shoe

62 filter
63 water table (groundwater level)
64 well casing
65 well head
66 hand pump

1–46 fire service drill
(extinguishing, climbing, ladder,
and rescue work)

1–3 fire station
1 engine and appliance room
2 firemen's quarters
3 drill tower
4 fire alarm (fire alarm siren, fire
siren)
5 fire engine
6 blue light (warning light), a
flashing light (*Am.* flashlight)
7 horn (hooter)
8 motor pump, a centrifugal pump
9 motor turntable ladder (*Am.*
aerial ladder)
10 ladder, a steel ladder (automatic
extending ladder)
11 ladder mechanism
12 jack
13 ladder operator
14 extension ladder
15 ceiling hook (*Am.* preventer)
16 hook ladder (*Am.* pompier
ladder)
17 holding squad
18 jumping sheet (sheet)
19 ambulance car (ambulance)
20 resuscitator (resuscitation
equipment), oxygen apparatus
21 ambulance attendant
(ambulance man)
22 armband (armlet, brassard)
23 stretcher
24 unconscious man
25 pit hydrant
26 standpipe (riser, vertical pipe)
27 hydrant key
28 hose reel (*Am.* hose cart, hose
wagon, hose truck, hose carriage)
29 hose coupling
30 soft suction hose
31 delivery hose
32 dividing breeching
33 branch
34 branchmen
35 surface hydrant (fire plug)
36 officer in charge
37 fireman (*Am.* firefighter)

38 helmet (fireman's helmet, *Am.*
   fire hat) with neck guard (neck
   flap)
39 breathing apparatus
40 face mask
41 walkie–talkie set
42 hand lamp
43 small axe (*Am.* ax, pompier
   hatchet)
44 hook belt
45 beltline
46 protective clothing of asbestos
   (asbestos suit) or of metallic
   fabric
47 breakdown lorry (*Am.* crane
   truck, wrecking crane)
48 lifting crane
49 load hook (draw hook, *Am.* drag
   hook)
50 support roll
51 water tender
52 portable pump
53 hose layer
54 flaked lengths of hose
55 cable drum

56 winch
57 face mask filter
58 active carbon (activated carbon,
   activated charcoal)
59 dust filter
60 air inlet
61 portable fire extinguisher
62 trigger valve
63 large mobile extinguisher
   (wheeled fire extinguisher)
64 foam–making branch (*Am.* foam
   gun)
65 fireboat
66 monitor (water cannon)
67 suction hose

Ordering of Entries

In the index the entries are ordered as follows:
1. Entries consisting of single words, e.g.: 'hair'.
2. Entries consisting of noun + adjective. Within this category the adjectives are entered alphabetically, e.g. 'hair, bobbed' is followed by 'hair, closely-cropped'.

   Where adjective and noun are regarded as elements of a single lexical item, they are not inverted, e.g.: 'blue spruce', not 'spruce, blue'.
3. Entries consisting of other phrases, e.g. 'hair curler', 'ham on the bone', are alphabetized as headwords.

Where a whole phrase makes the meaning or use of a headword highly specific, the whole phrase is entered alphabetically. For example 'ham on the bone' follows 'hammock'.

Index

References

The numbers in bold type refer to the sections in which the word may be found, and those in normal type refer to the items named in the pictures. Homonyms, and in some cases uses of the same word in different fields, are distinguished by section headings (in italics), some of which are abbreviated, to help to identify at a glance the field required. In most cases the full form referred to by the abbreviations will be obvious. Those which are not explained in the following list:

Agr.	Agriculture/Agricultural	Hydr. Eng.	Hydraulic Engineering
Alp. Plants	Alpine Plants	Impl.	Implements
Art. Studio	Artist's Studio	Inf. Tech.	Information Technology
Bldg.	Building	Intern. Combust. Eng.	Internal Combustion Engine
Carp.	Carpenter	Moon L.	Moon Landing
Cement Wks.	Cement Works	Music Not.	Musical Notation
Cost.	Costumes	Overh. Irrign.	Overhead Irrigation
Cyc.	Cycle	Platem.	Platemaking
Decid.	Deciduous	Plant. Propagn.	Propagation of Plants
D.I.Y.	Do-it-yourself	Rm.	Room
Dom. Anim.	Domestic Animals	Sp.	Sports
Equest.	Equestrian Sport	Text.	Textile[s]
Gdn.	Garden	Veg.	Vegetable[s]

A

abattoir **5**
abrasive wheel combination **22** 28, 35
absorption dynamometer **54** 97-107
absorption muffler **101** 16
absorption silencer **101** 16
abutment *Bridges* **126** 27, 29, 45
abutment pier **126** 29
acceleration rocket **145** 22, 48
accelerator **102** 46
accelerator pedal **102** 46, 94
accelerometer **141** 10
acceptance **161** 12, 23
accessories **26** 43-105
accessory shoe **25** 4; **26** 20
accessory shop **107** 24
access ramp **110** 15
accommodation **57** 33
accommodation bureau **115** 28
accommodation ladder **132** 98
accommodation module **57** 33
account, private ~ **161** 4
accounting machine **147** 26
accumulator railcar **122** 55
acetylene connection **52** 31
acetylene control **52** 32
acetylene cylinder **52** 2, 22
actuating transistor **106** 19
acuity projector **22** 47
adapter **23** 55
adapter, four-socket ~ **38** 8
adapter, four-way ~ **38** 8
adapter ring **26** 82
adapter unit **153** 34
address **147** 42
address display **147** 41
addressing machine, transfer-type ~ **156** 7
address label **147** 4
address system, ship's ~ **135** 30
A-deck **134** 28-30
adhesion railcar **125** 1
adhesive, hot ~ **160** 61
adhesive binder *Bookbind.* **95** 1

adhesive binder *Office* **160** 61
adhesive tape dispenser **158** 27
adhesive tape dispenser, roller-type ~ **158** 28
adhesive tape holder **158** 28
adjusting cone **98** 58
adjusting equipment **59** 61-65
adjusting knob **27** 54
adjusting nut **54** 35
adjusting screw *Bldg. Site* **30** 79
adjusting screw *Inf. Tech.* **153** 78
adjusting screw *Mach. parts etc.* **54** 107
adjusting spindle **137** 51
adjusting washer **98** 55
adjustment, coarse ~ **23** 4
adjustment, fine ~ *Drawing Off.* **62** 66
adjustment, fine ~ *Joiner* **44** 36
adjustment, fine ~ *Optic. Instr.* **23** 5
adjustment, fine ~ *Photog.* **27** 33
administration building *Airport* **144** 16
administration building *Coal* **55** 18
advertisement **9** 2; **115** 10
aerial **124** 4
aerial ladder **164** 9
aero engines **143** 33-60
aerogenerator **66** 42
aeroplane **141** 67-72
aeroplane, propeller-driven ~ **142** 1-6
aeroplane, types of ~ **142** 1-33
aftercastle **129** 23
after deck **134** 32
afterpeak **138** 28
aft fan-jet **143** 42
agate **86** 22
aggregate scraper **111** 13
agitator *Paperm.* **83** 47
aileron **141** 52
aileron, inner ~ **140** 43
aileron, outer ~ **140** 41
air blast **50** 56

air-blast circuit breaker **63** 34; **64** 51-62
air-bleed duct *Intern. Combust. Eng.* **101** 12
air blower, primary ~ **71** 11
air brake **140** 44
airbridge **144** 14
airbus **142** 17
air cleaner **102** 55
air compressor *Offshore Drill.* **57** 23
air compressor *Painter* **40** 33
air compressor *Railw.* **122** 14, 44; **123** 34, 58, 72
air compressor, diesel-powered ~ **111** 39
air compressor, mobile ~ **111** 39
air-conditioning equipment **150** 15
air correction jet **103** 3
aircraft **140**; **141**; **142**; **143**
aircraft, propeller-driven ~ **142** 1-6
aircraft, single-engine ~ **141** 1-31, 32-66; **142** 1, 2
aircraft, tilt-wing ~ **143** 26
aircraft, twin-boom ~ **140** 34
aircraft, twin-engine ~ **142** 3
aircraft, twin-jet ~ **142** 7
aircraft, types of ~ **142** 1-33
aircraft engines **143** 33-60
aircraft tractor **144** 23
aircraft tug **144** 23
air duct **66** 35
air extraction vent **65** 21
air extractor pipe **44** 40
air feed pipe **58** 29
air filler neck **107** 21
air filter **102** 55
air flow **110** 45
air flow, secondary ~ **143** 50
air hose *Garage* **106** 54
air hose *Serv. Stat.* **107** 18
air inlet and outlet **3** 14
air inlet *Fire Brig.* **164** 60
air inlet *Lorries etc.* **105** 16
air intake *Car* **103** 60

275

audio recording level control **154**
11
audio sync head **154** 24
audio systems **152**
audio track **154** 32
audio typist **159** 33
audiovision **154**
audio-visual camera **154** 1-4
audio-visual projector **153** 16
auger *Carp.* **31** 65
auto **102** 1-56; **106** 34
auto changer **152** 18
autoclave **81** 12, 33
autofocus override switch **28** 11
automatic flight control panel **146**
23
automatic-threading button **28** 83
automobile **102** 1-56; **103; 104;**
106 34
automobile models **104** 1-36
automobile tire **102** 15; **107** 27
automotive mechanic **106** 53
autopilot **135** 18
auto-soling machine **11** 2
auxiliary brake valve **122** 23
auxiliary-cable tensioning
mechanism **125** 48
auxiliary engine room **134** 70
auxiliary parachute bay **146** 59
AV **154**
aviation fuel **56** 57
avionics console **146** 22
awning *Ship* **15**; **132** 116
awning crutch **129** 14
axe **31** 73; **164** 43
axial-flow pump **128** 47-52
axis, lateral ~ **141** 68
axis, longitudinal ~ **141** 72
axis, normal ~ **141** 70
axis, polar ~ **24** 15, 18
axis, vertical ~ **141** 70
axis mount, English-type ~ **24**
222
axis mounting, English-type ~ **24**
22
axle **98** 61, 76, 81
axle, coupled ~ **121** 36
axle, floating ~ *Motorcycle* **100**
34
axle, live ~ **103** 65-71
axle, rigid ~ **103** 65-71
axle bearing **121** 10
axle drive shaft **112** 13

B

back *Bookbind.* **96** 41
back *Car* **104** 35
back *Mills* **2** 2
backbone *Bookbind.* **96** 41
back *Roof* **33** 86
back comb **16** 6
back fat **6** 40
back gauge **94** 17; **96** 4, 7
backing **163** 29
backing disc, rubber ~ **45** 22
backing paper *Paperhanger* **39** 5
backing paper *Photog.* **25** 21

back-pedal brake **98** 63
back plate **51** 36
back-pressure valve, hydraulic ~
52 8
backrest *Railw.* **118** 66
backrest *Weaving* **77** 37
backrest, reclining ~ **102** 35
back scouring valve **127** 61
back standard adjustment **25** 55
backstay **130** 19
backstitch seam **13** 1
backwater **83** 26
bacon **7** 2
badging **102** 12
baggage loader **144** 22
baggage retrieval **144** 38
baggage terminal **144** 5, 16
bag, paper ~ **9** 48
bag, postman's ~ **147** 54
baguette **8** 12
bakehouse **8** 55-74
baker's shop **8** 1-54
bakery **8** 55-74
baking ingredients **9** 8-11; **10** 62
balance *Paperm.* **84** 9
balance cable **125** 46
balance cable sleeve **125** 74
balance weight **153** 50
balance wheel **21** 39
balancing cabins **125** 25
balancing knob **27** 39
balcony, projecting ~ **129** 57
bale **80** 34; **81** 62; **117** 10, 11, 23
bale breaker **74** 7
bale opener **74** 7
baling press **80** 33
ball *Aircraft* **141** 12
ball *Bicycle* **98** 31
ball, steel ~ **54** 70
ball and socket head **25** 47
ballast *Railw.* **123** 66
ballast *Station* **116** 61
ballast tank **134** 78
ball bearing **54** 69; **98** 56, 68
ball mill **72** 1
ball of clay **72** 9
ball race **98** 68
baluster **34** 51
balustrade **34** 22, 50
bamboo cane **47** 31
banana **10** 90
banana-handling terminal **137** 22
banana saddle **99** 59
band, fluorescent ~ **110** 8
band, iron ~ **41** 16
band, steel ~ **74** 5
band brake **54** 104
band of barrel **41** 8
bandsaw **45** 50; **68** 48
bandsaw, horizontal ~ **68** 48
bandsaw blade **68** 53
band wheel **15**
bandwheel cover **44** 32
bank *Bank* **161**
bank *Post* **148** 43
bank acceptance **161** 12
bank branch **115** 31
bank clerk **161** 5
bank employee **162** 7
bank of oars **129** 12

bank protection **127** 51-55
bank slope **128** 28
bank stabilization **127** 51-55
bank statement **158** 44
bar *Office* **157** 29
bar, flat ~ **54** 10
bar, round ~ **54** 8
bar bender **30** 21
barb *Mach. Parts etc.* **54** 44
barber **17** 1
barber's shop **17** 1-42
barge **127** 22, 25; **136** 8
barge and push tug assembly **132**
92
bargee **127** 26
bargeman **127** 26
barge sucker **127** 59
bark *Carp.* **31** 86
bark *Ship* **130** 1-72; **131** 21-23
bark, five-masted ~ **131** 32-34
bark, four-masted ~ **131** 29
bark schooner **131** 20
barley, germinated ~ **3** 23
barley elevator **3** 33
barley hopper **3** 2
barley reception **3** 41
barley silo **3** 31
barouche **97** 35
barque **130** 1-72; **131** 21-23
barque, five-masted ~ **131** 32-34
barque, four-masted ~ **131** 29
barque schooner **131** 20
barrage **128** 57-64, 65-72
barrel *Cooper* **41** 5
barrel *Mach. Tools* **60** 27
barrel, aluminium ~ **4** 17
barrelhead **41** 10
barrel stave **41** 9
barrel store **4** 16
barrier *Hydr. Eng.* **128** 65
barrier *Railw.* **113** 40
barrier *Supermkt.* **10** 5
barrow *Station* **116** 32
barrow, road sweeper's ~ **110** 9
barrow, street sweeper's ~ **110** 9
bar set **157** 30
base *Bookbind.* **94** 25
base *Floor etc. Constr.* **34** 21, 63
base *Mills* **2** 33
base *Optic. Instr.* **23** 3; **24** 2
base *Road Constr.* **111** 59
base, horizontal ~ **23** 72
base, round ~ *Basketm.* **47** 19
base, round ~ *Electrotyp. etc.* **89**
10
base, round ~ *Hairdresser* **16** 27
base, woven ~ **47** 20
base course *Carp.* **31** 28
base course *Road Constr.* **111** 59
base course *Street Sect.* **109** 3
base course, concrete ~ **29** 2
base frame **88** 40
baseboard *Photog.* **27** 27
basement **29** 1
basement stairs **34** 16
basement wall **34** 1
basement window **29** 3
base of goblet **73** 42
base of machine **79** 54
base of support **125** 81

base plate

cable

column box **30** 11, 73
comb *Hairdresser* **16** 6
comb, adjustable ~ **76** 26
comb, top ~ **74** 67·
comber **74** 56, 63
comber draw box **74** 60
combination cutting pliers **37** 60; **38** 53
combination lever **121** 30
combination rib weave **82** 25
combination toolholder **60** 41
combing cylinder **74** 68
combing machine **74** 56
comb setting **76** 36
combustion chamber **143** 37
combustion chamber, external ~ **58** 16
command key **158** 21
command section **145** 65
commencement of speed restriction **114** 39, 42
common salt **81** 13
communication line **38** 23
communication link **148** 50
communications satellite **148** 52
commutator cover **122** 18
companion ladder **132** 123; **134** 24
companionway **132** 123; **133** 23; **134** 24
company account **161** 4
company messenger **147** 17
compartment *Railw.* **118** 13; **119** 24
compartment, secretarial ~ **116** 37; **120** 25
compartment, special ~ **116** 26
compartment, twin-berth ~ **118** 38
compartment, two-berth ~ **118** 38
compartment, two-seat ~ **118** 38
compartment door **118** 14
compartment window **118** 52; **119** 8
compass *Drawing Off.* **62** 52
compass, fluid ~ **135** 46
compass, gyroscopic ~ **135** 31, 51-53
compass, liquid ~ **135** 46
compass, magnetic ~ **134** 6; **135** 46; **141** 6
compass, mariner's ~ **134** 6
compass, ratchet-type ~ **62** 64
compass, spirit ~ **135** 46
compass, wet ~ **135** 46
compass bowl **135** 49
compass brick **70** 25
compass bridge **134** 4-11; **138** 24
compass card **135** 47
compasses **135** 46-53
compass flat **134** 4-11; **138** 24
compass head **62** 53
compass plane **43** 28
compass platform **134** 4-11; **138** 24
compass repeater **135** 31, 52, 53
compass saw **31** 63; **37** 70; **43** 3
compensating airstream **103** 4
compensating roller **92** 45
compensation pendulum **20** 33

compensator **92** 45
compensator level **23** 69
composing frame **85** 2
composing room **85; 86; 87**
composing rule **85** 14
composing stick **85** 13
composition *Composing Rm.* **86** 1-17
composition, computer controlled ~ **87** 14
compositor **85** 5
compressed-air braking system **119** 21
compressed-air hose **85** 38
compressed-air inlet **64** 53
compressed-air line *Blacksm.* **49** 5
compressed-air line *Joiner* **44** 45
compressed-air pipe *Forging* **50** 22
compressed-air pipe *Metalwkr.* **51** 17
compressed-air reservoir *Offshore Drill.* **57** 21
compressed-air supply **124** 20
compressed-air system **49** 1
compressed-air tank *Blacksm.* **49** 4
compressed-air tank *Power Plant* **64** 51
compressed-air vessel **163** 17, 50
compressed-gas container **145** 32
compressed-helium bottle **145** 14
compressed-helium tank **145** 43, 50
compressor *Blacksm.* **49** 3
compressor *Energy Sources* **66** 4
compressor *Office* **158** 43
compressor *Oil, Petr.* **56** 45
compressor *Painter* **40** 33
compressor *Ship* **134** 51
compressor, high-pressure ~ **143** 36
compressor, low-pressure ~ **143** 35
computer **88** 70; **106** 1
computer cable **106** 3, 38
computer centre **155**
computer data **149** 13
computer harness **106** 3, 38
computer socket, main ~ **106** 2, 39
computer test, automatic ~ **106** 33
computing scale **9** 12
concentrator **83** 24, 42, 44, 48, 62
concrete, heavy ~ **30** 72
concrete aggregate **29** 36; **30** 26
concrete bucket **30** 38
concrete mixer **29** 33; **30** 29; **112** 23
concrete-mixing plant **112** 19
concrete pump hopper **112** 24
concreter **30** 9
concrete, rammed ~ **29** 1
concrete, tamped ~ **29** 1
concrete road construction **112** 1-24
concrete scraper **111** 13
concrete spreader **112** 5

concrete spreader box **112** 6
concrete tamper **30** 83
concrete test cube **30** 84
concrete-vibrating compactor **112** 10
concrete vibrator **30** 88
condensate **83** 17
condenser *Brew.* **3** 6
condenser *Energy Sources* **66** 8
condenser *Nucl. Energy* **65** 17, 35
condenser *Oil, Petr.* **56** 44
condenser *Optic. Instr.* **23** 8; **24** 32
condenser *Paperm.* **83** 30
condenser *Synth. Fibres* **81** 5
condensing locomotive **121** 69
condensing tender **121** 69
condition report **106** 7
conductor *Power Plant* **64** 34, 43
conductor, copper ~ **38** 43
conductor, electrostatic ~ **141** 51; **142** 27
conductor, high-voltage ~ **63** 33
cone *Bicycle* **98** 58
cone *Mach. Parts etc.* **54** 67
cone *Synth. Fibres* **80** 27
cone, cross-wound ~ **76** 8, 24
cone, pyrometric ~ **72** 6
cone breaker **83** 82
cone creel **76** 9
cone drum box **74** 30
cone refiner **83** 27, 60, 73, 83
cone-winding frame **76** 1
cone-winding machine **80** 26
confectionery **8** 17-47; **9** 75-86
confectionery unit **8** 67-70
conference circuit **153** 22
conference connection **153** 22
conference grouping **157** 31-36
conference hook-up **153** 22
conference table **157** 31
configuration, angular ~ **159** 39
confluence **135** 90
connecting corridor **119** 11
connecting door, sliding ~ **118** 19
connecting element **159** 48
connecting hose **119** 16, 21
connecting rod *Intern. Combust. Eng.* **101** 21
connecting rod *Railw.* **121** 11
connecting-rod bearing **103** 25
connecting seal, rubber ~ **118** 8; **119** 12
connecting system, automatic ~ **148** 25
connection, internal ~ **156** 14
connection, pneumatically sprung ~ **105** 45
connection, rubber ~ **105** 45
connection of modules **153** 70
connection rebar **30** 10, 71
connector *Weaving* **77** 52
connector, thermoplastic ~ **38** 29
consignment, general ~ **117** 4
consignment, mixed ~ **117** 4
consignment note **117** 30
console *Joiner* **44** 24
console *Serv. Stat.* **107** 29
console operator **155** 3
console typewriter **155** 4

copper plate

288

door, folding

extractor support **53** 16
extrusion press **70** 11; **72** 7
eye *Blacksm.* **48** 29
eyebrow *Roof* **32** 23
eyecup **26** 73; **28** 14
eyelet embroidery **13** 11
eyelet *Glaz.* **35** 23
eyelet *Shoem.* **11** 63
eyelet *Weaving* **77** 28
eyelet, hook, and press-stud
   setter **11** 53
eye *Mills* **2** 19
eye *Weaving* **77** 28, 29
eyepiece **24** 20; **26** 42; **28** 14
eyepiece focusing knob **23** 56

F

fabric *Bldg. Site* **29** 1-49
fabric *Knitting* **78** 48
fabric *Text. Finish.* **79** 39, 51, 64
fabric *Weaves* **82** 29
fabric, air-dry ~ **79** 22
fabric, metallic ~ **164** 46
fabric, non-woven ~ **14** 27
fabric, printed ~ **79** 57
fabric, raised ~ **79** 36
fabric, shrink-resistant ~ **79** 26
fabric, tubular ~ **78** 1, 9
fabric, woollen ~ *Dressm.* **14** 27
fabric, woollen ~ *Text. Finish.* **79**
   1
fabric, woven ~ **77** 12
fabric box **78** 10
fabric container **78** 10
fabric drum **78** 10
fabric-finishing machine,
   decatizing ~ **79** 49
fabric for upholstery **45** 60
fabric guide roller **79** 5
fabric-plaiting device **79** 30
fabric-raising machine **79** 31
fabric rol **78** 29
fabric roller **77** 20
fabric shaft **82** 21, 23
fabric wallhanging **39** 18
face *Blacksm.* **48** 28
face *Clocks* **21** 25
face *Composing Rm.* **85** 31; **86** 42
face compress **17** 25
face mask filter **164** 57
face mask *Fire Brig.* **164** 40
face par **162** 12
facsimile telegraph **156** 1
factory number **98** 51
factory ship *Sea Fish.* **1** 11
factory ship *Ship* **132** 86
fairing **100** 43
fairing, integrated ~ **100** 44
fairing, metal ~ **99** 50
fairway **127** 21
fairway, main ~ **135** 92
fairway, secondary ~ **135** 93
fairway markings **135** 84-102
fairway marks **135** 68-83
fall **132** 106
fan *Aircraft* **143** 34, 43
fan *Energy Sources* **66** 14
fan *Intern. Combust. Eng.* **101** 7

fan *Refuse Coll.* **110** 35, 46
fan *Weaving* **76** 23
fan, low-pressure ~ **110** 33
fan blower **90** 22
fan clutch **101** 8
fan drift **55** 22
fan fold sheet, continuous ~ **159**
   47
fan-jet turbine **143** 38
farm vehicle engineering **49**
fascia panel **102** 57-90
fascine **127** 53
fashion catalogue **15** 6
fashion journal **15** 4
fashion magazine **15** 4
fast and slow motion switch **28** 87
fastback **104** 29
fast breeder **65** 1
fast-breeder reactor **65** 1
fastening *Station* **117** 12
fat end **6** 53
faucet *Electrotyp. etc.* **89** 34
faucet *Plumb. etc.* **37** 34
fault *Coal* **55** 51
F-contact **26** 14
feather *Mach. Parts etc.* **54** 73
feed *Iron & Steel* **58** 51
feed *Mach. Tools* **60** 9
feed adjustment **11** 28
feed board **91** 32, 49, 67; **92** 4, 21,
   30; **96** 9
feed chain **83** 67
feed chain drive **83** 69
feed channel **68** 55
feed conveyor **147** 33
feed drum **91** 33, 34
feed gearbox **60** 8
feed gear lever **60** 10
feed guide **95** 23
feed hopper *Bookbind.* **96** 26
feed-in **84** 13
feed indicator **68** 9
feeder *Bookbind.* **96** 25
feeder *Brickwks.* **70** 7
feeder *Letterpress* **92** 22, 24
feeder *Offset Print.* **91** 31, 48, 68,
   74
feeder, automatic ~ **92** 5
feeder broom **110** 44
feeder mechanism **92** 22
feeder panel **64** 4
feeder-selecting device **78** 40
feeder skip **29** 35
feeding apparatus **92** 22
feeding-in **75** 15
feed mechanism *Mach. Tools* **60**
   18
feed mechanism *Post* **147** 48
feed motor **88** 43
feed pawl **68** 44
feed pipe **7** 50
feed pump *Nucl. Energy* **65** 13
feed pump *Railw.* **121** 9
feed roller **68** 4, 40
feed roller, fluted ~ **74** 52
feed runner **58** 22
feed screw **60** 15
feed setting **11** 28
feed shaft **60** 33

feed spool **28** 31
feed table *Bookbind.* **95** 12, 21;
   96 9, 34
feed table *Letterpress* **92** 4, 21, 30
feed table *Offset Print.* **91** 32, 49,
   67
feed table *Sawmill* **68** 63
feed-through insulator **64** 12, 35
feed-through terminal **64** 12, 35
feed trip **60** 18
feed tripping device **60** 18
feed valve **121** 20
feedwater heater **121** 23
feedwater line **65** 12, 30
feedwater preheater **121** 23
feedwater steam circuit **65** 45
feedwater tank **63** 17
feedwater tray, top ~ **121** 29
feeler *Weaving* **77** 32
feeler gauge **51** 53
felt **84** 51
felt, dry ~ **84** 23
felt nail **33** 96
felt tip pen **158** 11
fence adjustment handle **43** 66
fence *Aircraft* **142** 8
fence *Joiner* **43** 65
fence *Refuse Coll.* **110** 13
fence, timber ~ **29** 44
fence, wicker ~ **127** 54
fender *Docks* **136** 12
fender *Hydr. Eng.* **128** 9
fender *Tram* **108** 12
fender, front ~ *Bicycle* **98** 13
fender, front ~ *Car* **102** 3; **102** 3,
   13
fender, integral ~ **104** 33
fender, wooden ~ **129** 26
fender pile *Hydr. Eng.* **128** 9
fender pile *Shipbuild.* **133** 35
fermentation room **8** 72
fermentation thermometer **4** 9
fermentation trolley **8** 73
fermentation vessel **4** 8
fermenter **4** 8
fermenting cellar **4** 7
ferries **132**
ferroconcrete construction **30** 1-
   89
ferryboat **127** 11, 15; **136** 11
ferry, flying ~ **127** 10
ferry cable **127** 2
ferry landing stage **127** 7
ferryman **127** 17
ferry rope **127** 2
fettler **59** 43
fettling shop **59** 38-45
fibre, glass ~ **62** 48
fibre, loose ~ **79** 43
field illumination **23** 33
field lens **26** 40
figurehead **129** 16
filament **80** 17, 22; **81** 44
filament, continuous ~ **80** 1-34
filament, solid ~ **80** 15
filament lamp **38** 56
filament tow **80** 28, 30
file *Metalwkr.* **51** 16
file *Office* **156** 6; **158** 37; **159** 5
file, flat ~ **19** 49; **51** 27

file, half-round ~ **51** 29
file, rough ~ **51** 8
file, round ~ **19** 47; **51** 29
file, smooth ~ **51** 8
file handle **19** 50
filet **13** 22
file tab **159** 4
filigree work **13** 30
filing cabinet **156** 4
filing clerk **159** 6
filing drawer **159** 2, 23
filing machine **51** 15
filing shelf **159** 10
fill, sanitary ~ **110** 10
filler *Paperhanger* **39** 3
filler *Power Plant* **64** 38
filler *Tobacc. etc.* **18** 7
filler hoist **111** 51
filler hole **124** 19
filler opening **111** 52
filler rod **52** 12
fillet *Bookbind.* **94** 3
fillet *Carp.* **31** 45
fillet *Floor etc. Constr.* **34** 57 67
fillet *Meat* **6** 13
fillet, tilting ~ **32** 31
fillet gauge **53** 36
fillet of beef **6** 24
fillet of pork **6** 44
filling compound **64** 38
filling end **73** 2
filling *Hydr. Eng.* **128** 7
filling *Water* **163** 29
filling knife **39** 35
filling station **107** 1-29
film *Composing Rm.* **87** 25
film *Photog.* **25** 9
film, cine ~ **28**
film, exposed ~ **28** 42
film, unexposed ~ **28** 41
film advance **25** 32
film advance lever, single-stroke
~ **26** 16
film agitator, automatic ~ **27** 19
film and sound cutting table **28** 96
film and tape synchronizing head
28 102
film back **26** 80
film cassette **23** 65
film cassette, miniature ~ **25** 7
film cassette, universal ~ **153** 44
film clip **27** 14
film copier, automatic ~ **87** 28
film drier **27** 23
film feed spool **28** 79
film former **89** 24
film gate **28** 30
film gate opening **28** 40
filming agent **89** 24
filming speed selector **28** 12
film magazine **24** 40
film marker **28** 95
film matrix case **87** 17
film of fluorescent material **151** 19
film perforator **28** 95; **153** 10
film processor, automatic ~ **88** 72
filmsetter **87** 7
filmsetting **87**
film speed setting **28** 18
film spool **25** 8

film spool holder **149** 6
film transport **25** 32
film transport handle **27** 7
film turntable **28** 99
film viewer **28** 91; **153** 8
film wind **25** 32
film window **25** 18; **26** 28, 34
filter *Paperm.* **83** 20
filter *Synth. Fibres* **81** 32
filter *Water* **163** 62
filter *Weaving* **76** 14
filter adjustment **27** 43, 44, 45
filter bed **163** 10
filter bottom **163** 11
filter cake **72** 13
filtered water outlet **163** 12
filter gravel **163** 10
filter lens **53** 40
filter mount **26** 6
filter pick-up **23** 57
filter press *Porcelain Manuf.* **72**
12
filter press *Synth. Fibres* **80** 12
filter screen **27** 22
final image tube **24** 39
final picture quality checking
room **149** 60-65
fine cut **18** 25
fine focusing indicator **135** 36
finger hole *Office* **158** 39
finger plate **148** 11
finger stop **148** 12
fining bath **73** 4
fining lap **22** 37, 38
finish, gloss ~ **39** 32
finished malt collecting hopper **3**
20
finishing **79** 1-65; **81** 57
finishing layer **34** 40
finishing machine **11** 3
finishing of textile fabrics **79**
finishing press **94** 4
finishing train **59** 71
fin, vertical ~ *Aircraft* **140** 24; **141**
59; **142** 6; **143** 7
fin, vertical ~ *Space* **146** 1
fin post **146** 3
fire, blacksmith's ~ **48** 1-8; **49** 34
fire alarm **164** 4
fire alarm siren **164** 4
fire appliance building **144** 8
fireboat **164** 65
firebox **121** 4
fire department **164**
firedoor handle handgrip **121** 63
fire engine **164** 5
fire extinguisher **107** 9
fire extinguisher, portable ~ **164**
61
fire extinguisher, wheeled ~ **164**
63
firefighter **164** 37
fire-fighting equipment **138** 25;
139 20
fire gable **32** 9
fire gun **132** 4
fire hat **164** 38
firehole door **121** 61
firehole shield **121** 60
fireman **164** 37

fire nozzle **132** 4
fire plug **164** 35
fire service **164**
fire service drill **164** 1-46
fire siren **164** 4
fire station **164** 1-3
fire tube **121** 17
firing mould **72** 4
firing process **72** 2
firing sequence insert **106** 13
firmer chisel **45** 30
first aid station **115** 44
first-class section **118** 17
first floor **29** 7
first-floor landing **34** 23
fishbolt **113** 13
fishbone stitch **13** 7
fish *Grocer* **9** 19
fish, canned ~ **7** 28
fish-canning factory **136** 59
fish dock **136** 56
fisheye **26** 44
fishing boat **1** 24
fishing lugger **1** 1
fishing tackle, suspended ~ **1** 29
fish market **136** 57
fishplate **113** 12
fishtail bit **56** 21
fitch **40** 19
fitter **51** 1
fitting of the frame **22** 10
fitting-out quay **133** 5-9
fittings **37** 38-52
fix **135** 45
flag dressing **132** 85
flame regulator **18** 31
flan case **8** 47
flange *Cooper* **41** 28
flange *Electrotyp. etc.* **89** 44
flange *Hydr. Eng.* **128** 67
flange *Mach. Parts etc.* **54** 2, 5
flange, bottom ~ **126** 10
flange, top ~ **126** 9
flange mount **41** 20
flanging, swaging, and wiring
machine **36** 25
flank *Bldg. Site* **30** 6
flank *Meat* **6** 2, 15-16
flank, thick ~ **6** 15, 36
flank, thin ~ **6** 16
flans **8** 22-24
flap *Aircraft* **140** 37
flap, double-slotted ~ **140** 48
flap, extending ~ **140** 51
flap, normal ~ **140** 46
flap, slotted ~ **140** 47
flaps, plain ~ **140** 46-48
flap, split ~ **140** 49
flaps, simple ~ **140** 46-48
flaps, split ~ **140** 49-50
flap valve **103** 63
flare, pork ~ **6** 45
flash, battery-portable ~ **25** 65
flash, electronic ~ **25** 65, 68
flash, single-unit ~ **25** 68
flash bar **25** 75
flash contact **25** 30
flash cube **25** 74
flash cube contact **25** 13
flash cube unit **25** 73

generator *Intern. Combust. Eng.*
101 76
generator *Nucl. Energy* **65** 15, 47,
53
generator *Railw.* **122** 46
generator *Ship* **134** 74
generator exhaust **57** 2
generator unit **142** 33
gentlemen's toilet **144** 47
geyser *Plumb. etc.* **37** 12-13
gherkin, pickled ~ **9** 29
gib *Mach. Parts etc.* **54** 74
gib *Plumb.* **36** 3
gig **97** 34
gilder **94** 2
gilding *Bookbind.* **94** 1
gilding *Painter* **40** 40
gilding and embossing press **94** 26
gimbal ring **135** 50
gimbal suspension **152** 23
gimlet **31** 65
gimping **13** 28
gimping needle **13** 29
gingerbread **8** 51
girder, steel ~ **54** 3-7
girt **31** 50
glass, armoured ~ **20** 29
glass, bullet-proof ~ **161** 3
glass, frosted ~ **35** 5
glass, laminated ~ **35** 5
glass, lined ~ **35** 6
glass, molten ~ **73** 23, 31, 50
glass, ornamental ~ **35** 6
glass, patterned ~ **35** 5
glass, raw ~ **35** 6
glass, shatterproof ~ **35** 5
glass, stained ~ **35** 6
glass, thick ~ **35** 5
glass, wired ~ **35** 6
glassblower **73** 38
glassblowing **73** 38-47
glass cloth **41** 29
glass cutter, diamond ~ **35** 25
glass cutters **35** 25-26
glass cutter, steel ~ **35** 26
glass-drawing machine **73** 8
glasses **22** 9
glass fibre, production of ~ **73** 48-
55
glass fibre products **73** 56-58
glass filament **73** 52
glass furnace **73** 1, 49
glass holder **35** 9
glasshouse pot, covered ~ **73** 46
glassmaker **73** 38
glassmaking **73** 38-47
glass paper **46** 25
glass pliers **35** 19
glass ribbon **73** 10
glass wool **73** 58
glassworker **35** 8
glazier **35**; **35** 82
glazing sheet **27** 58
glazing sprig **35** 24
glove box lock **102** 89
glove compartment lock **102** 89
glow plug **101** 66
glue, joiner's ~ **43** 13
glue-enamel plate **90** 32
glue pot **43** 12, 13; **94** 15 **147** 5

glue roller **96** 33
glue size **39** 4
glue tank **95** 9; **96** 32
glue well **43** 13
gluing **94** 14
gluing machine **96** 31
gluing mechanism **95** 4
goaf **55** 37
gob *Coal* **55** 37
gob *Glass Prod.* **73** 40
goblet, hand-blown ~ **73** 41
gob of molten glass **73** 23, 31
Godet wheel **80** 16
GO gauging member **60** 57
GO side **60** 60
goggles **51** 21
gold and silver balance **19** 35
gold cushion **94** 6
gold finisher **94** 2
gold knife **94** 7
gold leaf **31** 45, 52; **94** 5
gold size **40** 44
goldsmith **19** 17
golf ball *Office* **160** 15
golf ball cap **160** 30
golf ball typewriter **160** 1
gondola cableway **125** 19
gondola *Railw.* **125** 20
gondola *Supermkt.* **10** 23, 43, 62
goods, bulky ~ **117** 18
goods, general ~ **117** 4
goods lorry **117** 15
goods office **117** 26
goods shed **117** 7, 26-39
goods shed door **117** 37
goods shelf **9** 14
goods station **117**
goods van **117** 6; **124** 22
goods van, covered ~ **124** 14
goods wagon, covered ~ **124** 14
goods wagon, open ~ **124** 8
gooseberry flan **8** 22
gouge **43** 9; **46** 15
governor **135** 56
gown **16** 34; **17** 4
grade crossing, protected ~ **113**
39
grade crossing, unprotected ~
113 49
grade crossings **113** 39-50
grader **111** 19
grader levelling blade **111** 21
grader ploughshare **111** 21
grain *Brew.* **3** 50
grandfather clock **21** 24
gran turismo car **104** 32
grape **10** 89
grapnel **129** 11
grapple **129** 11
grappling iron **129** 11
grass **47** 26
grass verge **111** 56
grate **110** 33
graticule *Photomech. Reprod.* **88**
4
gravel **29** 36; **30** 26
gravel filter layer **110** 23
graver **86** 33
gravity hammer, air-lift ~ **50** 24

gravity mixer **29** 33
gravure cylinder **93** 10
gravure cylinder, etched ~ **93** 22
gravure cylinder, printed ~ **93** 17
gravure etcher **93** 18
gravure printing **93**
grease gun **106** 30
grease nipple **54** 81
great primer **86** 30
green liquor, uncleared ~ **83** 41
green liquor preheater **83** 43
grenzanhydrite **65** 67
grid *Cotton Spin.* **74** 26
grid *Water* **163** 11
grid hearth **50** 1
grill *Painter* **40** 12
grill *Station* **115** 38
grinder *Metalwkr.* **51** 18
grinder *Painter* **40** 29
grinder, continuous ~ **83** 53, 66
grinder, pneumatic ~ **59** 44
grinder chuck **68** 46
grinding cylinder **72** 1
grinding machine **51** 18
grinding machine, universal ~ **61**
1
grinding machine bed **61** 6
grinding machine table **61** 7
grinding-roller bearing **74** 41
grinding stone *Papem.* **83** 71
grinding wheel *Blacksm.* **48** 19;
49 8
grinding wheel *D.I.Y.* **45** 23
grinding wheel *Mach. Tools* **61** 4
grinding wheel *Metalwkr.* **51** 19
grinding wheel *Sawmill* **68** 43
grindstone **83** 71
grip *Bicycle* **98** 3
grip *Cine Film* **28** 61
grip *Photog.* **25** 37
gripper **91** 65
gripper bar **91** 56
gripping jaw **60** 36
grip sole **12** 19
grist **3** 42
grit guard **59** 40
gritter, self-propelled ~ **111** 41
grocer **9** 41
grocer's shop **9** 1-87
groceryman **9** 41
grocery store **9** 1-87
groom *Carriages* **97** 27
groove *Iron Foundry etc.* **59** 59
groove *Sawmill* **68** 6
grooving **68** 6
ground **34** 9
ground floor **29** 7
ground-floor landing **34** 23
ground-nut oil **9** 24
ground power unit **144** 22
ground tackle **134** 49-51
groundwater level **163** 1, 42, 63
groundwater stream **163** 3
groundwood **83** 68
groundwood mill **83** 53-65
groundwood pulp **83** 77, 78
group instruction **153** 1
group selector switch **149** 42
growler **97** 26
groyne head *Rivers* **127** 20

groyne *Rivers* **127** 19
grub screw **54** 48
GT car **104** 32
guard *Blacksm.* **49** 9
guard *Metalwkr.* **51** 20
guard, protective ~ **79** 45
guard board **29** 29
guard cam **78** 57
guard for V-belt **91** 58
guard iron **121** 34
guard netting **29** 90
guard rail *Floor etc. Constr.* **34** 53
guard rail *Railw.* **113** 23
guard rail *Ship* **132** 121
guard rail *Shipbuild.* **133** 66
guard rail *Weaving* **76** 31
gudgeon pin **103** 26
guest rope **138** 14
gugelhupf **8** 33
guide, stationary ~ **154** 21
guide bar *Cotton Spin.* **75** 17
guide bar *Weaving* **76** 38
guide bearing **24** 14
guide block **85** 48; **87** 18
guide groove **128** 75
guide notch **28** 36
guide pin **154** 21
guide rail *Railw.* **125** 56
guide rail *Weaving* **76** 3
guide rod **111** 27
guide roller *Cotton Spin.* **75** 18
guide roller *Sawmill* **68** 5
guide step **28** 36
guide tractor **52** 19
guiding slot *Weaving* **76** 11
guillotine *Bookbind.* **94** 16; **96** 1
guillotine *Plumb.* **36** 26
guillotine cutter, automatic ~ **96** 1
gull wing, inverted ~ **140** 14
gun **129** 50
gun, pneumatic ~ **5** 3
gunport **129** 59
gunport shutter **129** 60
gutter *Bookbind.* **96** 55
gutter *Street Sect.* **109** 10
gutter, parallel ~ **33** 83
gutter bracket **33** 32
gutter Roof **33** 28, 92
guy pole **63** 31
guy wire *Energy Sources* **66** 44
gypsum crusher **71** 14
gypsum store **71** 13
gyro compass **135** 31, 51-53
gyro compass unit **135** 51-53
gyrodyne **143** 29
gyro horizon **141** 3
gyro repeater **135** 52

H

hack **97** 26
hacking knife **39** 37
hackney carriage **97** 26
hackney coach **97** 26
hacksaw **45** 3, 17; **47** 40; **49** 23; **51** 9; **61** 14
hacksaw frame **37** 71
haematite **19** 48

haft **48** 30
hairbrush **16** 10
hair clip **16** 11
hair curler **17** 31
haircut **17** 3
haircutting scissors **16** 7; **17** 34
hairdresser **16** 35; **17** 1
hairdresser *Airport* **144** 53
hairdresser, ladies' ~ **16**
hairdresser, men's ~ **17**
hairdresser's tools **16** 1-16
hairdressing salon, ladies' ~ **16** 1-39
hairdressing salon, men's ~ **17** 1-42
hair drier, hand-held ~ **16** 33; **17** 22
hair-fixing spray **16** 24
hairpin *Needlewk.* **13** 29
hairpin work **13** 28
hair spray **16** 24
hairstyle **17** 3
hair tonic **17** 10
half-barrier crossing **113** 45
half nonpareil **86** 20
half nut **90** 19
half-title **96** 43, 44
halftone dot **89** 39
hall, main ~ **147** 1-30; **161** 1-11
halogen lamp **88** 31
halved joint **32** 86
halving joint **32** 86
ham **6** 51
hammer, bricklayer's ~ **29** 53
hammer, brickmason's ~ **29** 53
hammer, carpenter's ~ **31** 74
hammer crusher *Cement Wks.* **71** 2
hammer crusher *Quarry* **69** 20
hammer cylinder **50** 30
hammer drill **69** 11
hammer drill, electric ~ **45** 43
hammer, flat-face ~ **48** 35
hammer, glazier's ~ **35** 18
hammer, machinist's ~ *D.I.Y.* **45** 40
hammer, machinist's ~ *Metalwkr.* **51** 23
hammer, shoemaker's ~ **11** 37
hammer, stonemason's ~ **69** 35
hammer forging **50**
hammer guide **50** 29
hammer **37** 78; **45** 7; **48** 26; **50** 26
hammer mill **71** 2
ham on the bone **7** 1; **10** 52
hand bindery **94** 1-38
hand bookbindery **94** 1-38
hand brace **51** 13
hand brake **98** 5; **102** 72; **123** 33
hand brake lever **99** 33; **102** 93
hand brake wheel **123** 64, 80
hand camera, large-format ~ **25** 36
handcart **31** 6
handclap **28** 69
hand-composing room **85** 1
hand compositor **85** 5
hand control **106** 8
hand cream **10** 27
hand die **37** 85

hand die, electric ~ **36** 12
hand drill **51** 13
hand flat knitting machine **78** 35
hand glass *Hairdresser* **16** 23; **17** 7
hand glass *Optician* **22** 16
handgrip *Bicycle* **98** 3
handgrip *Cine Film* **28** 5, 61
handgrip *Navig.* **135** 9
handgrip *Photog.* **25** 37
hand guard **5** 10
hand hair drier **16** 33; **17** 22
hand hammer, blacksmith's **48** 23
hand-ironing pad **15** 30
hand-iron press **14** 18
hand ladle **59** 23
hand lamp **164** 42
hand lead **135** 58
handlebar **98** 2; **99** 45
handlebar, adjustable ~ **99** 3
handlebar, semi-rise ~ **99** 11
handlebar fittings **99** 30-35
handlebar grip **98** 3
handlebar stem **98** 3
handle *Carriages* **97** 12
handle *D.I.Y.* **45** 47
handle *Hairdresser* **17** 37
handle *Joiner* **43** 10, 18
handle *Metalwkr.* **51** 5
handle, double ~ **59** 15
handle, fixed ~ **40** 7
handle, insulated ~ **38** 54
hand lever *Bookbind.* **94** 31
hand lever *Joiner* **43** 55
hand-lever press **94** 26
hand luggage **105** 19
hand mirror *Hairdresser* **16** 23; **17** 7
hand mirror *Optician* **22** 16
hand pump **163** 66
handrail *Floor etc. Constr.* **34** 53, 79
handrail *Ship* **132** 122
handrailing **126** 70
hand rammer **59** 32
hand-removing tool **20** 10
handrest **23** 58
hand saw **31** 60; **37** 72; **45** 27
handscrew **43** 14
handset **148** 7; **156** 15
handset cord **148** 14
handset cradle **148** 13
hand-setting room **85** 1
hand shank **59** 14
hand shears *Bldg. Site* **30** 87
hand shears *Tailor* **15** 11
hand spray *Hairdresser* **16** 30; **17** 13
hand spray *Offset Platem.* **90** 7
hand spray *Painter* **40** 35
handstamp **147** 45
hand steel shears **30** 22
hand towel **17** 24
hand vice **51** 24
handwheel *Bookbind.* **94** 23
handwheel *Cooper* **41** 19
handwheel *Cotton Spin.* **74** 18
handwheel *Knitting* **78** 7, 30
handwheel *Paperm.* **83** 74
handwheel *Road Constr.* **112** 9
handwheel *Shoem.* **11** 24

mortise and tenon joint **32** 84, 85
mortise axe **31** 72
mortise chisel **43** 8
mortise lock **51** 36-43
mortiser **31** 17
mortising chain, endless ~ **43** 50
motion, longitudinal ~ **60** 17
motor *Electrotyp. etc.* **89** 14
motor *Iron Foundry etc.* **59** 64
motor *Tram* **108** 5, 7
motor *Watchm.* **20** 13
motor *Water* **163** 45
motor *Weaving* **76** 12, 34
motor, auxiliary ~ **122** 17
motor, built-in ~ **75** 2
motor, built-on ~ **75** 33
motor, electric ~ *Blacksm.* **49** 2
motor, electric ~ *Railw.* **123** 34
motor, electric ~ *Ship* **134** 69
motor, electric ~ *Weaving* **77** 18
motor, synchronous ~ **87** 19
motor, three-phase ~ **75** 35
motor base plate **75** 36
motor bedplate **75** 36
motorboat landing stage **127** 7
motor car **102** 1-56; **103**; **104**; **195** 34
motor car mechanic **106** 53
motor coach **105** 17
motorcycle **100**
motorcycle, heavyweight ~ **100** 31
motorcycle, light ~ **99** 39; **100** 1, 16
motorcycle, lightweight ~ **100** 1
motorcycle chain **100** 22
motorcycles **99**
motorcycles, heavy ~ **100** 31-58
motorcycles, heavyweight ~ **100** 31-58
motorcycles, large-capacity ~ **100** 31-58
motorcycle stand **100** 21
motorcycle tyre **100** 26
motor drive **26** 76
motor drive, attachable ~ **26** 78
motor drive gear **78** 31
motor ferry **127** 6
motor grader **111** 19
motor pump **164** 8
motor safety switch **163** 46
motor scooter **99** 47
motor ship **134**
motor truck, heavy ~ **105** 20
motor turntable ladder **164** 9
motor uniselector **148** 42
motor vehicle mechanic **106** 53
motorway *Docks* **136** 54
mould *Bldg. Site* **30** 84
mould *Glass Prod.* **73** 47
mould *Iron & Steel* **58** 37
mould *Paperm.* **84** 48
mould, fixed ~ **89** 22
moulder *Bakery* **8** 57
moulder *Iron Foundry etc.* **59** 30
moulding box, closed ~ **59** 18
moulding box, open ~ **59** 33
moulding department **59** 30-37
moulding press, hydraulic ~ **89** 7
moulding sand **59** 35

moulding shop **59** 30-37
mould loft **133** 3
mould wall **59** 29
mountain railroads **125** 1-14
mountain railways **125** 1-14
mounting, German type ~ **24** 16
mounting, underfloor ~ **38** 22
mount of the frame **22** 10
mouth *Joiner* **43** 21
mouth piece *Electrotyp. etc.* **89** 17
mouthpiece *Post* **148** 9
mouthpiece *Tobacc. etc.* **18** 40
movable half **126** 66
moving iron **48** 39
mud drum **121** 28
mudguard, front ~ **98** 13
mudguard, rear ~ **98** 43
mud pump **56** 16
muffle furnace **51** 11
muffler *Car* **102** 29
muffler *Railw.* **120** 12, 22, 24; **122** 49
mule cop **76** 15
mule *Shoes* **12** 25
mule, open-toe ~ **12** 22
mull **94** 33; **96** 20
mull roll holder **96** 19
multiple cable system **126** 51
multiple drying machine **80** 31
multiple-frame viewfinder **25** 41
multiple meter **38** 41
multiple-unit train **122** 60
multiplier phototube **23** 51
multirole helicopter, light ~ **143** 11
Munich beer **4** 26
Muschelkalk **65** 58, 59, 60
music systems **152**
mustard *Grocer* **9** 28
mutton spanker **129** 29

N

nail, galvanized ~ **33** 74
nail, wire ~ **32** 95; **33** 74; **54** 51
nail, wooden ~ **32** 92
nail bag **33** 72
nail claw **31** 75
nail grip **11** 56
nail polish **10** 32
nail puller **11** 47
nail punch **45** 32
nail varnish **10** 32
name plate **29** 47
narghile **18** 42
narghileh **18** 42
narrow-gauge diesel locomotive **111** 24
narrow-gauge track system **70** 4
natural-gas engine **66** 5
naum keag **11** 7
navigating bridge **134** 14; **139** 22, 23, 24
navigating officer **135** 37
navigation **135**
navigational marks, floating ~ **135** 68-108
navigational television receiver mast **132** 37

navigation light indicator panel **135** 29
navigation light, left ~ **141** 50
navigation light, right ~ **141** 44
navvy **29** 76
navy plug **18** 25
navy yard **133** 1-43
neck *Mach. Parts etc.* **54** 64
neck *Meat* **6** 6, 20
neck *Weaves* **82** 33
neck brush **17** 27
neck flap *Fire Brig.* **164** 38
neck guard *Fire Brig.* **164** 38
neck interlocking point **82** 35
needle bar **78** 28
needle bed **78** 51, 55
needle butt **78** 60
needle cage **54** 75
needle cam **78** 14
needle cylinder *Bookbind.* **96** 21
needle cylinder *Knitting* **78** 8, 11
needle *Drawing Off.* **62** 56
needle *Mach. Parts etc.* **54** 76
needle, right-angle ~ **62** 67
needle, tapered ~ **101** 51
needled part of the cylinder **74** 70
needle file **19** 22
needle holder, cylindrical ~ **78** 8, 11
needle hook **78** 64
needle-matching system **25** 29
needlepoint **13** 30
needle point attachment **62** 54
needlepoint lace **13** 30
needle-raising cam **78** 59
needle roller bearing **54** 75-76
needles in parallel rows **78** 53
needle trick **78** 15
needlework **13**
negative carrier **27** 30
net *Sea Fish.* **1** 8
net background **13** 16
net sonar cable **1** 14
net sonar device **1** 17
netting **13** 22
netting loop **13** 23
netting needle **13** 26
netting thread **13** 24
neutral conductor **38** 13
neutral point **64** 22
newel **34** 43
newel, open ~ **34** 76
newel, solid ~ **34** 77, 78
newel post **34** 43
newscaster **149** 21
news dealer **116** 17
newspaper **93** 31; **116** 51
newspaper, folded ~ **92** 56
newspaper delivery unit **93** 29
newspaper typesetting **87** 29
newsreader **149** 21
news trolley **116** 16
news vendor **116** 17
nib **33** 51
nib size **62** 40
nick **86** 47
night-care cream **10** 27
nipper, bottom ~ **74** 65
nipper, top ~ **74** 66

pile hammer **137** 38
pile shoe **163** 61
piling **68** 25
pillar *Mach. Tools* **61** 21
pillar *Shipbuild.* **133** 61
pillar guide **50** 42
pillar stand *Optic. Instr.* **23** 32
pillar tap **37** 31
pillion footrest **99** 44
pillow lace **13** 18
pilot *Railw.* **121** 34
pilot, automatic ~ **135** 18
pilot boat **132** 95
pilot tone socket **28** 7
Pilsener beer **4** 26
pimehinketone **81** 20
pincers *Basketm.* **47** 37
pincers *D.I.Y.* **45** 13
pincers *Metalwkr.* **51** 69
pincers *Plumb. etc.* **37** 65
pincers *Shoem.* **11** 40, 41
pinch bar **69** 32
pinch roller **154** 25
pinch roller, rubber ~ **28** 35
pincushion **15** 20
pin *Mach. Parts etc.* **54** 31
pin *Metalwkr.* **51** 47
pin *Roof* **32** 93
pin *Turner* **46** 9
pin, cylindrical ~ **54** 40
pin, grooved ~ **54** 40
pin, split ~ **54** 19, 25, 78
pin, tapered ~ **54** 37
pineapple **10** 85
pin groove **54** 49
pin holder **20** 16
pinion *Mach. Parts etc.* **54** 92
pin slit **54** 49
pin slot **54** 49
pin vice **20** 16
pin wire **35** 28
pipe *Ship* **132** 3
pipe, briar ~ **18** 39
pipe, cement ~ **111** 62
pipe, clay ~ **18** 34
pipe, Dutch ~ **18** 34
pipe, earthenware ~ **163** 35
pipe, long ~ **18** 35
pipe, perforated ~ **111** 62
pipe, short ~ **18** 33
pipe, vertical ~ *Fire Brig.* **164** 26
pipe bender **36** 28
pipe-bending machine *Plumb.* **36** 28
pipe-bending machine *Plumb. etc.* **37** 82
pipe bowl **18** 36
pipe cleaner **18** 46, 48
pipe clip *Plumb. etc.* **37** 56
pipe clip *Roof* **33** 31
pipe cutter **37** 84
pipe-cutting machine **37** 10
pipeline **56** 65
piperack *Offshore Drill.* **57** 4
pipe repair stand **37** 11
pipe scraper **18** 45
pipe stem **18** 38
pipe still **56** 36
pipe supports **37** 53-57
pipe vice **37** 81

pipe wrench **37** 61; **38** 4777; **45** 11
pirn **77** 30
pirn, empty ~ **77** 21
pirn holder, spring-clip ~ **77** 33
pistol, captive-bolt ~ **5** 3
pistol grip *D.I.Y.* **45** 44
piston *Drawing Off.* **62** 60
piston *Inf. Tech.* **153** 46
piston *Intern. Combust. Eng.* **101** 37
piston, hydraulic ~ **50** 41
piston pin **103** 26
piston ring **101** 37
piston rod *Car* **103** 75
piston rod *Intern. Combust. Eng.* **101** 21
piston rod *Railw.* **121** 33
pit *Blacksm.* **49** 17
pitching **141** 67
pitching, stone ~ **127** 55
pitch of rivets **54** 60
pit *Coal* **55** 1-51
pithead building **55** 4
pithead frame **55** 3
pithead gear **55** 1
pit hydrant **164** 25
pivot bearing **2** 10
pivot *Bridges* **126** 69
pivot *Hairdresser* **17** 36
pivoting half **126** 66
pivoting section **126** 66
pivoting span **126** 66
pivot pier **126** 65
place of issue **161** 13
place of payment **161** 15
plain *Railw.* **118** 10-21, 26-32. 38-42, 61-72, 76
plain part of the cylinder **74** 69
plain-tile roofing **33** 2
plait **8** 41
plaiter **79** 30, 35
plaiting-down platform **79** 37
plan *Drawing Off.* **62** 19
plane *Aircraft* **141** 67-72
plane *Carp.* **31** 64
plane, high-wing ~ **140** 1; **142** 2
plane, low-wing ~ **140** 5, 14; **142** 1
plane, midwing ~ **140** 4
plane, propeller-driven ~ **142** 1-6
plane, shoulder-wing ~ **140** 3
plane, types of ~ **142** 1-33
plane iron **43** 20
planer, two-column ~ **61** 8
planer table **61** 11
planes **43** 15-28
planing machine, two column ~ **61** 8
planking **30** 52
plank **29** 87; **31** 1, 91; **68** 34, 35
plank, unsquared ~ **31** 94
plank platform **29** 28
plank roadway **29** 79
plan of locomotive **122** 10-18
planter **159** 13
plant, indoor ~ **159** 14
plant, pneumatic ~ **3** 12
plant stand **159** 13
plaster *Paperhanger* **39** 2
plaster cup **45** 18

plasterer **29** 83
plastering **29** 83-91
plaster mould **72** 15
plaster of Paris **39** 2
plate, curved ~ **89** 21
plate, halftone ~ **89** 38
plate, presensitized ~ **90** 31
plate, sliding ~ **94** 28
plate, steel ~ **7** 54
plate clamp *Electrotyp. etc.* **89** 27
plate clamp *Offset Platem.* **90** 8
plate-coating machine **90** 1
plate cylinder *Letterpress* **92** 51, 60
plate cylinder *Office* **160** 50
plate cylinder *Offset Print.* **91** 25, 38, 53, 62
plate-drying cabinet, vertical ~ **90** 27
plate girder bridge **126** 52
plate magazine **24** 40
plate mount **89** 41
plate mounting **89** 41
platen *Bookbind.* **94** 24
platen *Letterpress* **92** 13, 15, 29
platen *Office* **160** 18
platen knob **160** 22
platen machine **92** 13, 29
platen press **92** 13, 29
platen variable **160** 25
plate rack **89** 35
plate rod **89** 6
plate whirler **90** 1
platform *Bldg. Site* **29** 87; **30** 52
platform *Shoes* **12** 8
platform *Station* **116** 1, 14
platform, covered ~ **129** 49
platform, intermediate ~ **56** 5
platform, operator's ~ **79** 23
platform clock **116** 46
platformer **56** 47
platform lighting **116** 48
platform loudspeaker **116** 27
platform mailbox **116** 56
platform number **116** 4
platform post box **116** 56
platform railing **29** 24
platform roofing **116** 5
platform scale **115** 5
platform seat **116** 54
platform sole **12** 8
platform telephone **116** 57
platform truck **105** 6
playback deck **149** 4
playback deck, single ~ **149** 56
pleasure steamer **132** 101-128; **136** 29
pleasure vehicle **97** 33
pliers, flat-nose ~ **37** 62; **51** 66
pliers, multiple ~ **45** 12
pliers, round-nose ~ **37** 64; **38** 50
pliers, shoemaker's ~ **11** 38
plinth *Carp.* **31** 28
plough *Brew.* **3** 24
plugboard **153** 69
plug, earthed ~ **38** 9
plug gauge **60** 56
plugging **34** 69
plugging sand bucket **69** 29
plug *Metalwkr.* **51** 45

315

release *Weaving* 76 35
release/lock lever 158 42
release valve 121 58
remitter 161 19
remnant 14 16
remote control jack 28 9
remote control panel 68 14
remote control socket 28 9
rendering coat 34 6
rendering, exterior ~ 33 38
rendezvous point 144 29
repair bay 107 22
repairer 72 19
repair quay 133 10
repair shop 107 22
reproducing head 152 59
re-reeler 84 41
re-reeling machine 84 41
rescue cruiser 132 18; 139 14
rescue helicopter 132 20; 139 16
research microscope 23 1, 66
reserve fuel tank 123 60
reserve tank 143 20
reservoir *Hydr. Eng.* 128 39-46
reservoir, impounded ~ 128 57
reset button *Car* 102 77
reset button *Cine Film* 28 86
resetting button 38 20
resetting spring 148 49
residue 56 43
resin, synthetic ~ 41 26
resistor 64 56
restaurant 144 50
restaurant car 118 22-32
restaurant car, self-service ~ 118 73
restoring spring 148 49
resuscitation equipment 164 20
resuscitator 164 20
retailer 9 41
retail shop 9 1-87
retail store 9 1-87
retaining plate 78 56
retarder 117 48
reticella lace 13 30
reticule 26 61
retoucher 93 14
retouching and stripping desk 88 19
retrofocus position 26 84
retro-rocket 145 37
return pipe 37 24
return spring *Car* 103 55
return spring *Knitting* 78 37
rev counter 100 41; 102 38; 123 22; 141 8
rev counter, electric ~ 102 70
rev counter, electronic ~ 99 40
reveal 29 10; 31 31
revenue stamp 18 26
reverse gear 103 44
reverse shaft 60 34
reversing clutch 26 27
reversing gear 121 18; 122 53; 123 74
reversing ring 26 83
reversing wheel 121 56
revertive signal panel 64 7
revetment 127 51-55

revolution counter 100 41; 102 38; 123 22; 141 8
revolution counter, electric ~ 102 70
revolution counter, electronic ~ 99 40
rewind 25 6; 26 12
rewind bench 149 59
rewind button 160 73
rewind cam 26 29
rewind crank 25 6; 26 12
rewinder *Cine Film* 28 93
rewinder *Paperm.* 84 41
rewind handle *Cine Film* 28 93
rewind handle *Photog.* 25 6, 26 12
rewinding 81 50
rewind release button 26 27
rewind station 84 41
rhubarb flan 8 22
rib *Aircraft* 141 46
rib *Basketm.* 47 24
rib *Floor etc. Constr.* 34 36
rib *Meat* 6 3
rib *Shipbuild.* 133 58
rib, annular ~ 146 47
rib, flat ~ 6 21
rib, fore ~ 6 18
rib, main ~ *Space* 146 10
rib, middle ~ 6 19
rib, prime ~ 6 18
rib, top ~ 6 31
ribbon cassette 160 16
ribbon of glass 73 10
ribbon selector 160 11
rib randing 47 2
rib weave, combined ~ 82 19
rice *Grocer* 9 38
ridge *Roof* 33 93
ridge beam 32 48
ridge board 32 48
ridge capping piece 33 99
ridge course 33 47, 79
ridge course tile 33 4
ridge hook 33 65
ridge joint 33 79
ridge purlin 32 43
ridge rope 132 118
ridge tile 33 3, 8, 22
ridge turret 32 14
riffler 83 2; 84 13
riflegrip *Photog.* 26 100
rig 130 1-72
rigging 130 1-72
rigging, running ~ 130 67-71
rigging, standing ~ 130 10-19
right tank fuel gauge 141 17
rim *Bicycle* 98 28
rim *Car* 102 16; 103 77
rim *Motorcycle* 100 25
rim brake 98 5
rind 31 86
ring cake 8 33; 10 22
ring *Cotton Spin.* 75 51, 54
ring, front ~ 24 7
ring for the carrying strap 26 9
ring frame 75 34
ring gauge 19 25, 27
ring net 1 25
ring rail 75 42, 54
ring-rounding tool 19 26

revolution counter, standard ~ 75 45
ring spindle, standard ~ 75 45
ring spinning frame 75 34
ringtube *Cotton Spin.* 75 52
ring tube *Weaving* 76 15
ripper 111 20
riprap 127 51
rise adjustment 44 21
rise adjustment wheel 44 22
rise and fall adjustment wheel 43 60
riser *Fire Brig.* 164 26
riser *Floor etc. Constr.* 34 33, 48
riser *Iron Foundry etc.* 59 22
riser *Water* 163 19
riser gate 59 22
riser pipe 163 19
river *Rivers* 127 31
river arm, blind ~ 127 18
river arm 127 3
riverbank 127 5
river branch, blind ~ 127 18
river branch 127 3
river engineering 127
river ferry 127 10
river island 127 4
river islet 127 4
river police 128 24
rivers 127
river tug 127 23
rivet 54 57-60
rivet head 54 57
riveting 54 56
riveting machine 49 27
rivet shank 54 58
road, bituminous ~ 111 55
road building 111; 112
road-building machinery 111 1-54
road coach 97 39
road construction 111; 112
road form 112 15
road layers 109 1-5
road making 111; 112
road-metal spreading machine 111 31
road ripper 111 20
road roller 111 36
roadster *Bicycle* 98 1
roadster *Car* 104 26
road surface 126 8; 128 1
road sweeper 110 5
road-sweeping lorry 110 41
roadway, orthotropic ~ 126 2
roasting chicken 9 6
roasting drum 9 71
roasting round 6 11
rock bit 56 21
rock, coal-bearing ~ 55 49
rocker arm 101 33
rocker arm mounting 101 34
rocker switch 38 4
rocket apparatus 139 1
rocket engine, liquid-fuelled ~ 146 36
rocket engine, main ~ 146 36
rocket gun 139 1
rocket *Life-Sav.* 139 2
rocket line 139 3
rocket stage, first ~ 145 3
rocket stage, second ~ 145 18
rocket stage, third ~ 145 33

scouring tunnel **128** 62
scouring wheel **11** 6
scrag **6** 6
scrag end **6** 6
scrambling motorcycle **100** 16
scrap box **52** 15
scraper *Butch.* **7** 42
scraper *Painter* **40** 23
scraper *Paperhanger* **39** 10
scraper, pointed ~ **51** 63
scraper, triangle ~ **51** 63
scraper blade **111** 17
scrap iron charging box **58** 26
scrap iron feed **58** 65
scray entry, curved ~ **79** 47
screed **34** 41
screeding beam **112** 14
screeding board **112** 14
screen *Bldg. Site* **29** 85
screen *Inf. Tech* **153** 84
screen *Paperm.* **83** 57
screen *Post* **147** 40
screen *Refuse Coll.* **110** 11
screen, all-matt ~ **26** 58, 59, 60, 65
screen, centrifugal ~ **83** 22, 56
screen, crystal glass ~ **90** 24
screen, ground glass ~ **23** 24; **26** 58, 59, 60, 61, 65, 66; **88** 2, 34
screen, illuminated ~ **88** 20
screen, inner ~ **151** 20
screen, magnetic ~ **151** 20
screen, matt ~ *Optic. Instr.* **23** 24
screen, matt~ *Photog.* **26** 61, 66
screen, protective ~ **65** 74
screen, rotary ~ **83** 2
screen, secondary ~ **83** 58
screen, vibrating ~ **69** 21
screen frame, mobile ~ **79** 60
screen holder, hinged ~ **88** 3
screening **67** 14
screening, inner ~ **151** 20
screening, magnetic ~ **151** 20
screenings **69** 22
screen magazine **88** 9
screen printing **79** 59
screen printing operator **79** 65
screen table **79** 63
screen work **47** 4
screw *Life-Sav.* **139** 26
screw *Metalwkr.* **51** 4
screw *Weaving* **76** 36
screw, cheese-head ~ **54** 36
screw, cross-head ~ **54** 26
screw, feathering ~ **135** 19
screw, hexagonal socket head ~ **54** 27
screw, main ~ **59** 62
screw, self-tapping ~ **54** 26
screw, ship's ~ **132** 44; **133** 72; **134** 62
screw, slotted ~ **54** 36
screw, three-blade ~ **134** 62
screw base **38** 59
screw block **47** 8
screw clamp **31** 66
screw conveyor **3** 26
screw-cutting machine **36** 27; **37** 86
screw die **51** 61

screwdriver, cross-point ~ **45** 5
screwdriver **20** 6; **126** 69, **38** 46; **45** 4; **51** 62
screw groove **54** 38
screw joint **37** 42
screw log **135** 54
screw post **133** 71
screws **54** 13-50
screw slit **54** 38
screws lot **54** 38
screw tap **51** 60
screw wrench **37** 67
scrim **94** 33; **96** 20
scrim roll holder **96** 19
scroll-opening roller **79** 13
scrubber **67** 22, 23, 24
scrubbing agent **67** 37
scrubbing oil tank **67** 43
scrub board **34** 21, 63
scutcher, double ~ **74** 14
scutcher lap **74** 47
scutcher lap holder **74** 48
sea fishing **1**
seal **101** 69
seal, clay ~ **163** 39
seal, loam ~ **163** 39
sealadder **132** 91
sealing tape **37** 75
seam **55** 29
seamarks **135** 68-108
seam binding **14** 14; **15** 19
seamless engraving adjustment **88** 53
seam roller **39** 36
sea, open ~ **138** 4
seaplane **143** 1, 5
seaside pleasure boat **132** 15
seat **123** 63
seat, back ~ **104** 22
seat, captain's ~ **146** 17
seat, child's ~ **98** 21
seat, coachman's ~ **97** 8
seat, commander's ~ **146** 17
seat, conical ~ **54** 67
seat, co-pilot's ~ **141** 37; **146** 18
seat, double ~ **108** 19; **118** 63
seat, driver's ~ **97** 8; **102** 34; **121** 59
seat, engineer's ~ **121** 59
seat, fireman's ~ **121** 39
seat, folding ~ **104** 22; **118** 12
seat, pilot's ~ **141** 36; **146** 18
seat, rear ~ **102** 31
seat, reclining ~ **102** 34; **118** 44, 64
seat, single ~ **108** 17; **118** 62
seat, upholstered ~ **118** 44; **119** 25
seat pillar **98** 24
seat stay **98** 19
seat tube **98** 18
seat upholstery **118** 65
seawater desalination plant **57** 25
sea wing **143** 3
secondary **64** 16
second-class seating arrangement **122** 58
second-class section **118** 10; **119** 22

second indicator **21** 21
seconds timer **40** 39
secretary **120** 27
secretary, proprietor's ~ **159** 31
section *Bookbind.* **94** 12
section *Drawing Off.* **62** 28
section *Railw.* **114** 29
section, hollow ~ **126** 5
section, middle ~ **126** 68
section, tubular ~ **126** 5
section line *Drawing Off.* **62** 27
section of warp rib fabric **82** 14
sections **54**
securities **162** 11-19
security **162** 1-10
security, fixed-income ~ **162** 11-19
security, unlisted ~ **162** 5
security drawer **147** 22
sedan **104** 4, 25
Seger cone **72** 6
seggar **72** 2
seizing **1** 5
selector **148** 42
selector, electronic ~ **148** 42
selector fork **103** 42, 45
selector head **103** 44
selector motor **148** 48
self-discharge freight car **124** 24
self-discharge wagon **124** 24
self-service station **107** 1-29
self-threading guide **76** 18
self-time lever **26** 15
self-timer **26** 15
selvedge **77** 11; **82** 20, 24
selvedge shaft **82** 22
selvedge thread draft **82** 20
semaphore arm **114** 2
semaphore arm, supplementary ~ **114** 8
semaphore signal **114** 1, 7, 12
semibold **86** 3
semi-trailer *Lorries etc.* **105** 30-33
semi-trailer *Station* **117** 59
semolina **9** 36
separating rail **75** 30
separation plant **110** 31
separation rocket motor, aft ~ **146** 62
separation rocket motor, forward ~ **146** 60
separator *Bldg. Site* **30** 81
separator *Cotton Spin.* **75** 43
separator *Offshore Drill.* **57** 28
separator *Paperm.* **83** 31
separator, centralized ~ **83** 15
serial number *Stock Exch.* **162** 13
series of moulds **58** 36
service bridge **128** 72
service building **65** 36
service bunker **67** 3
service counter **161** 4
service girder, adjustable ~ **30** 78
service module main engine **145** 57
service riser **37** 7
service station **107** 1-29
service tray **16** 31
service vehicle **144** 22
serving area **118** 79

MORE OXFORD PAPERBACKS

Details of a selection of other books follow. A complete list of Oxford Paperbacks, including The World's Classics, Twentieth-Century Classics, OPUS, Past Masters, Oxford Authors, Oxford Shakespeare, and Oxford Paperback Reference, is available in the UK from the General Publicity Department, Oxford University Press (JH), Walton Street, Oxford OX2 6DP.

In the USA, complete lists are available from the Paperbacks Marketing Manager, Oxford University Press, 200 Madison Avenue, New York, NY 10016.

Oxford Paperbacks are available from all good bookshops. In case of difficulty, customers in the UK can order direct from Oxford University Press Bookshop, 116 High Street, Oxford, Freepost, OX1 4BR, enclosing full payment. Please add 10 per cent of published price for postage and packing.

THE OXFORD–DUDEN PICTORIAL
ENGLISH DICTIONARY:

Science and Medicine

Certain kinds of information are better conveyed visually than by written definitions. This dictionary offers more than an ordinary illustrated dictionary; it presents the vocabulary of a particular subject alongside a picture illustrating it. An alphabetical index is also provided for easy cross-reference.

This vocabulary of Astronomy, Geography, Dentistry, Mathematics, Natural History, and much more is given in this dictionary.

Oxford Paperback Reference

THE OXFORD–DUDEN PICTORIAL
ENGLISH DICTIONARY:

Leisure and the Arts

Certain kinds of information are better conveyed visually than by written definitions. *The Oxford–Duden Pictorial English Dictionaries* offer more than an ordinary illustrated dictionary; they present the vocabulary of a particular subject alongside a picture illustrating it. An alphabetical index is also provided for easy cross-reference.

This volume ranges from fine art and the theatre to sports, fashions, and the home, covering a wide-ranging vocabulary of use in everyday life.

Oxford Paperback Reference

THE CONCISE OXFORD DICTIONARY OF ENGLISH LITERATURE

Second Edition

Revised by Dorothy Eagle

This handy and authoritative reference book is essential for anyone who reads and enjoys English literature. It contains concise yet informative entries on English writers from the *Beowulf* poet to Samuel Beckett and W. H. Auden, defines literary movements and genres, and refers the reader to sources for more than a thousand characters from books and plays. It also includes a host of sources of influence on English literary achievement such as foreign books and writers, art, and major historical events.

The Concise Oxford Dictionary of English Literature is an abridgement of Paul Harvey's classic *Oxford Companion to English Literature*.

Oxford Paperback Reference

THE OXFORD DICTIONARY OF CURRENT ENGLISH

Edited by R. E. Allen

This is the most authoritative, comprehensive, and up-to-date dictionary of its size available, specially designed to be quickly and easily used in everyday life. Among its main features are:

* over 70,000 definitions

* senses arranged in order of comparative familiarity and importance

* pronunciations given in the International Phonetic Alphabet

* special markings for disputed and racially offensive uses

* extensive treatment of idioms and phrases

* generous coverage of terms used in technology and the information sciences

* clear layout and presentation with a minimum of special abbreviations and symbols

THE WAY PEOPLE WORK

Job Satisfaction and the Challenge of Change

Christine Howarth

What makes a job satisfying? How can we improve the quality of working life? Does greater job satisfaction mean greater efficiency?

These are some of the many questions which both managers and employees must ask themselves (and each other) if the organizations for which they work are to have any chance of success in today's harsh economic climate. Christine Howarth, who has many years' experience as an independent management consultant, has written this book as a *practical* guide to human relationships in employment.

An OPUS book

DEMOCRACY AT WORK

Tom Schuller

Should people play a significant part in decisions affecting their working lives? *Democracy at Work* takes a fresh look at the controversial question of industrial democracy in the light of recent changes in the structure of employment and in the balance of decision-making.

'This short but elegantly written book airs a number of important issues and points to the narrowness of much of the current perspectives in Britain on worker participation.' *Times Higher Education Supplement*

THE A–Z OF WOMEN'S HEALTH

Derek Llewellyn-Jones

Every woman needs to know the facts about herself. *The A–Z of Women's Health* puts those facts at her fingertips. Alphabetically arranged for easy reference, and complemented by many diagrams and photographs, this is an indispensable guide to female life and health.

'His understanding and compassion are as evident as his sense and expertise.' *The Times Educational Supplement*

'sensible and authoritative' *Journal of Obstetrics and Gynaecology*

Oxford Paperback Reference

A CONCISE DICTIONARY OF AMERICAN PLACE-NAMES

George R. Stewart

From Poxabog Pond and Headache Spring via Fort Necessity PA and Russiaville IN to Goshelpme Creek and Delusion Lake, a journey around the often extraordinary place-names of the American continent is bound to prove fascinating. This dictionary contains some 12,000 names of towns, cities, landmarks, and districts in the USA. It explains their meaning and derivation, and will prove useful to all those who have an interest in American history, geography, or folklore.

Oxford Paperback Reference

A CONCISE DICTIONARY OF LAW

This authoritative and up-to-date dictionary contains about 1,500 entries explaining the major terms, concepts, processes, and organization of the law. Compiled by practising lawyers, it is intended primarily for those, such as business men, civil servants, and local government officers, who require some legal knowledge in the course of their work. It will also be an extremely useful work of reference for law students and legal secretaries, and its simple, jargon-free presentation means that anyone who comes into contact with the law, whether as a housebuyer or motorist, will find it of considerable value.

Oxford Paperback Reference

A CONCISE DICTIONARY OF MODERN PLACE-NAMES IN GREAT BRITAIN AND IRELAND

Adrian Room

Why the 'Peace' in Peacehaven? Who was the Burgess of Burgess Hill? Why was a port named after a brand of soap? In answering questions like these, Adrian Room's dictionary reveals the origins of more than 1,000 names of towns and villages that have come into being since 1500, thus filling a major gap in the study of British and Irish place-names.

'thanks should be offered to Adrian Room for drawing attention to a category of topographical names that might otherwise have escaped notice' *Country Life*

Oxford Paperback Reference

DICTIONARY OF BRITAIN

Adrian Room

A dictionary of all those words and phrases, customs and institutions, that so puzzle visitors to Britain.

This dictionary has more than 3,000 alphabetically arranged entries explaining a wide range of topics, including public events, personalities, geography, food, work, tradition, and sport. It is illustrated throughout with photographs, maps, and attractive line drawings.

Oxford Paperback Reference

THE KING'S ENGLISH

Third Edition

H. W. Fowler and F. G. Fowler

Generations of students, scholars, and professional writers have gone to *The King's English* for answers to problems of grammar or style. The Fowler brothers were particularly concerned to clarify the more problematic and obscure rules and principles inherent in English vocabulary and composition, and also to illustrate with examples the most common blunders and traps. They wrote with characteristic good sense and liveliness, and this book has become a classic reference work.

A DICTIONARY OF MODERN ENGLISH USAGE

H. W. Fowler

Second Edition

Revised by Sir Ernest Gowers

This is the paperback edition of Fowler's *Modern English Usage,* which for over fifty years has been the standard work on the correct but easy and natural use of English in speech or writing. It deals with points of grammar, syntax, style, and the choice of words; with the formation of words and their spelling and inflexions; with pronunciation; and with punctuation and typography. But most of all Fowler is renowned for the iconoclasm and wit with which he writes.

'Let me beg readers as well as writers to keep the revised Fowler at their elbows. It brims with useful information.' Raymond Mortimer, *Sunday Times*

'Fowler is still the best available authority. For those who think that it matters to make their writing shipshape and water-tight, there is still no alternative. Apart from that, we read him because he was a funny, quirky, witty man, who used words to express complicated meanings with beautiful conciseness.' *Books and Bookmen*

THE OXFORD COMPANION TO CLASSICAL LITERATURE

Compiled by Sir Paul Harvey

This is a comprehensive classical dictionary with a literary emphasis. It includes 6 illustrations, 14 maps, and a date chart of classical literature.

'Outstandingly comprehensive brief guide covering every aspect of the classical background (and foreground) from the history of Rome to the hendecasyllable, ancient religion to the design of the trireme.' *Sunday Times*

Oxford Paperback Reference

THE OXFORD DICTIONARY OF ENGLISH CHRISTIAN NAMES

Third Edition

Edited by E. G. Withycombe

What's in a name? This 'standard reference work for those approaching the font' (*Scotsman*) is equally at home on the family bookshelf and in the scholar's library. Personal names from Aaron to Zoë, that have survived in use after the end of the fourteenth century, are listed alphabetically. Each entry includes early forms of the name, its equivalents in other languages, pet forms, and etymology, together with an account of its introduction into England and subsequent history, frequency of occurrence, fluctuations in fashion, etc. Some of the commoner Irish, Gaelic, and Welsh names have also been included. The introduction discusses the general history of personal names, and an appendix lists common words derived from Christian names.

Oxford Paperback Reference

THE OXFORD GUIDE TO THE ENGLISH LANGUAGE

Edited by E. S. C. Weiner and Joyce M. Hawkins

This is the ideal concise handbook for everyone who cares about using the English language properly. Combining between one set of covers Edmund Weiner's *Oxford Guide to English Usage* and a compact Oxford dictionary compiled by Joyce Hawkins, it is comprehensive and exceptionally convenient for regular quick consultation.

The dictionary contains nearly 30,000 words and phrases, and provides a compact and up-to-date guide to contemporary English—spelling, pronunciation, and meaning.

THE OXFORD GUIDE TO WORD GAMES

Tony Augarde

This is a unique guide to all kinds of word games and word play, from crosswords and scrabble to acrostics, rebuses, and tongue-twisters. Not only does it reveal the origins of games, outlining their fascinating history, but it describes how to play them, and their often equally interesting variants. Illustrating his descriptions with examples and diagrams, Tony Augarde builds up an intriguing and amusing picture of the British love of verbal ingenuity.

'very good value and fun' *Sunday Telegraph*

THE OXFORD PAPERBACK DICTIONARY

Edited by Joyce M. Hawkins

This dictionary was first published in 1979 and became an immediate success, attracting world-wide attention and praise for its clear definitions, up-to-date coverage of vocabulary, straightforward system of pronunciation, and especially for its notes on correct English usage. In this new enlarged edition these features have been retained and the coverage has been increased, especially in the field of computers, which have recently invaded not only the office but also the home.

'Every home, office, secretary and boss should have one.' *The Good Book Guide*

Oxford Paperback Reference